MINERAL
EQUILIBRIA

AT LOW TEMPERATURE AND PRESSURE

Robert M. Garrels

HARVARD UNIVERSITY

HARPER & BROTHERS, PUBLISHERS, NEW YORK

TO
W. C. KRUMBEIN,
*who insisted that I consider
more than one mineral at a time;*
AND TO
M. J. N. POURBAIX,
who showed me how to do it.

Contents

Editor's Introduction

GEOCHEMISTRY is generally considered to be one of the new and burgeoning interdisciplinary scientific fields. The evidence for such a belief is obvious. For example, the Geochemical Society is scarcely out of its swaddling clothes, but it is already a large and important international scientific organization. The very word "geochemistry" was not even included in the ten-volume *Oxford Universal English Dictionary* published as recently as 1937. During the Second World War and immediately thereafter, however, geochemical work was initiated at scores of universities and commercial laboratories. Thus by 1948 "geochemistry" was well enough established to be defined in *The American College Dictionary* as "the science dealing with chemical changes in, and the composition of, the earth's crust."

Geochemistry actually is far from new. The early prospectors and miners were aware of some of the rudiments of the subject, and many of the mineralogists and petrologists of the past century were much more than amateur geochemists. The United States Geological Survey for more than a half century has had an important chemical section, and F. W. Clarke's famous, but all too infrequently consulted, "Data of Geochemistry" was first issued as early as 1908.

Geochemistry in the completely modern sense, however, *is* a new and rapidly growing subject. This is true because more and more men, trained to a high level of technical competence in chemistry, have discovered that there are innumerable previously unsolved geological problems which yield results when subjected to a scientific attack based on chemical "know-how." So often has this been the case that the names of a number of the nation's leading chemists are now linked to spectacular geological "break-throughs."

Geologists themselves have also become active in geochemical work.

Partly this is true because foresighted improvements in the geological curriculum have resulted in a new generation of geologists who for the first time are reasonably sophisticated in chemistry. Partly, however, it stems from the fact that geologists became increasingly conscious of the importance of chemistry in their own work through the great activity in, and important results of, the search for uranium and other minerals and metals during and after World War II.

Robert M. Garrels is one of the leading American scientists who has risen to the top rungs of the geochemical ladder through the geological approach to the subject. A graduate of the University of Michigan, Dr. Garrels went to Northwestern University to study under Professor Charles Behre—now of Columbia University—who, as an economic geologist concerned with ore deposits, early became convinced of the importance of geochemistry in the solution of many geological problems. After receiving his doctorate in 1941, Dr. Garrels had a fruitful decade of teaching and research at Northwestern. In 1952 he joined the United States Geological Survey, where he had the advantage of working with a large and accomplished geochemical research team. Relatively recently Dr. Garrels has returned to academic pursuits as Professor of Geochemistry at Harvard University. With this rich background in geology and geochemistry, it is not surprising that Garrels' *Mineral Equilibria* is a somewhat unorthodox textbook. It differs notably from other books on the subject in that individual equations, rather than rectilinear graphs or triangular composition diagrams, are stressed in portraying equilibrium relations among minerals. Because chemical terminology is complex—and many notations are employed—Professor Garrels has prepared a helpful preliminary section of his book in which he clearly defines the terms and symbols employed. Thus, although the volume is of the pioneering type, the reasonably well-prepared student is lead by relatively easy and logical stages to the formulation and solution of equations pertinent to a number of geochemical problems. He then is instructed in the methods of erecting the properly coordinated graphical structures most useful in displaying or suggesting the chemical and geological interrelations which otherwise might not be obvious.

The possibilities for increased usefulness of the methods of study which Dr. Garrels advocates are unlimited. The body of thermochemical data is growing rapidly, and the eventual use of the facts will not be limited to any one theoretical aspect of geochemistry, or to any one practical phase of economic geology. It is probably not too broad

a statement to say that almost all aspects of physical geology are potentially involved in *Mineral Equilibria*. This is true because the purpose of the Garrels volume is to develop methods which lead to the determination of the thermodynamic concentration—or, as Garrels puts it, the *activity*—of a substance. For example, the relationships of the iron minerals can be determined, the effect of sulfur on iron-water-oxygen relations can be studied, and the influence of other constituents such as carbon dioxide or silica on the system can at least be suggested.

In addition to the examples cited, Chapter 7 outlines a number of geological applications of the Eh-pH diagrams. These range through the troublesome standard ore-deposition problems to the origin and alteration of chemical sediments, the formation of soils, the oxidation-reduction qualities of ground water above and below the water table, and similar applications.

It will be apparent even to the casual reader that Garrels has helped to pave the way for another step forward in making geology—at least in a number of its subdisciplines—less qualitative and more exact. For the average student of geology, the path through *Mineral Equilibria* may be rough in spots, but those who successfully complete the intellectual journey should be well rewarded. It is not too much to suggest that from their group will come the leadership of the next generation of geologists.

CAREY CRONEIS

The Rice Institute
Houston, Texas

Preface

Despite the tremendous increase in interest in geochemistry in the past ten years, there is no convenient text that summarizes those aspects of low-temperature aqueous chemistry most useful to geologists. The number of papers in current geologic journals that use solution chemistry is increasing rapidly, and comprehension of them requires a considerable range of knowledge of chemistry, especially selected aspects of physical chemistry and thermodynamics. In teaching a seminar in geochemistry at Harvard University for the past three years, I have found it necessary to develop at some length the basis for understanding of the recent literature, and I have ventured to describe the results in the following pages, in the hope that I will save others from duplicating the task of accumulating the same materials.

The subject matter of this text is devoted largely to chemical relations in aqueous solutions at low temperatures and pressures. The reasons for this restriction are numerous: among them are my own major interest in the field; the availability of suitable textbooks for students interested in igneous and metamorphic geology, where the reactions are to a large extent investigated as functions of temperature and total pressure; and what seems to me a remarkable neglect of the low temperature-low pressure environment, which after all includes the outer half mile of the earth—our region of direct observation.

Also, emphasis is to a large extent on representation of equilibrium relations among chemical compounds simulating minerals. I believe that until we have made extensive comparisons of natural systems and their idealized counterparts we are in no position to isolate the variables responsible for observed mineral relations.

I have attempted to give sufficient detail in the operations involved in the various calculations so that a geologist with two years of

inorganic chemistry can use the examples given to make similar calculations on systems of interest to him, and will have a good grasp of the limitations of his results in terms of their application to natural systems.

ROBERT M. GARRELS

June, 1959

Acknowledgments

THE material presented here has been accumulated over a number of years. Perhaps it is best to proceed historically in attempting to show the many people who are really responsible for this text. At Northwestern University I worked closely with John Castano and N. King Huber, who were graduate students at that time, and our interest was largely in relations among the iron minerals. At about this time discussion concerning field and laboratory aspects of sedimentary iron deposition with H. L. James, of the U.S. Geological Survey, were most invigorating. All my colleagues at Northwestern were helpful, but W. C. Krumbein was the person who opened my eyes to the possibilities of simultaneous representation of stability fields of minerals, and we collaborated in attempts to delineate the environments of chemical sediments. At the U.S. Geological Survey I became involved in studies of the geochemistry of the Colorado Plateau uranium deposits, and am indebted to so many of my colleagues there that it is hard to stop when I list the individuals whose help has been indispensable. C. L. Christ, A. D. Weeks, C. R. Naeser, H. T. Evans, E. S. Larsen, III, R. G. Coleman, V. E. McKelvey, and A. M. Pommer all have collaborated with me in various publications. The stimulus of daily contact and continual discussion with C. L. Christ, H. T. Evans, C. R. Naeser, and A. D. Weeks has provided me with a wealth of information and ideas. At Harvard University H. E. McKinstry influenced me back into studies of relationships among sulfide minerals and the development of the partial pressure diagrams. I have drawn heavily on his syntheses of mineral relationships. My other colleagues have been helpful; I have had many discussions with J. B. Thompson, Jr., and R. Siever. C. C. Stephenson of Massachusetts Institute of Technology has made many helpful suggestions and has contributed free energy values. Students in my classes have not only provided many of the diagrams used as illustrations but also have been a constant source of fresh ideas and new techniques. I have used diagrams originally prepared by J. A. Silman,

J. Smith, R. Natarajan, P. Hostetler, D. Emery, U. Peterson, P. Howard, J. Anthony, R. Honea, J. Anderson, R. Notkin, K. Linn, E. Hilton, W. McIntyre, I. Barnes, J. Reitzel, and E. Gaucher.   The diagrams were drafted by C. Goodwin.

Ramifying all through this development is the influence of the work of M. J. N. Pourbaix, Director of the Belgian Institute for the Study of Corrosion.   I have had access to the many publications of the Institute on Eh-pH diagrams, as well as to M. Pourbaix's classic book on the subject.   My early papers are crude indeed when compared with the elegant methods Pourbaix and his co-workers have developed, methods I have tried to emulate.

The sponsors of the work are implicit in the foregoing discussion: The Northwestern University Graduate School; the U.S. Geological Survey (largely in work done on behalf of the U.S. Atomic Energy Commission); and the Committee on Experimental Geology at Harvard University.

The length of this list, which is far from inclusive of all to whom I owe a debt, shows how much has come from others and to what a large extent this text is synthesized with their help.   I hope that colleagues I have not indicated by name will know that I am nonetheless appreciative of their help.

MINERAL EQUILIBRIA

1

Introduction

A LARGE part of the following discussion is devoted to a simple theme—the simultaneous representation of various chemical reactions. It is a little surprising, considering the importance always accorded to mineral associations, that few methods of portraying equilibrium relations among minerals are in general use. By far the largest percentage of diagrams portrays stability relations as functions of temperature and pressure, by using rectilinear graphs, or, alternatively, shows compositional relations at constant temperature and pressure, by using triangular or tetrahedral axes. There are in addition numerous combinations, such as triangular composition diagrams with isotherms or isobars superimposed.

These methods are essentially as important as their widespread use would indicate, and in any comprehensive treatment of methods of portrayal of chemical relations would occupy a large part of the text. But because they are in such common use, and because adequate texts are available that discuss their construction and interpretation, they will be considered here only in their relation to other types of diagrams. As a result, anyone who might use this book as a guide to all the methods available, treated at a length consistent with their importance, would find it lopsided. But it is largely a vehicle for making available a large number of diagrams of other types that should be useful to geologists.

EQUATIONS AS THE BASIS OF REPRESENTATION

All methods of representation must be synthesized from individual chemical reactions. Such a statement perhaps emphasizes the

obvious, but there is so great a tendency to use pressure-temperature-composition diagrams to show the fields of stability of solids that the methods by which the relations are obtained are ofttimes neglected. If a return is made to individual equations as the building blocks, it can be seen that the graphical structures useful in portraying their inter-connections are many, and that the ones chosen should depend upon the problem to be solved.

Because chemical terminology has become so complex, and various notations are used, it is advisable to devote a preliminary section to definitions of terms and symbols before attempting even the simpler chemical equations.

TERMS AND SYMBOLS

The formulas of compounds will be written in the standard manner, i.e., H_2O, CO_2. The subscripts generally will indicate only the atomic ratios of the elements, and will be whole numbers. From place to place larger numbers may be used if knowledge of structural con-stitution is important. On the one hand, H_4SiO_4 indicates only that H, Si, and O are in the atomic ratios of $4/1/4$, and carries no implica-tion, unless stated otherwise, that the molecular species involved is not $H_8Si_2O_8$ or $H_{16}Si_4O_{16}$. On the other hand, if a formula is written with larger than minimum whole number subscripts, such as V_3O_9, structural information has been taken into account.

To indicate polymerization of unknown degree, the minimum sub-script formula may be enclosed in parentheses, and the whole given a subscript x, i.e., $(H_4SiO_4)_x$. To designate solid solution relations fractional subscripts are used within parentheses. The formula of a certain magnesian calcite would be written $(Ca_{0.9}Mg_{0.1})CO_3$.

Lower case subscripts following a formula are used to designate the state of the substance, or to provide other descriptive information, as follows:

c	crystalline
l	liquid
g	gas
aq	in aqueous solution
1 atm.	at one atmosphere pressure

As an example, O_2, g, 25°, 1 atm., means molecular gaseous oxygen at 25°C and 1 atmosphere pressure. $S_{c,rh}$ means crystalline rhombic

sulfur. The most commonly used subscripts are those listed above indicating state. Where other descriptive terms are used throughout the text, they will be spelled out.

CONCENTRATION UNITS

Most low-temperature natural solutions are highly aqueous, therefore it is convenient to use the concentration units developed by chemists for dilute water solutions, such as molality and molarity, as opposed to mol fraction, which is perhaps more useful for solutions of all types.

Molality, m, is expressed as moles of solute per 1000 grams of water; formality,[1] f, is moles of solute per 1000 grams of solution, and molarity, M, is moles of solute per 1000 milliliters of solution. In the ensuing calculations molality will be used almost exclusively. In most instances the difference between m, f, and M is so small that it can be neglected, because it is overshadowed by other uncertainties, such as the errors in free energy values.

The interrelations of these three concentration units are:

$$\text{molality} = m = \frac{\text{weight solute} \times 1000}{\text{formula weight solute} \times \text{weight water}} \qquad (1.1)$$

$$\text{formality} = f = \frac{\text{weight solute} \times 1000}{\text{formula weight solute} \times \text{weight solution}} \qquad (1.2)$$

$$\text{molarity} = M = \frac{\text{weight solute} \times 1000}{\text{formula weight solute} \times \text{volume solution}} \qquad (1.3)$$

Dividing (1) by (2):

$$\frac{m}{f} = \frac{\text{weight solution}}{\text{weight water}} \qquad (1.4)$$

Since weight water = weight solution − total weight solutes:

$$m = f \frac{\text{weight solution}}{\text{weight solution} - \text{total weight solutes}} \qquad (1.5)$$

Dividing (1.3) by (1.2):

$$\frac{M}{f} = \frac{\text{weight solution}}{\text{volume solution}} \qquad (1.6)$$

[1] There seems to be no consistent definition of formality as used in the chemical literature. The definition used here is from *Webster's Unabridged Dictionary*, 1955.

Since weight solution $=$ volume $\times$ density:

$$M = f \times \text{density of solution} \qquad (1.7)$$

From (1.4) and (1.7):

$$m = M \frac{\text{weight solution}}{(\text{weight solution} - \text{total weight solutes})} \times \frac{1}{\text{density}} \qquad (1.8)$$

As an example of the application of the relations, a calculation will be made of the formality, molality, and molarity of sodium ion in a brine with a density of 1.018 containing 10,000 ppm total dissolved solids, and in which the sodium ion is 1000 ppm. Inasmuch as the analysis is expressed in weight of solutes per weight of solution, the first step is to obtain the formality from equation (1.2):

$$f = \frac{\text{weight Na}^+ \times 1000}{\text{formula weight Na}^+ \times \text{weight solution}} = \frac{1000 \times 1000}{23 \times 1{,}000{,}000} = 0.0435$$

Then, from equation (1.5):

$$m = 0.0435 \frac{\text{weight solution}}{\text{weight solution} - \textit{total} \text{ weight solutes}}$$

$$= \frac{0.0435 \times 1{,}000{,}000}{1{,}000{,}000 - 10{,}000} = 0.0439$$

From equation (1.7):

$$M = f \times \text{density of solution} = 0.0435 \times 1.018 = 0.0442$$

Consequently, for such a brine, which is fairly characteristic of waters encountered underground, $f = 0.0435$, $m = 0.0439$, and $M = 0.0442$. These differences increase with increasing total solutes. However, a great many natural waters are so dilute, that the difference can be disregarded.

The *mole fraction* of a given constituent in solution is defined as the ratio of the number of moles of the given constituent to the total moles of constituents:

$$N_1 = \frac{\text{moles}_1}{\text{moles}_1 + \text{moles}_2 + \text{moles}_3 + \text{moles}_x}$$

No distinction is made between solute and solvent; the mole fraction of NaCl in a 1.0 molal solution is:

$$N_{\text{NaCl}} = \frac{1}{1 + 55.51} = 0.0177$$

The value 55.51 is the number of moles of water in 1000 grams.

We will use mole fraction from time to time in calculating the partial pressures of gases, based on the relation:

$$\frac{\text{partial pressure gas}_1}{\text{total gas pressure}} = \text{mole fraction gas}_1$$

Molality and partial pressure are the concentration terms that will be used almost exclusively in this text. Molality of a given species will be designated either as a small m followed by a subscript indicating the species, as $m_{Fe^{++}}$, or the chemical symbol of the species will be enclosed in parentheses (Fe^{++}). Partial pressure is symbolized by a capital P followed by a subscript indicating the species, as P_{O_2}, P_{CO_2}.

THERMODYNAMIC CONCENTRATION—ACTIVITY

Most of the calculations used in this book will result in obtaining the thermodynamic concentration or *activity* of a substance. The activity of a solute, for example, is defined in such a way that the ratio of the activity to the molality becomes unity at infinite dilution. At very moderate molalities there is a significant deviation of activity and molality. By an activity of one we mean a concentration identical numerically to a molality of one, under the particular condition that the behavior of the solution is ideal. Very few real solutions fulfill this criterion of ideal behavior; thus a solution at an activity of one is only roughly comparable to a solution in which $m = 1$. For our purposes it is sufficient to recognize the following relations:

1. The activity of solids and pure liquids is one.

2. The activity of a gas is numerically equal to the partial pressure of the gas as calculated from its mole fraction, under the condition for which calculations will be made here, that is, for pressures of a few atmospheres or less at 25°C. This relation holds, in fact, in the range through which a given gas behaves ideally, which means that the validity of the near-identity of activity and partial pressure differs with the particular gas considered, and calculations involving hydrogen, for example, could be extended well beyond the "few atmospheres" general limit.

3. The activity of a solute is numerically equal to its molality only in highly dilute solution. Again, the near identity holds in the range of ideal solution behavior, which is very restricted, especially for polar solutes in water. Methods of obtaining the relation between activity

and molality in relatively concentrated solutions is the subject of the next chapter.

To denote activity of a given species the symbol *a* will be used, followed by a subscript indicating the species, as $a_{Fe^{++}}$, or the chemical symbol of the species will be enclosed in brackets [Fe^{++}].

For an excellent discussion of the development of the concept of activity, the reader is referred to Glasstone (Samuel Glasstone, *Thermodynamics for Chemists*. D. Van Nostrand Co., Princeton, N.J., 1947, pp. 350–376).

THE LAW OF MASS ACTION AND THE EQUILIBRIUM CONSTANT

One of the cornerstones of the development of stability relations among minerals is the *Law of Mass Action*. It was discovered long ago that the driving force of a chemical reaction to right or to left could be related to the concentrations of the reactants and the products. When a reaction is at equilibrium, that is to say that the rates to the right and left are equal, and that any small change in the concentrations will be followed by a reversion to the original state, the relations of the concentrations of the reactants and products can be stated, "The product of the activities of the reaction products, each raised to the power indicated by its numerical coefficient, divided by the product of the activities of the reactants, each raised to a corresponding power, is a constant at a given temperature and pressure."

The basic simplicity of the law is obscured by the words necessary to state it. If the reaction of *b* moles of *B* with *c* moles of *C* has come to equilibrium with the products *d* moles of *D* and *e* moles of *E*:

$$bB + cC = dD + eE$$

Then

$$\frac{a_D^d \, a_E^e}{a_B^b \, a_C^c} = k = \text{equilibrium constant}$$

STANDARD FREE ENERGY OF FORMATION, ΔF_f°

When the interrelations of chemical reactions and their energy changes are considered, a new definition of equilibrium can be formulated. Equilibrium is attained when the energy released or absorbed

by a reaction is zero. Any spontaneous reaction not at equilibrium releases energy. On that basis:

$$\sum \text{energy products} - \sum \text{energy reactants} = 0$$

defines an equilibrium condition.

The next step in this development is to relate energy changes of reactions to their equilibrium constants, and it becomes necessary to define the energy content of various types of substances. It will be necessary only to obtain the *standard free energy of formation*, the energy of the reaction to form one mole of the substances in their standard states from the elements under standard conditions.

The standard or reference conditions in general use are at 25°C and 1 atmosphere total pressure, a great convenience because the discussions in this text are concerned almost exclusively with such conditions. The standard states of various types of substances are as follows:

1. The standard state of an element is the one that occurs stably at the standard conditions. Examples are Fe_c, O_{2g}, Hg_l, $S_{c, rhombic}$. The standard free energy of formation of a mole of the elements is zero by convention.

2. The standard state of a compound is defined similarly to that for an element. For those compounds that are solid or liquid, the standard free energy of formation is the energy change (in kilocalories) in the formation of one mole of the compound from the elements. For gaseous compounds, the standard free energy of formation is the energy change in forming one mole of the compound at a partial pressure of one.

3. The standard state of a species dissolved in water is at an activity of one, and the standard free energy is the energy change for the reaction from the elements to the dissolved species in the standard state.

The standard free energy of formation is symbolized ΔF_f°. Tables for substances of geologic interest are given in Appendix A. Much more comprehensive lists are given in Latimer (W. M. Latimer, *Oxidation Potentials*: Prentice-Hall, Inc., Englewood Cliffs, N.J., 1952, 392 pp.); in *U.S. Bureau of Standards Circular 500* (R. D. Rossini, D. D. Wagman, W. H. Evans, Samuel Levine, and Irving Jaffe, Selected values of chemical thermodynamic properties, *Natl. Bur. Standards Circ. 500*, U.S. Dept. Commerce, 1952, 1268 pp. [plus later supplements]); in various bulletins of the U.S. Bureau of Mines, in technical reports of the Belgian Center for the Study of Corrosion (cf. Enthalpies libres de

formation standards, a 25°C, *Rapport Tech. 28*, 1955, Centre Belge
d'Etude de la Corrosion, Bruxelles, pp. 1–9). The data compiled in
Latimer's book are probably most easily used in conjunction with this
text, inasmuch as they are restricted to standard conditions.

STANDARD FREE ENERGY OF REACTION AND THE EQUILIBRIUM CONSTANT

The standard free energy of a reaction is the sum of the free energies
of formation of the products in their standard states, minus the free
energy of formation of the reactants in their standard states:

$$\Delta F_R^\circ = \sum \Delta F_{f\,\text{products}}^\circ - \Delta F_{f\,\text{reactants}}^\circ$$

The standard free energy of reaction is related to the equilibrium
constant by:

$$\Delta F_R^\circ = - RT \ln k$$

where R is the gas constant and T the absolute temperature. For
almost all relations to be discussed, which are at 25°C and 1 atmosphere
total pressure:

$$\Delta F_R^\circ \,(\text{kcal}) = -0.00198 \text{ kcal/deg} \times 298.16° \times 2.303 \log k$$
$$\Delta F_R^\circ = -1.364 \log k$$

This relation is the basis of all following calculations.

REACTION TYPES

REACTIONS INVOLVING ONLY SOLIDS

Equilibrium is attained only when the free energy change of a reaction is zero. When solids react to produce solids, the free energy of
the reaction at 25°C and 1 atmosphere total pressure is the standard
free energy of the reaction, and cannot be varied because the activity
of solids is fixed. Thus only by merest chance can equilibrium among
solids occur at an arbitrarily selected temperature and pressure.

This relation is a useful one, because it puts solid-solid reactions into
a go-no-go category. Any such proposed reaction can quickly be
tested to see if the proposed reactant(s) or product(s) is the stable
species. If the standard free energy of the reaction is negative—i.e.,

energy is released—then the product(s) is stable; if the standard free energy is positive, the reactant(s) is stable relative to the product(s).

For example, there are two monoxides of lead—a red and a yellow variety. For the reaction:

$$PbO_{c\,red} \rightleftarrows PbO_{c\,yellow}$$
$$\Delta F_f^\circ\,PbO_{yellow} - \Delta F_f^\circ\,PbO_{red} = \Delta F_R^\circ$$
$$-45.05 - (-45.25) = +0.20 \text{ kcal}$$

Thus PbO_{red} is the stable phase. The method is a convenient test for the relative stability of any polymorphs.

For a reaction of geologic interest involving two reactants and two products:

$$PbCO_{3\,c} + CaSO_{4\,c} \rightleftarrows PbSO_{4\,c} + CaCO_{3\,c\,calcite}$$
$$\Delta F_{f\,PbSO_4}^\circ + \Delta F_{f\,CaCO_3}^\circ - \Delta F_{f\,PbCO_3}^\circ - \Delta F_{f\,CaSO_4}^\circ = \Delta F_R^\circ$$
$$(-193.89) + (-269.78) - (-149.7) - (-315.56) = +1.59 \text{ kcal}$$

Therefore cerussite and anhydrite are stable with respect to anglesite and calcite. If reactions go to completion in nature, anglesite and calcite should be an unknown association under standard conditions. Only by changing the temperature or the pressure or both could all four species be brought into equilibrium.

REACTIONS INVOLVING ONLY SOLIDS AND NEARLY PURE WATER

Reactions that involve only solids and pure or nearly pure liquid water can be treated like solid-solid reactions, inasmuch as the activity of pure water also is fixed. This gives a test for such relations as stability of oxides versus hydroxides, or of oxides versus hydrates in dilute water solution. For example:

$$Al_2O_3 \cdot H_2O_{c,\,boehmite} + 2H_2O_l = Al_2O_3 \cdot 3H_2O_{gibbsite}$$
$$\Delta F_{f\,gibbsite}^\circ - \Delta F_{f\,boehmite}^\circ - 2\Delta F_{f\,H2O}^\circ = \Delta F_R^\circ$$
$$(-554.6) - (-435.0) - (-113.4) = -6.2 \text{ kcal}$$

Gibbsite is the stable phase relative to boehmite in dilute aqueous solution.

REACTIONS INVOLVING A GAS PHASE

If a reaction involves a gas phase, equilibrium can usually be achieved under standard conditions by varying the partial pressure

(activity) of the gas. For example, if a single gas is involved, as in the reaction:

$$FeO_c + CO_{2g} = FeCO_{3c}$$

The equilibrium constant is:

$$k = \frac{[FeCO_3]}{[FeO]\, P_{CO_2}}$$

Because the activities of the solids are constant, the expression reduces to:

$$k = \frac{1}{P_{CO_2}}$$

Thus a reaction involving solids and a single gas phase is at equilibrium under standard conditions at a single fixed partial pressure of the gas. In this instance:

$$\Delta F^\circ_{f\,FeCO_3} - \Delta F^\circ_{f\,FeO} - \Delta F^\circ_{f\,CO_2} = \Delta F^\circ_R$$

$$(-161.06) - (-58.4) - (-94.26) = -8.40 \text{ kcal}$$

Then

$$-1.364 \log k = -8.40$$

$$\log k = 6.1$$

and

$$P_{CO_2} = 10^{-6.1} \text{ atm.}$$

This indicates that at the earth's surface FeO is unstable relative to siderite, inasmuch as the partial pressure of CO_2 in the atmosphere is about $10^{-3.5}$ atmosphere. On the other hand, FeO may be unstable relative to other compounds as well, so that the reaction cited tests only the $FeO-FeCO_3$ pair. Yet it does give a specific answer to the specific question.

Many reactions can be expressed in terms of two or even more gas pressures. The determination of the equilibrium constant is similar to that for a single gas:

$$Fe_c + CO_{2g} + \tfrac{1}{2}O_{2g} = FeCO_{3c}$$

$$\Delta F^\circ_{f\,FeCO_3} - \Delta F^\circ_{f\,Fe} - \Delta F^\circ_{f\,CO_2} - \tfrac{1}{2}\Delta F^\circ_{f\,O_2} = \Delta F^\circ_R$$

$$(-161.06) - (0) - (-94.26) - \tfrac{1}{2}(0) = -67.00 \text{ kcal}$$

$$-1.364 \log k = -67.00$$

$$\log k = 49.1$$

Then

$$\log \frac{1}{P_{CO_2} P_{O_2}^{1/2}} = 49.1$$

For many applications it is convenient to keep the relation in logarithmic form. Rearranging

$$\log P_{CO_2} = -49.1 - \tfrac{1}{2} \log P_{O_2}$$

On a log-log plot of the partial pressures of oxygen and CO_2, the reaction for equilibrium between iron and siderite would plot as a straight line with a slope of $-\tfrac{1}{2}$, and an intercept of -49.1.

REACTIONS INVOLVING DISSOLVED SPECIES

As for gases, reactions involving dissolved species can be expressed in terms of the activities of the dissolved species. Abundant thermochemical data to handle this kind of reaction are available only under standard conditions, but we are on the verge of having data available for a wide range of temperatures and pressures. In many ways the unique aspect of this text is the extensive use of data for dissolved species, which are completely unavailable for the high temperature–high pressure reactions. Strangely enough, little use has been made of the thermochemical data by investigators interested in low temperature–low pressure systems of geologic interest.

What happens when hematite is put into water? What is the activity of ferric ion? Questions of this kind can be answered, at least in part, by writing the reaction:

$$Fe_2O_{3\,c} + 3H_2O_l = 2Fe^{3+}_{aq} + 6OH^-_{aq}$$

The equilibrium constant for the reaction is:

$$k = \frac{[Fe^{3+}]^2[OH^-]^6}{[Fe_2O_3][H_2O]^3}$$

The activities of $Fe_2O_{3\,c}$ and H_2O_l are unity, so

$$k = [Fe^{3+}]^2[OH^-]^6$$

The standard free energy of the reaction is:

$$2\varDelta F^\circ_{f\,Fe^{3+}} + 6\varDelta F^\circ_{f\,OH^-} - \varDelta F^\circ_{f\,Fe_2O_3} - 3\varDelta F^\circ_{f\,H_2O} = \varDelta F^\circ_R$$

$$(2 \times -2.53) + (6 \times -37.6) - (-177.1) - (3 \times -56.69) = 116.51 \text{ kcal}$$

Then

$$-1.364 \log k = 116.51$$
$$\log k = -85.4 = \log [Fe^{3+}]^2[OH^-]^6$$

Rearranging and simplifying:

$$\log [Fe^{3+}] = -42.7 - 3 \log [OH^-]$$

Therefore the ferric ion is a function of the cube of the hydroxyl activity in the solution. The stability of Fe_2O_3 in water can be plotted as a linear equation if $\log [Fe^{3+}]$ and $\log [OH^-]$ are used as coordinates.

As compared to partial pressure diagrams, such plots can be termed activity-activity diagrams. Activity-activity diagrams can obviously be used to show stability relations using any activities of dissolved species as the axes. Because so many reactions of geologic interest involve the activity of hydrogen ions or can be rewritten to include activity of hydrogen ions, special attention is directed toward writing reactions so that the activity of hydrogen ions becomes one of the variables plotted.

REACTIONS INVOLVING DISSOLVED SPECIES

THE ROLE OF pH

Because the activity of hydrogen ions is involved in, or can, by a little effort, become involved in reactions with dissolved species, and because experimental techniques permit accurate measurement of the activity of hydrogen ions, there has been a tendency to use a_{H^+} as a characterizing variable whenever possible, so as to help provide a common reference activity for a variety of reactions. Also, because so many representations of activities are most conveniently shown as logarithmic functions, the term pH was developed long ago:

$$pH = -\log a_{H^+}$$

If we reconsider the reaction discussed in the previous section:

$$Fe_2O_{3\,c} + 3H_2O = 2Fe^{3+}_{aq} + 6OH^-_{aq}$$

We see that it can be rewritten, by adding the reaction for the dissociation of water:

$$Fe_2O_{3\,c} + 3H_2O = 2Fe^{3+}_{aq} + 6OH^-_{aq}$$
$$6OH^-_{aq} + 6H^+_{aq} = 6H_2O_l$$
$$\overline{\phantom{Fe_2O_{3\,c} + 6H^+_{aq} = 2Fe^{3+}_{aq} + 3H_2O_l}}$$
$$Fe_2O_{3\,c} + 6H^+_{aq} = 2Fe^{3+}_{aq} + 3H_2O_l$$

The only variable activities are those of Fe^{3+}_{aq} and H^+_{aq}. The equilibrium constant is:

$$\log k = \log \frac{[Fe^{3+}]^2}{[H^+]^6}$$

Rearranging:

$$\log k = 2 \log [Fe^{3+}] - 6 \log [H^+]$$

But by substituting the relation

$$pH = - \log [H^+]$$

we obtain

$$\log k = 2 \log [Fe^{3+}] + 6pH$$

The number of reactions that can be expressed with pH as a variable is remarkable, not only reactions involving oxides, hydroxides, and basic salts, but also those including carbonates, silicates, and sulfides.

THE ROLE OF Eh

Just as pH can be developed as a variable in a great many reactions, so can the oxidation potential, Eh, be used to compare equilibrium conditions among diverse substances. Here it is convenient to develop the concept of Eh through those of pH and partial pressures of gases.

The first step in the development of Eh is the splitting of oxidation-reduction reactions into *half-cells* or *half-reactions*. For the oxidation of ferrous ions to ferric ions by reaction with hydrogen ions:

$$Fe^{++}_{aq} + H^+_{aq} = Fe^{3+}_{aq} + \tfrac{1}{2}H_{2\,g} \qquad (1.9)$$

Ferrous ions are oxidized to ferric ions, and hydrogen ions are reduced to hydrogen. We can think of the overall reaction as the sum of two processes—oxidation of ferrous ion to ferric, with an electron left over:

$$Fe^{++}_{aq} = Fe^{3+}_{aq} + e \qquad (1.10)$$

And reduction of hydrogen ion to hydrogen, accompanied by the acceptance of an electron.

$$H^+_{aq} + e = \tfrac{1}{2}H_{2\,g} \qquad (1.11)$$

Either of these half reactions is called a half-cell, or half-reaction. Now consider the free energy relation:

$$\Delta F^{\circ}_{f\,Fe^{3+}} + \Delta F^{\circ}_{f\,e} - \Delta F^{\circ}_{f\,Fe^{++}} = \Delta F^{\circ}_{R(1.10)}$$

$$\tfrac{1}{2}\Delta F^{\circ}_{f\,H_2} - \Delta F^{\circ}_{f\,H^+} - \Delta F^{\circ}_{f\,e} = \Delta F^{\circ}_{R(1.11)}$$

In other words, $\Delta F^\circ_{R(1.10)} + \Delta F^\circ_{R(1.11)} = \Delta F^\circ_{R(1.09)}$ or the sum of the free energies of reaction of the half-cells is identical to that of the whole reaction. Note also that ΔF°_{fe} disappears during the addition. When we examine ΔF°_R for the hydrogen half-cell: $H^+_{aq} + e = \frac{1}{2}H_{2\,g}$ it is found that:

$$\tfrac{1}{2}\Delta F^\circ_{f\,H_2} - \Delta F^\circ_{f\,H^+\,aq} - \Delta F^\circ_{fe} = \Delta F^\circ_R$$

and

$$\tfrac{1}{2}\Delta F^\circ_{f\,H_2} - \Delta F^\circ_{f\,H^+\,aq} = \Delta F^\circ_R + \Delta F^\circ_{fe}$$

Similarly, for $Fe^{++}_{aq} = Fe^{3+}_{aq} + e$

$$\Delta F^\circ_{f\,Fe^{3+}} = \Delta F^\circ_R - \Delta F^\circ_{fe}$$

Therefore the actual value for ΔF°_{fe} is unimportant, for it drops out in the addition of the free energies of any two half-cell reactions. Henceforth we can treat ΔF°_{fe} as if it were zero. Then

$$H^+_{aq} + e = \tfrac{1}{2}H_{2\,g}$$
$$\tfrac{1}{2}\Delta F^\circ_{f\,H_2} - \Delta F^\circ_{f\,H^+} = \Delta F^\circ_R$$
$$0 - 0 = 0$$

The standard free energy of reaction of the hydrogen half-cell is zero. Consequently any oxidation-reduction reaction can be written as two half-reactions with the hydrogen half-reaction as the reducing or oxidizing part of the two couples, and the standard free energy change attributed entirely to the oxidation or reduction half-cells, ignoring the ΔF°_f of the electrons. A specific example will help to clarify this statement. For the reaction:

$$Fe^{++}_{aq} + Cu^{++}_{aq} = Fe^{3+}_{aq} + Cu^+_{aq} \qquad (1.12)$$

we can write:

$$Fe^{++}_{aq} = Fe^{3+}_{aq} + e \qquad (1.13)$$
$$Cu^{++}_{aq} + e = Cu^+_{aq} \qquad (1.14)$$
$$\Delta F^\circ_{f\,Fe^{3+}} - \Delta F^\circ_{f\,Fe^{++}} = \Delta F^\circ_{R(1.13)}$$
$$\Delta F^\circ_{f\,Cu^+} + - \Delta F^\circ_{f\,Cu^{++}} = \Delta F^\circ_{(1.14)}$$
$$\Delta F^\circ_{R(1.13)} + \Delta F^\circ_{R(1.14)} = \Delta F^\circ_{R(1.12)}$$

$\Delta F^\circ_{R(1.13)}$ and $\Delta F^\circ_{R(1.14)}$ are the standard free energies of the half reactions. Thus if we have a series of standard free energies for half reactions available, we can take any pairs we choose to obtain the overall free energy of the oxidation-reduction reaction.

This leads to a relation between free energies of reactions and voltage measurements of galvanic cells. Let us suppose we have a copper electrode dipping into a solution containing cupric ions at unit activity, and a hydrogen electrode consisting of an inert platinum electrode dipping into a solution at unit activity of hydrogen ions, and saturated with hydrogen gas at 1 atmosphere pressure (also unit activity).

If the electrodes are connected, electrons will flow through the circuit. At the copper electrode, copper will be deposited by discharge of cupric ions:

$$Cu_{aq}^{++} + 2e = Cu_c^\circ$$

and at the hydrogen electrode hydrogen will release electrons to become H^+:

$$H_{2g} = 2H_{aq}^+ + 2e$$

Thus the overall reaction is:

$$Cu_{aq}^{++} + H_{2g} = Cu_c^\circ + 2H_{aq}^+$$

The voltage between the electrodes can be measured at the very beginning of the process, before any sensible change in activities has occurred because of the reactions, and will be found to be 0.337 volt. When the reaction comes to equilibrium, the voltage will decrease to zero.

Thus in the beginning there is a voltage corresponding to a reaction under standard conditions and at unit activity of all substances; at the end, the voltage disappears when the free energy change becomes zero. This suggests a relation between voltage and standard free energy change, which has been found to be:

$$\Delta F_R^\circ = E_R^\circ n\mathscr{F} \tag{1.15}$$

where E_R° is the voltage of the reaction when all substances involved are at unit activity; n is the number of electrons involved (2 in the case cited for the copper-hydrogen cell), and $\mathscr{F}$ is a constant, the faraday. A faraday is 23.06 kcal per volt-gram equivalent—the units necessary to express the faraday to have it be consistent with the other units used.

The equation relating E_R° directly to the equilibrium constant under standard conditions is:

$$E_R^\circ = -\frac{1.364}{n\mathscr{F}} \log k \tag{1.16}$$

The standard free energy of the hydrogen half-cell reaction is zero; correspondingly its voltage is also used as a zero reference. The

voltage of any circuit, when a given standard half-cell is measured
against the standard hydrogen cell, can be attributed entirely to the
given standard half-cell and used to obtain its standard free energy of
reaction.

Consider the standard copper-cupric ion electrode. Its EMF
measured against the standard hydrogen electrode is 0.337 volt, and
two electrons are involved. From equation (1.15):

$$\Delta F_R^\circ = E^\circ n \mathscr{F}$$
$$\Delta F_R^\circ = 0.337 \times 2 \times 23.06 = 15.54 \, \text{kcal}$$

By writing the reaction and using ΔF_f° values:

$$Cu^\circ = Cu_{aq}^{++} + 2e$$
$$\Delta F_{f\,Cu^{++}}^\circ - \Delta F_{f\,Cu^\circ}^\circ = \Delta F_R^\circ$$
$$15.53 - 0 = 15.53 \, \text{kcal}$$

Now let us consider the situation when the potential of a copper
electrode immersed in a solution of cupric ions is measured against a
standard hydrogen electrode, but the *activity of the cupric ions is not
unity.* For this situation we can write:

$$\text{Eh} = E^\circ + \frac{RT}{n\mathscr{F}} \ln \frac{[Cu^{++}]}{[Cu^\circ]} \tag{1.17}$$

where Eh is the potential under experimental conditions measured
against the standard hydrogen electrode, E° is the potential of the
reaction under standard conditions, R the gas constant, T the absolute
temperature, n the number of electrons, and $\mathscr{F}$ the faraday. At $25\,°C$
and 1 atmosphere total pressure this expression can be rewritten:

$$\text{Eh} = E^\circ + \frac{0.059}{n} \log \frac{[Cu^{++}]}{[Cu^\circ]} \tag{1.18}$$

The term $[Cu^{++}]/[Cu^\circ]$ is known under these conditions as a reaction
constant Q, as opposed to the equilibrium constant k for a complete
reaction.

If the measured potential is 0.100 volt, then remembering the
activity of Cu° is unity, and the number of electrons involved is 2:

$$0.100 = 0.337 + \frac{0.059}{2} \log [Cu^{++}] \tag{1.19}$$

$$[Cu^{++}] = 10^{-8.03}$$

The relation for any half-cell whose potential is measured against a standard hydrogen half-cell can be generalized:

$$bB + cC = dD + eE + ne$$

$$Eh = E° + \frac{0.059}{n} \log \frac{[D]^d[E]^e}{[B]^b[C]^c} \tag{1.20}$$

Many oxidation-reduction reactions of geologic interest can be defined by Eh alone, by Eh and pH alone, or by Eh, pH and the activity of a single dissolved species. Thus plots of Eh versus pH can be used to compare stability relations of many reactions. Also, both Eh and pH can be measured by simple equipment under field and laboratory conditions, whereas the activities of individual ions or the partial pressures of gases are more difficult to obtain.

To show the use of Eh and pH as characterizing variables, even though many diagrams will be developed in detail in later chapters, let us answer the question: Which will oxidize first under alkaline conditions, V_2O_3 to V_2O_4 or MnO to Mn_2O_3?

The procedure is to write the half-cells, *always putting the oxidation products on the right, and writing the reactions in terms of water, hydrogen ions, and electrons wherever possible.* For the vanadium reaction:

$$V_2O_{3c} + H_2O_1 = V_2O_{4c} + 2H^+_{aq} + 2e \tag{1.21}$$
$$\Delta F°_{fV_2O_4} + 2\Delta F°_{fH^+} - \Delta F°_{fV_2O_3} - \Delta F°_{fH_2O} = \Delta F°_R$$
$$-318 + 2(0) - (-271) - (-56.69) = +9.7 \text{ kcal}$$

From equation (1.15) ($\Delta F°_R = E°n\mathscr{F}$):

$$9.7 = E° \times 2 \times 23.06$$
$$E° = 0.210 \text{ volt}$$

From equation (1.20) ($[V_2O_3]$, $[V_2O_4]$, $[H_2O] = 1$):

$$Eh = 0.210 + \frac{0.059}{2} \log [H^+]^2$$
$$= 0.210 + 0.059 \log [H^+]$$

Because pH $= -\log [H^+]$

$$Eh = 0.210 - 0.059 \text{ pH} \tag{1.22}$$

For the manganese reaction:

$$2MnO_c + H_2O_1 = Mn_2O_{3c} + 2H^+_{aq} + 2e \tag{1.23}$$
$$\Delta F°_{fMn_2O_3} + 2\Delta F°_{fH^+} - 2\Delta F°_{fMnO} - \Delta F°_{fH_2O} = \Delta F°_R$$
$$-212.3 + 0 - (2 \times -86.8) - (-56.69) = +18.0 \text{ kcal}$$

From equation (1.15) $(\Delta F_R^\circ = E^\circ n \mathscr{F})$:

$$18.0 = E^\circ \times 2 \times 23.06$$

$$E^\circ = 0.390 \text{ volt}$$

From equation (1.20) $([Mn_2O_3], [MnO], [H_2O] = 1)$:

$$Eh = 0.390 + \frac{0.059}{2} \log [H^+]^2$$

By substituting $-pH$ for $\log [H^+]$:

$$Eh = 0.390 - 0.059 \, pH \tag{1.24}$$

Equation (1.22) is the boundary between V_2O_3 and V_2O_4, and equation (24) is the boundary between MnO and Mn_2O_3. The equations are of the same form, being linear on an Eh-pH plot, and they have the same slope. Figure 1.1 shows the equations plotted on an Eh-pH grid. Clearly V_2O_3 oxidizes to V_2O_4 at a lower potential under all conditions than MnO oxides to Mn_2O_3.

SUMMARY

The various terms and symbols to be used in following chapters have been defined. The molality, m, was chosen as the analytical concentration unit of dissolved species and partial pressure as the concentration unit for gases. The activity, a, is the thermodynamic concentration resulting from thermochemical calculations.

The basis for later development of stability relations was derived in terms of several equations. They are: (1) expression for the equilibrium constant, $k = a_D^d a_E^e / a_B^b a_C^c$; (2) the relation between standard free energy of reaction and the equilibrium constant, $\Delta F_R^\circ = - RT \ln k$; (3) the relation between standard free energy of formation and the standard electrode potential, $\Delta F_R^\circ = E^\circ n \mathscr{F}$; (4) the relation between measured reaction potential, standard potential, and the reaction constant,

$$Eh = E^\circ + \frac{RT}{n\mathscr{F}} \ln \frac{a_D^d a_E^e}{a_B^b a_C^c}$$

The use of the relations has been demonstrated by a consideration of reactions of various types under standard conditions, those involving only solids, those expressed in terms of gas pressures, and those expressed in terms of the activities of dissolved species. Special emphasis has been given to expression of equilibrium relations as a function of Eh and pH.

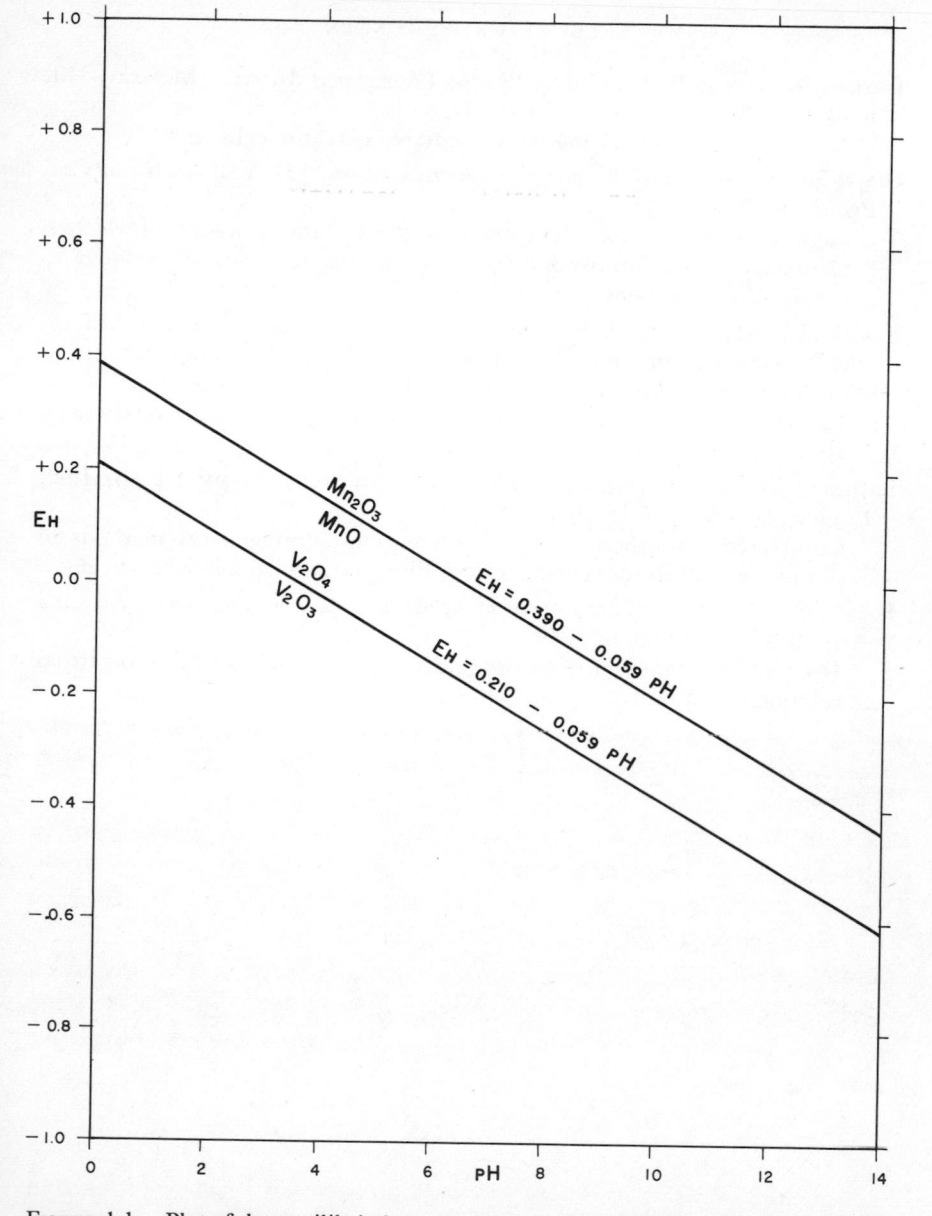

FIGURE 1.1. Plot of the equilibria between V_2O_3 and V_2O_4 and between MnO and Mn_2O_3 as functions of Eh and pH, showing that V_2O_3 oxidizes to V_2O_4 at a lower potential under all pH conditions than that for $MnO–Mn_2O_3$. Diagram at 25°C and 1 atm. total pressure.

SELECTED REFERENCES

Darken, L. S., and R. W. Gurry, *Physical Chemistry of Metals*.   McGraw-Hill
Book Co., New York, 1953, Chap. 17.
   A concise summary of the basic theory of galvanic cells.

Glasstone, Samuel, *An Introduction to Electrochemistry*.   D. Van Nostrand Co.,
Princeton, N.J., 1942.
   General reference for all aspects of theory and practice of electrochemistry; good for trouble shooting on specific problems related to
   details of calculations.

Kolthoff, I. M., and E. B. Sandell, *Textbook of Quantitative Inorganic Analysis*.
The Macmillan Company, New York, 1952, Chaps. IV (Mass Action), V
(Solubility and Solubility Product), X (Theory of Electroanalysis).
   Excellent introduction at the second year level to the basic relations of
   chemical equilibria.

Latimer, W. M., *Oxidation Potentials*, 2nd edition.   Prentice-Hall, Inc.,
Englewood Cliffs, N.J., 1952, Chap. I.
   Condensed discussion of units, conventions, and general methods of
   obtaining equilibrium constants and Eh equations from free energy data.

Pourbaix, M. J. N., *Thermodynamics of Dilute Aqueous Solutions*.   Edward
Arnold & Co., London, 1949.
   Detailed development of theory and practice of pH-oxidation potential
   relations.

2

Activity-Concentration Relations

A_{LL} the relations to be deduced are based on thermodynamic concentrations, or activities. But the geologist wants to be able to calculate solubilities of substances in various aqueous environments. This requires development of a relation between the activities of dissolved species of a given element and total concentration of the element as determined by chemical analysis.

It must be recognized from the beginning that calculation of solubilities is still more of an art than a science, and that any values determined entirely theoretically are suspect. The solubility of a given element is the sum of the stoichiometric concentrations of all dissolved species containing the element. Thus accurate calculation of solubility requires knowledge of all species contributing to the result of chemical analysis, plus a relation between concentration of a given species and its activity.

Therefore to make solubility calculations, the geochemist needs detailed knowledge of the chemistry of the element in question; it might almost be said that the result, to be trusted, has to be known in advance from experimental work. Yet it is possible in many instances to calculate a *minimum solubility* that is nearly as useful as the true solubility in answering geochemical questions.

The concentration of a given element in aqueous solution as determined by quantitative analysis can be described as:

$$m_A = \sum m_S$$

where m_A is the total molality defined as:

m_A = moles per 1000 grams of water

$$= \frac{\text{weight of element obtained by analysis} \times 1000}{\text{atomic weight of element} \times \text{weight of containing water}}$$

Then $\sum m_S$ is the sum of the molalities of all species containing the element, where the molality of a given species is defined similarly to m_A, on the assumption that the species could be isolated and determined quantitatively.

To relate m_A to calculated activities of individual species, a connection between activity and molality of individual species is required:

$$a_S = \gamma_S m_S; \quad m_S = \frac{a_S}{\gamma_S}$$

where γ_S is the *activity coefficient*. Then

$$m_A = \sum m_S = \sum \frac{a_S}{\gamma_S}$$

As an example, assume that water is saturated with carbon dioxide under a given partial pressure, and that the amount dissolved is determined by loss of weight of the gas from the source container.   Then

$$m_{A(CO_2)} = \sum m_S$$

In this instance, knowledge of the chemistry tells us that important dissolved species are H_2CO_3, HCO_3^-, and CO_3^{--}.   Then

$$m_{A(CO_2)} = m_{H_2CO_3} + m_{HCO_3^-} + m_{CO_3^{--}} + m_x + m_y + \cdots$$

The terms m_x, m_y, etc., are used to denote those species undoubtedly present of which we have no current knowledge.   Thus if only H_2CO_3, HCO_3^-, and CO_3^{--} are considered, the value of $m_{A(CO_2)}$ obtained by summing them up will be less than the analytical value by the sum of the molalities of these unknowns.   If their sum is negligible in terms of analytical error, then the approximation:

$$m_{A(CO_2)} = m_{H_2CO_3} + m_{HCO_3} + m_{CO_3^{--}} \tag{2.1}$$

is satisfactory.   But at any rate $m_{A(CO_2)}$ will not be less than their sum.

If we wish to calculate $m_{A(CO_2)}$ from thermochemical considerations, we can, knowing the partial pressure of CO_2 used, calculate values for $a_{H_2CO_3}$, $a_{HCO_3^-}$, and $a_{CO_3^{--}}$.   If we also know values for $\gamma_{H_2CO_3}$, $\gamma_{HCO_3^-}$, and $\gamma_{CO_3^{--}}$, we can write:

$$m_{A(CO_2)} = \frac{a_{H_2CO_3}}{\gamma_{H_2CO_3}} + \frac{a_{HCO_3^-}}{\gamma_{HCO_3^-}} + \frac{a_{CO_3^{--}}}{\gamma_{CO_3^{--}}} \tag{2.2}$$

This approximation is subject to the same limitations as equation (2.1), plus any uncertainties that may arise specifically in the determination of activities and activity coefficients.

In summary, an approximation of the solubility of a given element can often be obtained by thermochemical calculations if detailed information is available on all dissolved species contributing to the solubility, and if accurate values of their activity coefficients can be obtained. When anything less than this knowledge is available, the calculated value is less than the observed one,[1] and underestimation may be serious indeed.

ACTIVITY COEFFICIENTS

In ideal solutions, the activity of a dissolved species is proportional to its concentration (expressed as a mole fraction). In the solutions discussed here, consisting chiefly of polar compounds dissolved in water, behavior is far from ideal for the ionic species formed. Only at extreme dilution does the numerical value of activity approach that of concentration. Because of the dissociation of solids into ions, interaction takes place between ions and water, as well as between ions. For calculation of solubilities it is necessary to obtain individual ion activity coefficients, and there is no way of measuring them. Instead they are obtained indirectly from the gross behavior of the dissolved compound.

Fortunately, many solutions of geologic interest are dilute; that is the mole fraction of total dissolved materials is small because of the overwhelming proportion of water. In sea water, for example, in which the chief dissolved material is sodium chloride, the mole fraction of NaCl is only about 0.02. Even so, there is no good theoretical basis for handling such solutions; satisfactory theory extends only up to mole fractions of about 0.0002. But semi-empirical methods have been developed that give some useful activity coefficient values in complex solutions over much of the range of geologic interest.

IONIC STRENGTH

Semi-empirical values for individual ion activity coefficients stem from the development of the concept of ionic strength by Lewis and

---

[1] In highly concentrated solutions, a_i may exceed m_i, and the calculated value may exceed the observed one. This effect is rare at concentrations less than one molal.

Randall.[2]   They showed that the effects of solutions of electrolytes on properties such as the solubility of a solid are remarkably uniform if cognizance is taken of the charges on the ions as well as of their concentrations.   They defined the ionic strength as:

$$\text{ionic strength} = \mu = \tfrac{1}{2} \sum c_i z_i^2$$

where c_i is the concentration of a given ion, and z_i is its charge. For example, the ionic strength of a 1 molal $CaCl_2$ solution is:

$$\mu = \tfrac{1}{2}(m_{Ca^{++}} \cdot 2^2 + m_{Cl^-} \cdot 1^2) = \tfrac{1}{2}(1 \times 4 + 2 \times 1) = 3$$

whereas the ionic strength of a 1 molal NaCl solution is:

$$\mu = \tfrac{1}{2}(m_{Na^+} \cdot 1^2 + m_{Cl^-} \cdot 1^2) = \tfrac{1}{2}(1 \times 1^2 + 1 \times 1^2) = 1$$

The ionic strength of natural waters can be calculated from chemical analyses, inasmuch as the analyses are usually expressed in terms of major ionic species, or in terms of dissolved salts.

Analysis of a water from the Madison sand of Mississippian Age from the Cut Bank oil field in Montana provides the values given in Table 2.1.[3]

TABLE 2.1.   Analysis of Water from a Mississippian Sand (ppm)

Na^+	Ca^{++}	Mg^{++}	SO_4^{--}	Cl^-	CO_3^{--}	HCO_3^-
2187	39	57	232	1680	84	2850

The first step is conversion from parts per million to molality (Table 2.2), from the relation[4]

$$\text{molality} = \frac{\text{parts per million}}{\text{gram formula weight}} \times 10^{-3}$$

TABLE 2.2.   Analysis of Water from a Mississippian Sand (molality)

Na^+	Ca^{++}	Mg^{++}	SO_4^{--}	Cl^-	CO_3^{--}	HCO_3^-
0.0951	0.00097	0.0024	0.00242	0.0474	0.0014	0.0467

Taking the ions as they appear from left to right in the table:

$$\mu = \tfrac{1}{2}(0.0951 \times 1^2 + 0.00097 \times 2^2 + 0.0024 \times 2^2 + 0.00242 \times 2^2 + 0.0474 \times 1^2 + 0.0014 \times 2^2 + 0.0467 \times 1^2) = 0.1082$$

[2] G. N. Lewis and Merle Randall, *J. Am. Chem. Soc.*, *43*, 1112 (1921).

[3] James G. Crawford, 1951, Water analysis (Characteristics of oilfield waters of the Rocky Mountain Region), in *Subsurface Geologic Methods*, Colorado School of Mines, 1951, p. 193.

[4] A correction should be made here because (Chap. 1, p. 3) the analysis is expressed as a weight fraction, i.e., grams/10^6 g solution, and not grams/10^6 g H_2O.   The error involved is, however, very small.

This value of ionic strength is about average for the waters in rocks. It corresponds to a mole fraction of dissolved solids of about 0.002. Stream and lake waters commonly run about $1/10$ of this value, whereas the oceans are about 10 times higher.

Ionic strength is a relation useful in comparing solutions of diverse compositions because the specific electrical effects of the interactions of the variously charged ions present are taken into consideration. Because electrical effects are functions of the square of the charge on the ions, use of ionic strength gives a more useful criterion of the behavior of a solution than does concentration. It is not a cure-all, but it does remove one complexity that otherwise tends to obscure specific compositional effects. Determination of ionic strength is, like determination of solubility, a process requiring successive approximations. To calculate an ionic strength we must know the major ions present. The process consists, as in the example cited, of a first consideration of known major species. If the presence of other species is deduced, as a result of theory or experiment, the ionic strength must be changed by taking cognizance of them. In general the major species of natural waters are sufficiently well known so that the presentation of ions in typical chemical analyses provides a value of ionic strength that is little changed by more detailed study. Undoubtedly the water from the Madison sand contains traces of boron and iodine, as well as small amounts of potassium, but their total contribution would be unlikely to change the ionic strength determined by more than a percent or two.

MEAN ACTIVITY COEFFICIENTS

Although individual ion activity coefficients are not measurable, the mean activity coefficients of individual salts in solution can be obtained accurately. For example, the relation between the molality of calcium chloride in aqueous solution and the lowering of the vapor pressure above the solution gives a measure of the ratio a/m, the relation between activity and stoichiometric concentration as determined by the observed effect of a weighed addition of salt on the properties of the solution. A variety of methods is available for obtaining activity coefficients for salts, and values for a wide range of concentration are available in standard chemical references.[5]

---

[5] Cf. I. M. Klotz, *Chemical Thermodynamics.* Prentice-Hall, Inc., Englewood Cliffs, N.J., 1950, Chap. 21; W. M. Latimer, *Oxidation Potentials.* Prentice-Hall, Inc., Englewood Cliffs, N.J., 1952, pp. 349–358; H. S. Harned and B. B. Owen, *The Physical Chemistry of Electrolytic Solutions,* 3rd edition. Reinhold Publishing Corporation, New York, 1958, Appendix A.

The overall activity coefficient of the dissolved salt is denoted $\gamma\pm$, and it is related to the coefficients of the individual ions by:[6]

$$\gamma\pm = [(\gamma_+)^{v+}(\gamma_-)^{v-}]^{1/v\pm} \qquad (2.3)$$

where $\gamma+$ is the activity coefficient of the positive ion, $\gamma-$ the activity coefficient of the negative ion, $v+$ is the number of moles of positive ions obtained by ionization of 1 mole of the salt, $v-$ is the number of moles of negative ions obtained from one mole of the salt, and $v\pm$ is the total number of moles of ions from one mole of the salt. For calcium chloride:

$$CaCl_2 = Ca^{++} + 2Cl^-$$

$v+$ is 1 and $v-$ is 2. The relation in equation (2.3) indicates that the overall activity coefficients are the geometric mean of the contributions of the individual ions.

The behavior of KCl in solution is the basis for obtaining individual ion activity coefficients. Various lines of evidence indicate that $\gamma_{K^+_{aq}}$ and $\gamma_{Cl^-_{aq}}$ are similar.[7] Therefore as a reasonable approximation:

$$\gamma\pm_{KCl} = [(\gamma_{K^+})(\gamma_{Cl^-})]^{1/2} = \gamma_{K^+} = \gamma_{Cl^-} \qquad (2.4)$$

Once values are obtained for γ_{K^+} and γ_{Cl^-}, a bridge of values usually can be built to obtain individual ion activity coefficient values for other cations or anions.

INDIVIDUAL ION ACTIVITY COEFFICIENTS FROM MEAN ACTIVITY COEFFICIENTS

From knowledge of γ_{K^+} and γ_{Cl^-}, values for the cationic activity coefficients for other halides can be obtained from the relations:

$$\gamma\pm_{MCl} = (\gamma_{M^+}\gamma_{Cl^-})^{1/2} = (\gamma_{M^+}\,\gamma\pm_{KCl})^{1/2} \qquad (2.5)$$

or, for a divalent cation:

$$\gamma\pm_{MCl_2} = (\gamma_{M^{++}}\gamma^2_{Cl^-})^{1/3} = (\gamma_{M^{++}}\gamma^2\pm_{KCl})^{1/3} \qquad (2.6)$$

For other salts of potassium, the reverse relation can be used to obtain activity coefficients for anions:

$$\gamma\pm_{K_2SO_4} = (\gamma^2_{K^+}\gamma_{SO_4^{--}})^{1/3} = (\gamma^2\pm_{KCl}\gamma_{SO_4^{--}})^{1/3} \qquad (2.7)$$

[6] I. M. Klotz, *op. cit.*, p. 308.
[7] G. N. Lewis and Merle Randall, *Thermodynamics.* McGraw-Hill Book Co., New York, 1923, p. 381.

Then

$$\gamma_{SO_4^{--}} = \frac{\gamma^3 \pm_{K_2SO_4}}{\gamma^2 \pm_{KCl}} \tag{2.8}$$

For a salt like $CuSO_4$, a double bridge must be used to obtain $\gamma_{Cu^{++}}$:

$$\gamma \pm_{CuSO_4} = (\gamma_{Cu^{++}} \gamma_{SO_4^{--}})^{1/2} \tag{2.9}$$

From equation (2.8):

$$\gamma_{SO_4^{--}} = \frac{\gamma^3 \pm_{K_2SO_4}}{\gamma^2 \pm_{KCl}} \tag{2.10}$$

By substituting in equation (2.9), and rearranging:

$$\gamma_{Cu^{++}} = \frac{\gamma^2 \pm_{CuSO_4} \gamma^2 \pm_{KCl}}{\gamma^3 \pm_{K_2SO_4}} \tag{2.11}$$

The errors involved become greater as the bridge becomes longer and are difficult to estimate. The best check is always against observational data.

Figure 2.1 illustrates typical curves resulting from a plot of mean activity coefficient against ionic strength. The values illustrate well the marked effect of valence in determining activity coefficients. KCl, a uniunivalent salt, has the highest values; Na_2SO_4 and $CuCl_2$, which are combinations of a divalent ion and two univalent ions, correspond well up to an ionic strength of 0.1; $CuSO_4$, a didivalent salt, exhibits the lowest activity coefficients.

INDIVIDUAL ION ACTIVITY COEFFICIENTS FROM DEBYE-HÜCKEL THEORY

The empirical method just described is the best method for obtaining individual ion activity coefficients in solutions of ionic strengths higher than about 0.05. In the more dilute region the Debye-Hückel theory gives values that check well with the empirical method and have the added advantage of providing a way of extrapolating into the range of infinite dilution.

In dilute solutions, current practice shows individual ionic activity coefficients can be obtained from an approximation of the Debye-Hückel theory, in which:

$$\log \gamma_i = - \frac{A z_i^2 \sqrt{\mu}}{1 + \mathring{a} B \sqrt{\mu}} \tag{2.12}$$

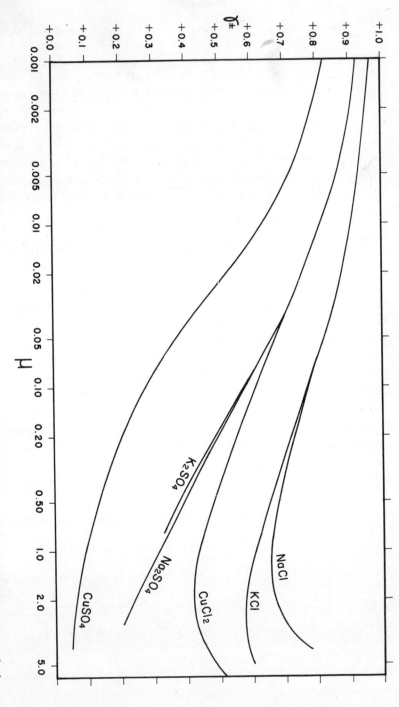

FIGURE 2.1.   Mean activity coefficients of typical salts.   Note the similarity of behavior of salts of the same valence type at ionic strengths up to 0.10.

where A and B are constants characteristic of the solvent (water) and of the temperature and pressure; z_i, as before, is the valence of the ion considered, μ is the ionic strength, and $\mathring{a}$ is a value dependent upon

TABLE 2.3. Values of $\mathring{a}_i$ for Some Individual Ions in Aqueous Solutions[a]

$a_i \times 10^8$	Ion
2.5	Rb^+, Cs^+, NH_4^+, Tl^+, Ag^+
3.0	K^+, Cl^-, Br^-, I^-, NO_3^-
3.5	OH^-, F^-, HS^-, BrO_3^-, IO_4^-, MnO_4^-
4.0–4.5	Na^+, HCO_3^-, $H_2PO_4^-$, HSO_3^-, Hg_2^{++}, SO_4^{--}, SeO_4^{--}, CrO_4^{--}, HPO_4^{--}, PO_4^{---}
4.5	Pb^{++}, CO_3^{--}, SO_3^{--}, MoO_4^{--}
5.0	Sr^{++}, Ba^{++}, Ra^{++}, Cd^{++}, Hg^{++}, S^{--}, WO_4^{--}
6	Li^+, Ca^{++}, Cu^{++}, Zn^{++}, Sn^{++}, Mn^{++}, Fe^{++}, Ni^{++}, Co^{++}
8	Mg^{++}, Be^{++}
9	H_3O^+ (H^+), Al^{+++}, Cr^{+++}, trivalent earths
11	Th^{4+}, Zr^{4+}, Ce^{4+}, Sn^{4+}

[a] Adapted from I. M. Klotz, *Chemical Thermodynamics.* Prentice-Hall, Inc., Englewood Cliffs, N.J., 1950, p. 331.

the "effective diameter" of the ion in solution. An excellent discussion of the basis for the equation is found in Klotz (I. M. Klotz, *Chemical Thermodynamics.* Prentice-Hall, Inc., Englewood Cliffs, N.J., 1950, pp. 328–336). The value for $\mathring{a}$ is determined largely from experiment; a list of values for many ions of interest is given in Table 2.3. Values of A and B as a function of temperature are given in Table 2.4.

TABLE 2.4. Values of Constants for Use in Debye-Hückel Equation (Aqueous Solution)[a]

Temperature °C	A	B ($\times 10^{-8}$)
0	0.4883	0.3241
5	0.4291	0.3249
10	0.4960	0.3258
15	0.5000	0.3226
20	0.5042	0.3273
25	0.5085	0.3281
30	0.5130	0.3290
35	0.5175	0.3297
40	0.5221	0.3305
45	0.5271	0.3314
50	0.5319	0.3321
55	0.5371	0.3329
60	0.5425	0.3338

[a] G. G. Manov, R. G. Bates, W. J. Hamer, S. F. Acree, 1943; *J. Am. Chem. Soc.*, *65*, 1765 (1943).

The physical significance of $\overset{\circ}{a}$, which is commonly related to the diameter of the ion in solution, merits a brief digression. The values of $\overset{\circ}{a}$ listed in Table 2.3 are larger than values of ionic diameters given for ions in crystals. This difference presumably stems from the envelope of water molecules that surrounds the ions in water. Some attempts have been made to interpret $\overset{\circ}{a}$ values structurally, but a clear-cut picture of the coordination of water molecules around the charged ions has not yet emerged. Detailed discussion of the hydration problem is given by Robinson and Stokes [R. H. Robinson and R. H. Stokes, "The role of hydration in the Debye-Hückel theory": *Molecular Interaction, Ann. N.Y. Acad. Sci.*, *51*, pp. 593–604 (1949)].

COMPARISON OF ACTIVITY COEFFICIENTS DETERMINED FROM DEBYE-HÜCKEL AND FROM MEAN ACTIVITY COEFFICIENT METHOD

Figure 2.2 shows individual ion activity coefficients calculated for HCO_3^- and CO_3^{--} by the Debye-Hückel equation and, for comparison, several sets of values by the mean activity coefficient method, using the mean activity coefficient of KCl as an approximation of the individual ion activity coefficient of either K^+ or Cl^-, and then using various "bridges" to obtain $\gamma_{HCO_3^-}$ or $\gamma_{CO_3^{--}}$.

In calculating $\gamma_{HCO_3^-}$ at 25°C from the Debye-Hückel theory, the procedure was as follows:

From equation (2.12)

$$\log \gamma_{HCO_3^-} = -\frac{A z_i^2 \sqrt{\mu}}{1 + \overset{\circ}{a} B \sqrt{\mu}}$$

From Table 2.4, $A = 0.5085$ and $B = 0.3281 \times 10^{+8}$. From Table 2.3, $\overset{\circ}{a}$ for $HCO_3^- = 4.0 \times 10^{-8}$. The valence of HCO_3^- is one. Then

$$\log \gamma_{HCO_3^-} = -\frac{0.5085 \times 1^2 \times \sqrt{\mu}}{1 + 4.0 \times 10^{-8} \times 0.3281 \times 10^8 \sqrt{\mu}}$$

Substitution of successive values for μ yields values for $\gamma_{HCO_3^-}$. In calculation the powers of ten of the values of $\overset{\circ}{a}$ and B cancel, so standard practice is to drop the 10^{-8} and the 10^{+8} as coefficients. Values for $\gamma_{CO_3^{--}}$ were obtained by similar substitutions.

The procedure for obtaining individual ion activity coefficients from mean coefficients of salts is somewhat variable from species to

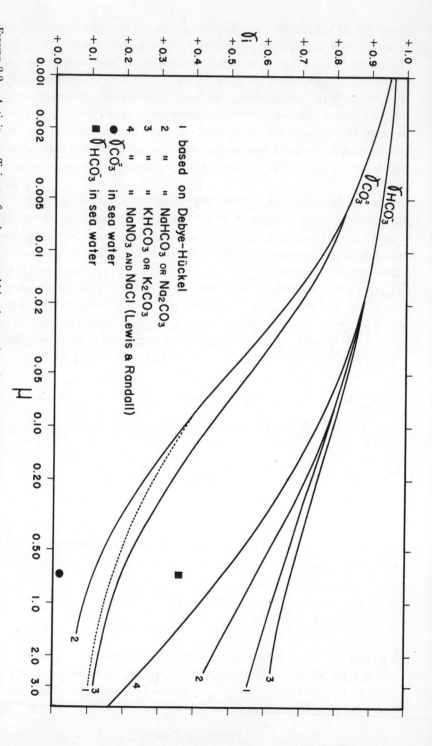

FIGURE 2.2. Activity coefficients of carbonate and bicarbonate ion, showing spread of values obtained by various methods of calculation. Note that Debye-Hückel values lie between those obtained from potassium and sodium salts.

species, so several methods for HCO_3^- are discussed and illustrated to show the range of values expectable.

In the first method, the mean activity coefficient of KCl is substituted into the expression for the mean activity coefficient of $KHCO_3$:

$$\gamma \pm _{KHCO_3} = (\gamma_{K^+} \gamma_{HCO_3^-})^{1/2}; \quad \gamma \pm _{KHCO_3} = (\gamma \pm _{KCl} \gamma_{HCO_3^-})^{1/2};$$

$$\gamma_{HCO_3^-} = \frac{\gamma^2 \pm _{KHCO_3}}{\gamma \pm _{KCl}}$$

In the second the mean activity coefficient of $NaHCO_3$ is used, and $\gamma_{HCO_3^-}$ obtained by an additional step which involves obtaining γ_{Na^+} by substituting $\gamma \pm _{KCl}$ into the expression for $\gamma \pm _{NaCl}$:

$$\gamma \pm _{NaCl} = (\gamma_{Na^+} \gamma_{Cl^-})^{1/2}; \quad \gamma \pm _{NaCl} = (\gamma_{Na^+} \gamma \pm _{KCl})^{1/2};$$

$$\gamma_{Na^+} = \frac{\gamma^2 \pm _{NaCl}}{\gamma \pm _{KCl}}$$

$$\gamma \pm _{NaHCO_3} = (\gamma_{Na^+} \gamma_{HCO_3^-})^{1/2}; \quad \gamma \pm _{NaHCO_3} = \left(\frac{\gamma^2 \pm _{NaCl}}{\gamma \pm _{KCl}} \gamma_{HCO_3^-}\right)^{1/2}$$

$$\gamma_{HCO_3^-} = \frac{\gamma^2 \pm _{NaHCO_3} \gamma \pm _{KCl}}{\gamma^2 \pm _{NaCl}}$$

As shown by Figure 2.2, all three sets of values obtained using mean activity coefficients, plus that obtained by Debye-Hückel, agree well up to an ionic strength of 0.1. Above 0.1 they diverge, with the Lewis and Randall method showing the greatest deviation from the mean. The results obtained through the mean activity coefficients of $KHCO_3$ and $NaHCO_3$ straddle Debye-Hückel results. The differences indicate the degree of failure of ionic strength alone in describing ionic interaction, and it is clear that there is less association of one type or another in potassium bicarbonate solutions than in sodium bicarbonate solutions. The same relation holds for $\gamma_{CO_3^{--}}$ values, also shown in Figure 2.2.

These results for bicarbonate and carbonate show that there should always be an attempt to use salts corresponding to those in the natural system under consideration when calculating individual ion activity coefficients. Unfortunately in many instances the composition of the natural solution is too complex to permit "matching" with one or two individual salts.

The low values for both ions in sea water are rather surprising inasmuch as sea water is chiefly a sodium chloride brine, and addition of chloride to carbonate solutions, so long as the cation is the same

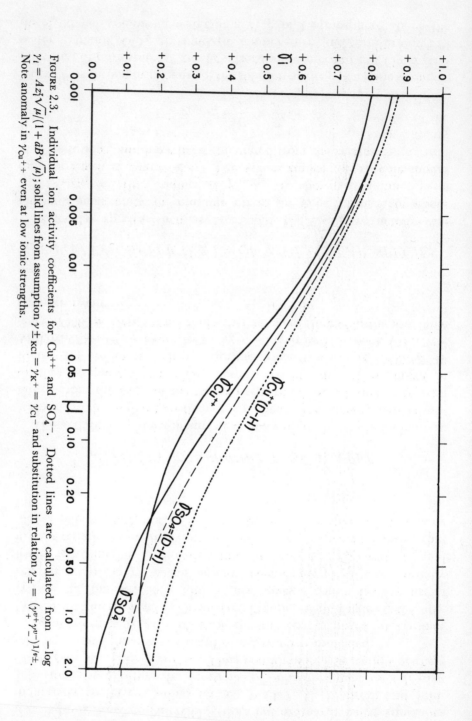

FIGURE 2.3. Individual ion activity coefficients for Cu^{++} and SO_4^{--}. Dotted lines are calculated from $-\log \gamma_i = Az_i^2\sqrt{\mu}/(1+\mathring{a}B\sqrt{\mu})$; solid lines from assumption $\gamma_{\pm \, KCl} = \gamma_{K^+} = \gamma_{Cl^-}$ and substitution in relation $\gamma_{\pm} = (\gamma_+^{v^+}\gamma_-^{v^-})^{1/v\pm}$. Note anomaly in γ_{Cu^+} even at low ionic strengths.

(i.e., adding NaCl to NaHCO$_3$), does not ordinarily cause anomalies in activity coefficient values [A. C. Walker, U. B. Bray, and John Johnston, Equilibrium in solutions of alkali carbonates. *J. Am. Chem. Soc.*, *49*, 1244 (1927)]. Thus considerable interaction of these ions with some minor constituent of sea water is indicated.

Values for many salts of geologic interest are listed in Latimer (W. M. Latimer, *Oxidation Potentials.* Prentice-Hall, Englewood Cliffs, N.J., 1952, pp. 354–356), and he also gives a comprehensive list of references (p. 357). Mean activity coefficients of salts are usually listed as a function of molality, but they can be compared at equal ionic strengths by multiplying the molality of 1–1 salts by three, that of 2–2 salts by four, that of 3–1 salts by nine, and that of 3–2 salts by fifteen.

ACTIVITY COEFFICIENT OF WATER

The activity of water remains near unity in dilute aqueous solutions. Values for the activity coefficient and hence the activity can be obtained from the ratio of the vapor pressure of the solution of interest to that of pure water. The activity coefficient values shown in Figure 2.4 are for the effect of adding NaCl to water at 25°C (E. B. Millard, *Physical Chemistry for Colleges.* McGraw-Hill Book Co., New York, 1936, p. 186). Effects of other salts are similar in the low ionic strength range.

ACTIVITY COEFFICIENTS OF MOLECULAR SPECIES

Molecular species, such as H$_2$S, and H$_2$CO$_3$, have activity coefficients near unity in solutions up to an ionic strength of about 0.5 ($\gamma_{H_2CO_3} = 1.10$). Values of $\gamma_{H_2CO_3}$ are shown as a function of ionic strength in Figure 2.4. The values shown are specifically for NaCl solutions, and have been calculated from the relation:

$$\gamma_{H_2CO_3} = \frac{C_0}{C_s} \times \frac{P_s}{P_0}$$

where P_s is the vapor pressure of the solution at the given ionic strength, P_0 is that of pure water, C_0 is the adsorption coefficient of CO$_2$ in pure water (volume CO$_2$ at standard temperature and pressure (STP) dissolved per volume of water at a P_{CO_2} of 1 atmosphere above the

solution), and C_s is the adsorption coefficient in the solution at the given ionic strength. Values for any other species such as H_2S can be calculated similarly.

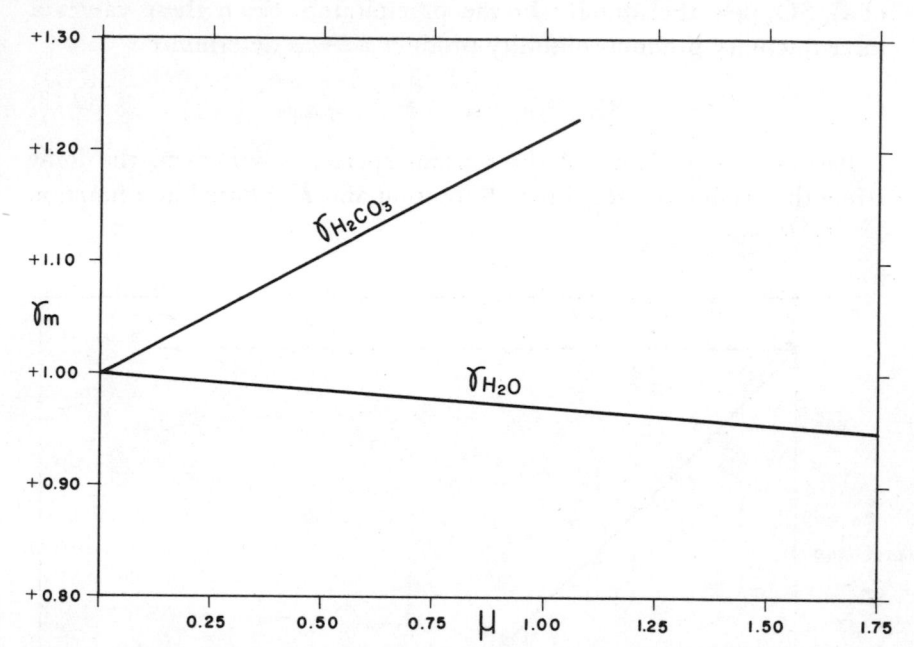

FIGURE 2.4. Activity coefficients of H_2CO_3 and of water in NaCl solution, showing relatively small change in γ values of molecular species as ionic strength is increased.

APPLICATION OF INDIVIDUAL IONIC ACTIVITY COEFFICIENT VALUES TO A STUDY OF BROCHANTITE SOLUBILITY

The use of mean activity coefficients in conjunction with Debye-Hückel values is best illustrated by an example. A study by J. Silman of the solubility and equilibrium constant of brochantite [$Cu_4(OH)_6SO_4$] (Ph.D. thesis, Harvard University, 1958) shows the techniques involved. Silman made up solutions of known molality of $CuSO_4$, then titrated them with NaOH to the midpoint of the precipitation curve (i.e., to the point at which half of the copper had been removed from the solution in the precipitate). The precipitate was then allowed to age for several weeks at 25 °C in the solution to be sure that equilibrium had been attained, and the pH measured. Inasmuch as pH is a measure of a_{H^+}, and $K_w = a_{H^+}a_{OH^-}$, the pH

values were used to obtain values of a_{OH^-} in equilibrium with the precipitate. Also, the molality of Cu^{++} was half the original concentration of copper, and the SO_4^{--} equal to the original concentration of $CuSO_4$ less the amount in the precipitate. From these values a mixed activity product-solubility product K' was determined:

$$m_{Cu^{++}}^4 \, a_{OH^-}^6 \, m_{SO_4^{--}} = K'_{\text{brochantite}} \tag{2.13}$$

Because the molality of the various species was known, the ionic strength was determined for each solution and K' plotted as a function of $\sqrt{\mu}$ (Figure 2.5).

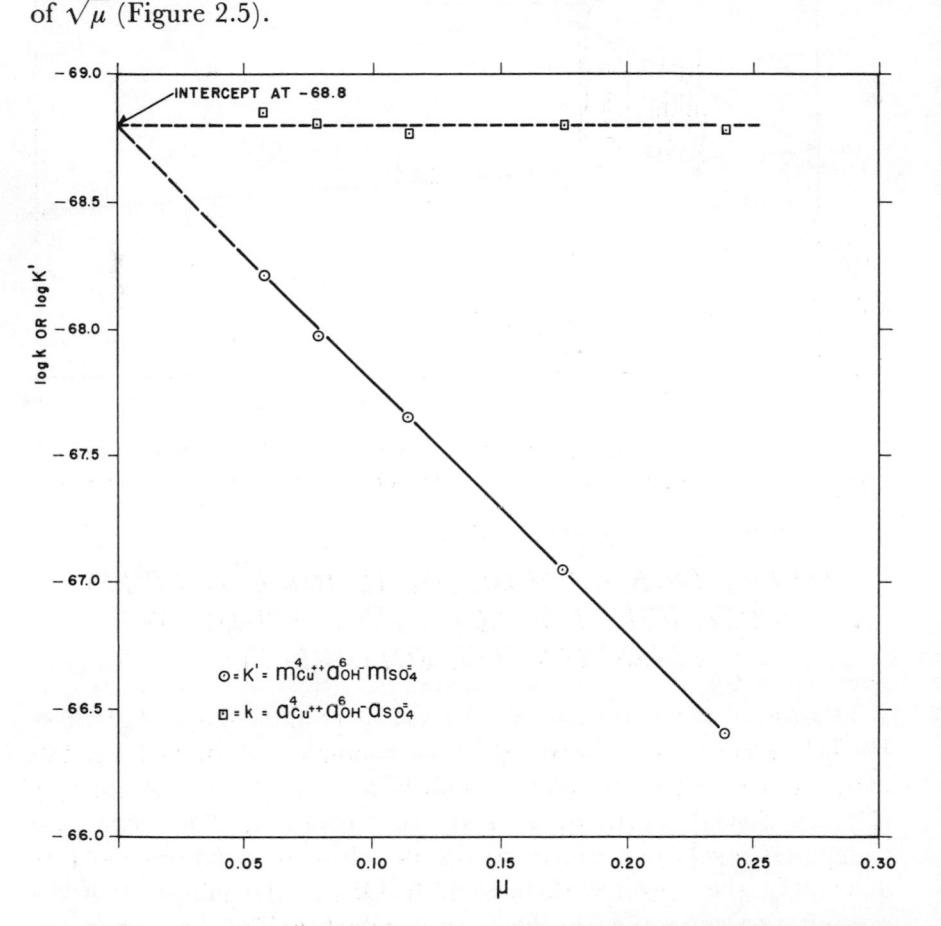

FIGURE 2.5. Determination of activity product of brochantite by extrapolation of K' values to infinite dilution by using Debye-Hückel theory to obtain the limiting slope (circles) and by individual calculations from experimental points, with activity coefficients for cupric ion and sulfate ion obtained by the mean coefficient method (solid lines in Figure 2.3).

From the relation:

$$m_i = \frac{a_i}{\gamma_i}$$

the expression for K' can be rewritten:

$$\left(\frac{a_{Cu^{++}}}{\gamma_{Cu^{++}}}\right)^4 a_{OH^-}^6 \left(\frac{a_{SO_4^{--}}}{\gamma_{SO_4^{--}}}\right) = K'_{brochantite} \qquad (2.14)$$

But the equilibrium constant for brochantite is:

$$a_{Cu^{++}}^4 a_{OH^-}^6 a_{SO_4^{--}} = k_{brochantite} \qquad (2.15)$$

By substituting k into equation (2.14):

$$k_{brochantite} = K' \gamma_{Cu^{++}}^4 \gamma_{SO_4^{--}} \qquad (2.16)$$

Inasmuch as the activity coefficients approach unity at infinite dilution, extrapolation of K' values to zero ionic strength should yield the value of the thermodynamic equilibrium constant k. Although the values of K' lie on a nearly straight line, a considerable extrapolation still has to be made. As a guide to the process, the Debye-Hückel theory can be used to determine the limiting slope. From equation (2.12):

$$-\log \gamma_{Cu^{++}} = \frac{4A\sqrt{\mu}}{1 + \mathring{a}B\sqrt{\mu}}; \quad -\log \gamma_{SO_4^{--}} = \frac{4A\sqrt{\mu}}{1 + \mathring{a}B\sqrt{\mu}} \qquad (2.17)$$

By taking logs of both sides of equation (2.16), and substituting activity coefficient values from equation (2.17):

$$\log k = \log K' - 4\left(\frac{4A\sqrt{\mu}}{1 + \mathring{a}B\sqrt{\mu}}\right) - \left(\frac{4A\sqrt{\mu}}{1 + \mathring{a}B\sqrt{\mu}}\right)$$

At very low ionic strength, the denominator of the two terms on the right becomes unity, and

$$\log k = \log K' - 5(4A\sqrt{\mu})$$

At 25°C, A is 0.5085, so as a close approximation:

$$\log k = \log K' - 10\sqrt{\mu} \qquad (2.18)$$

Therefore $\log K'$ is a linear function of the square root of the ionic strength, and the limiting slope is -10. Extrapolation to zero ionic strength was carried out using this slope, and a value of k of $10^{-68.8}$ is obtained.

It is also apparent from equation (2.16) that k can be obtained from K' at any ionic strength if values for the activity coefficients of Cu^{++} and SO_4^{--} are available. The small circles on Figure 2.5 are values of k obtained from K' and activity coefficients from Figure 2.3. Note that they differ slightly from determination to determination, but that the mean value is also $10^{-68.8}$.

In Silman's study the goal was a value for k, but it should be clear that with foreknowledge of k, values of K' can be used to obtain activity coefficients for the ions. The excellent agreement of k values calculated from individual ion activity coefficients shows that the values substituted for activity coefficients describe the behavior of cupric and sulfate ions in the $NaOH-CuSO_4$ mixtures used in the study.

Agreement of k determined by extrapolation and by calculation at specific values of ionic strength as demonstrated by Silman's study are unusually good, and perhaps in that respect are not typical of what can be expected when calculations are extended to more complex solutions. On the other hand, they do show that activity coefficients can be used in some cases to obtain accurate solubilities.

The point might be raised that if agreement had not been obtained, there would have been difficulty in ascribing the anomaly to cupric ion or to sulfate ion. Barton (Paul Barton, oral communication) has used an ingenious device to circumvent this possibility. After precipitating brochantite, he continued the titration until the brochantite was converted to cupric oxide. Inasmuch as the activity product of cupric oxide contains only cupric ions and hydroxyl ions, he could use the same technique as for brochantite, but in this case measurements of pH provide a value of the activity of the OH^- ion, so that differences between k and K' can be ascribed to the cupric ion alone. Then, after obtaining activity coefficients for the cupric ion, he could return to the brochantite precipitation and explain any anomalies in terms of the behavior of the sulfate ion.

COMPLEX IONS

Emphasis throughout this book is on equilibrium relations among solid phases, and the surrounding medium is used chiefly in stepping from one compound to another. Unfortunately, methods for determining the *composition* of the natural solution in equilibrium with a given solid or solids have not yet developed to the point where we can make calculations with any confidence. The activity coefficient for a

given dissolved species can, under propitious circumstances, be determined with fair accuracy. Our ignorance stems largely from current inability to predict all the dissolved species that are present in a given natural water. The reverse problem is equally difficult: given the composition of a natural water as determined by standard chemical analysis, what are the proportions of the various dissolved species that make up the total analysis of a given element?

Our progress on this problem is related to the total progress of solution chemistry. If anyone were entirely cognizant of all the work that has been done on aqueous solutions, he could probably make a fair estimate of the major dissolved species that would be encountered in a water yielding a particular standard analysis. Yet even such a hypothetical omniscient investigator would encounter many natural situations in which his best estimate of dissolved species would be in serious error. Therefore, calculations that attempt to bridge the gap between solution composition and the activities of the species contributing to that composition are partly science and partly art; their success depends not only upon the applications of standard methods by the investigator, but also upon his total knowledge, experience, judgment, and intuition.

At the present stage of development of solution chemistry dilute inorganic aqueous solutions can be handled fairly well, because the dissolved species tend to be relatively simple ions or molecules. But when the ionic strength rises above 0.1 (or in some instances above much lower values), interactions of simpler species tend to take place, so that complex species begin to make an important contribution to the total dissolved substances. Furthermore, the picture obtained by considering only inorganic substances is far from complete; natural systems usually contain important amounts of organic derivatives. Some of these are highly effective in binding metal ions, for example, into their structures, so that any calculation that ignores such species is not valid.

As the concentration of dissolved salts in aqueous solution increases, the ions, originally relatively far apart, begin to interact. The strictly electrical aspects of this interaction, that is, effects relating to the proximity of simple positive and negative ions, are the basis for Debye-Hückel theory; but in addition it is found that new species are formed that apparently behave as units in the solution. These complexes are, of course, in dynamic equilibrium with the simpler ions. This can be looked upon as the reason for the restricted range of applicability of

Debye-Hückel theory.   On the other hand, it also explains why the mean salt method, which automatically takes complexes into account, is relatively successful at moderate values of ionic strength.   To over-simplify the situation in order to develop a useful picture, it can be said that if a solution is concentrated so that interaction of dissolved species produces an infinite network of ions, a solid (a crystal structure), is produced.   On the other hand, many interactions produce relatively small finite groups that are prevented from continuous repetition by one cause or another.   These smaller groups remain dispersed through the medium, and can be regarded as soluble complexes.   Many such groups remain discrete because they are electrically charged; a solid requires interactions with a net charge balance.   Therefore one result of concentration is to develop ion groups simply by interaction of originally dispersed cations and anions, and the proportion of "free" ions diminishes.   We are so familiar with some of the common stable complexes that we hardly consider them as such; HCO_3^-, HSO_4^-, and $(C_2H_3O_2)^-$ are all complex ions.

Table 2.5 is given in an attempt to show the effects of some known inorganic complexes by showing the change in ratio of simple cation to bound cation as a result of an increase in concentration of one of the constituents of the complex.   As shown by the table, the effectiveness of a complex is commonly a power function of one or more of the constituent species.   Some complexes are highly effective at low concentrations, many do not "take hold" until some critical high value of concentration of the simple ions is reached, but once that value is exceeded, their proportions in the solution mount rapidly.   This power effect is shown by the copper-carbonate complex at the top of the table; the dicarbonate complex is of no consequence until $[CO_3^{--}]$ exceeds 10^{-5}, but its ratio to simple $[Cu^{++}]$ rises with the square of further added carbonate ion.

This "coming in" of more and more complexes as total concentration rises shows why we are so completely lost in trying to make calculations relating ionic activities to total concentration in such media as saline lakes.   On the other hand, lack of the chemical tools with which to decipher the complex behavior of dissolved species is hamstringing our efforts to recreate the solutions of the geologic past.

So much pessimism should be alleviated before passing on to a new topic.   The difficulties just discussed do not in any way affect the delineation of the fields of solids as functions of Eh, the activities of ions (including pH!), or the partial pressures of gases in the pressure range below 1 atmosphere.   Complexes have no effect on the fields of

TABLE 2.5. Effect of Complexes

Complex	Ionization Constant	Solution	Ratio Complex/Simple Cation	Solution	Ratio Complex/Simple Cation
$Cu(CO_3)_{2\,aq}^{--}$	$\dfrac{[Cu^{++}][CO_3^{--}]^2}{[Cu(CO_3)_2^{--}]} = 10^{-10}$	$10^{-5}[CO_3^{--}]$	10^0	$10^{-1}[CO_3^{--}]$	10^8
$CuCO_{3\,aq}$	$\dfrac{[Cu^{++}][CO_3^{--}]}{[CuCO_3]} = 10^{-6}$	$10^{-5}[CO_3^{--}]$	10^1	$10^{-1}[CO_3^{--}]$	10^5
$UO_2(CO_3)_{3\,aq}^{4-}$	$\dfrac{[UO_2^{++}][CO_3^{--}]^3}{[(UO_2^{++})(CO_3^{--})_3^{4-}]} = 10^{-24}$	$10^{-10}[CO_3^{--}]$	10^{-6}	$10^{-6}[CO_3^{--}]$	10^6
$PbCl_{aq}^+$	$\dfrac{[Pb^{++}][Cl^-]}{[PbCl^+]} = 10^{-1.5}$	$10^{-3}[Cl^-]$	$10^{-1.5}$	$10^0[Cl^-]$	$10^{1.5}$
$CdI_{4\,aq}^{--}$	$\dfrac{[Cd^{++}][I^-]^4}{[CdI_4^{--}]} = 10^{-6.3}$	$10^{-2}[I^-]$	$10^{-1.7}$	$10^0[I^-]$	$10^{6.3}$
$CuS_{5\,aq}^-$	$\dfrac{[Cu^+][S_5^{--}]}{[CuS_5^-]} = 10^{-21}$	$10^{-21}[S_5^{--}]$	10^0	$10^{-10}[S_5^{--}]$	10^{11}

stability of solids as delineated henceforth. If we are given solution
composition in the form of a standard chemical analysis, we cannot
calculate Eh and pH or gas partial pressure with assurance, but we
can measure these variables directly.

SUMMARY

The solubility of a given element in a natural water can be calculated
if the activities of all dissolved species in equilibrium with the stable
solid are known, and if the ratio of activities of the dissolved species to
their concentrations also are available. The activities of all known
species can be calculated if thermochemical data are available; the
chief errors that creep in are from ignorance of the presence of important species. This type of error is most likely to occur in concentrated solutions of mixed electrolytes, such as brines.

The relation between activities and concentrations of ionic species
can be handled well in dilute solution by using the ionic strength in
conjunction with the Debye-Hückel relation:

$$-\log \gamma_i = \frac{A z_i^2 \sqrt{\mu}}{1 + \mathring{a} B \sqrt{\mu}}$$

where

$$\gamma_i = \frac{a_i}{m_i}$$

In more concentrated solutions, provided that they are relatively simple
mixtures of salts, activity coefficients can be obtained by making the
assumption that $\gamma \pm_{KCl} = \gamma_{K^+} = \gamma_{Cl^-}$ and then calculating individual ion activity coefficients from the mean activity coefficients of
salts, with the general relation:

$$\gamma \pm = [\gamma_+{}^{v+} \gamma_-{}^{v-}]^{1/v \pm}$$

Whereas it is difficult to assess the magnitude of the error that
affects results obtained by these methods, they are valuable in recognizing complex ion formation over and above that from salt effects
alone. In other words, use of all the general tools at our command
gives an *expected* value of the solubility that can be used with the
measured value to deduce the degree of complex ion formation.

SELECTED REFERENCE

Klotz, I. M., *Chemical Thermodynamics*. Prentice-Hall, Inc., Englewood Cliffs,
    N.J., 1950, Chap. 21.
        Detailed discussion of activity coefficients of strong electrolytes.

3

Carbonate Equilibria

To many geologists, the carbonate rocks are the most important rock type in providing information about the geologic past. In addition to the abundant faunal and floral evidence they may contain, the fact that they are precipitates from their ancient environment means that if we are sufficiently astute we should be able to read from their minerals the conditions of their deposition and the events to which they have been subjected subsequently. A mere listing of the bibliography of investigations to this end would provide a larger volume than this. Here the emphasis is entirely on the mechanics of handling several typical situations that may occur geologically to show the equilibria involved and the procedures used in obtaining the activities of metal ions in equilibrium with solid carbonates. Also, the question of the calculation of the actual solubility of the metal is discussed.

The solubility values for carbonate minerals in the literature are many, conflicting and confusing. One of the reasons for this is the high degree of accuracy that is now expected from such work. To know the solubility of a mineral such as powellite ($CaMoO_4$) within an order of magnitude is most gratifying, but great labor has been expended to determine the difference in solubility of calcite and aragonite, in which the difference in free energy of formation of the dimorphs is somewhere between 0.2 and 0.5 kilocalorie. The other reason is one that will be discussed here, that so many variables have to be specified to fix the solubility of a carbonate mineral there is a tendency to compare values obtained under apparently similar but actually different conditions.

Five cases will be discussed.[1] These five sets of conditions cover many of the situations of geologic interest, and most others can be stipulated as combinations or permutations of the five. For convenience all calculations will be referred to calcite, with the recognition that the same procedures can be used for any other metal carbonate. The various sets of conditions are:

1. The reactions involved in placing pure calcite in pure water, with negligible gas phase present.

2. The reactions of calcite in pure water, but with the system open to CO_2; that is, in contact with a reservoir, such as the atmosphere, of fixed partial pressure of CO_2.

3. Equilibrium relations in a system with a fixed quantity of dissolved carbonate species but with pH arbitrarily fixed, i.e., controlled by other reactions in the system.

4. Equilibrium in a system connected to an external reservoir of fixed partial pressure of CO_2, but with pH arbitrarily determined.

5. Equilibrium resulting from addition of $CaCO_3$ to a system originally open to a CO_2 reservoir, but closed to that reservoir before addition of $CaCO_3$.

Case 1 can be regarded as that used for determining the solubility of calcite—it is the closed system $CaCO_3$–H_2O. It is, in fact, of little geologic utility, inasmuch as such a restricted composition is almost never encountered.

Case 2 is of considerable geologic importance—it represents relations in lakes and streams and other dilute natural waters in intimate contact with the atmosphere, in which the pH of the system is controlled entirely by the carbonate equilibria.

Case 3 can be represented by the questions raised by the analysis of an underground water. The analysis commonly gives total dissolved carbonate ($HCO_3^- + CO_3^{--} + H_2CO_3$), calcium concentration, and pH. Is such a solution in equilibrium with calcite? Is it in equilibrium with the atmosphere? If no analysis of calcium is given, but if the system is known to be in equilibrium with calcite, can calcium ion be calculated?

Case 4 is also of great geologic importance. Given knowledge that a system is in equilibrium with a given partial pressure of CO_2 and that it has a given pH, whatever the control may be, what is the

[1] The discussion of these five cases is developed largely from an unpublished manuscript by R. Siever and the author on stability of various carbonates in low-temperature aqueous solutions. I am indebted to Dr. Siever for releasing this part of the material.

activity of calcium ion in equilibrium with calcite? What is it necessary to know to approximate the solubility of calcite in such a system?

Case 5 can be illustrated by the situation in which rain water in equilibrium with the atmosphere sinks into the ground, perhaps through an unreactive soil, and comes into contact with calcite. What is the activity and concentration of calcium ion in the resultant solution at equilibrium? What is the equilibrium pH of the water?

GENERAL PATTERN OF SOLUTION OF CARBONATE EQUILIBRIUM PROBLEMS

In all five cases considered, the fundamental pattern of solution of the problem is the same. There are at most seven variables involved at constant temperature and pressure, assuming knowledge of activity coefficients for all species—they are P_{CO_2}, $a_{H_2CO_3}$,[2] $a_{HCO_3^-}$, $a_{CO_3^{--}}$, a_{H^+}, a_{OH^-}, $a_{Ca^{++}}$. In every case the activity product of $CaCO_3$, the first and second dissociation constants for carbonic acid, and the ion product constant for water are applicable, inasmuch as equilibrium with $CaCO_3$ is always stipulated, and internal equilibrium of all ionic species in the solution assumed. This gives 4 equations:

$$[Ca^{++}][CO_3^{--}] = k_{CaCO_3} = 10^{-8.3}_{25°C, 1 atm} \qquad (3.1)$$

$$\frac{[H^+][HCO_3^-]}{[H_2CO_3]} = k_{H_2CO_3} = 10^{-6.4}_{25°C, 1 atm} \qquad (3.2)$$

$$\frac{[H^+][CO_3^{--}]}{[HCO_3^-]} = k_{HCO_3^-} = 10^{-10.3}_{25°C, 1 atm} \qquad (3.3)$$

$$[H^+][OH^-] = k_{H_2O} = 10^{-14}_{25°C, 1 atm} \qquad (3.4)$$

These equations are then the backbone of each situation described. Note that they provide only ratios of activities. In every instance the remaining equations required can be considered as defining equations —they depend upon the special circumstances chosen. Furthermore, they provide, so to speak, the actual numbers involved necessary to solve the specific problem.

[2] There is another equilibrium sometimes cited, that between $CO_{2\ g}$ and $CO_{2\ aq}$. But we can write:

$$CO_{2\ g} = CO_{2\ aq}$$
$$\frac{CO_{2\ aq} + H_2O_1 = H_2CO_{3\ aq}}{CO_{2\ g} + H_2O_1 = H_2CO_{3\ aq}} \text{ (summary equilibrium).}$$

For the summary equilibrium we can consider all dissolved nonionized C-bearing species as $H_2CO_{3\ aq}$ and ignore the presence of $CO_{2\ aq}$.

In the solutions of the individual cases to follow, the values for the constants of equations (3.1)–(3.4) at 25°C and 1 atmosphere total pressure will be used.

CASE 1. $CaCO_3$ IN PURE WATER

When an excess of pure $CaCO_3$ is placed in pure water (experimentally water from which reactive gases such as CO_2 have been washed by bubbling with an inert gas such as nitrogen or helium), the ensuing process can be visualized as follows: calcium ions and carbonate ions dissociate into the water. So far as we know, the calcium ions do not interact appreciably with the water. On the other hand, the carbonate ions do, in a succession of reactions:

$$CO_{3\,aq}^{--} + H_2O_l = HCO_{3\,aq}^{-} + OH_{aq}^{-} \qquad (3.5)$$

$$HCO_{3\,aq}^{-} + H_2O_l = H_2CO_{3\,aq} + OH_{aq}^{-} \qquad (3.6)$$

The solution becomes alkaline because of the release of OH^- as the H^+ is used up to make HCO_3^- and H_2CO_3. Looked at another way, the reduction of H^+ by interaction with carbonate species causes dissociation of water to maintain the ion product of water. Furthermore, we can write:

$$H_2O_l + CO_{2\,g} = H_2CO_{3\,aq} \qquad (3.7)$$

But inasmuch as there is no gas space above the water, the amount of $CO_{2\,g}$ is negligible, and can be neglected as a contributor to the system.

Therefore in this system the species of importance are Ca_{aq}^{++}, $CO_{3\,aq}^{--}$ $HCO_{3\,aq}^{-}$, $H_2CO_{3\,aq}$, OH_{aq}^{-}, H_{aq}^{+}, $CaCO_{3\,c}$ and H_2O_l. The activity of $CaCO_{3\,c}$ is unity, and that of H_2O_l also can be considered unity, inasmuch as the solution is prerecognized as dilute. This leaves six variables. Equations (3.1)–(3.4) all hold for the system, so two more equations must be sought.

Because the original water is devoid of carbonate species, it follows that every species in solution containing a carbon atom must be matched by a calcium ion, for the source of such species is calcite, which cannot dissociate to free calcium in excess of carbons, or vice versa, without building up an electric charge. Then we can write:

$$m_{Ca^{++}} = m_{CO_3^{--}} + m_{HCO_3^{-}} + m_{H2CO3} \qquad (3.8)$$

Furthermore, the solution must remain electrically neutral, so that the sum of the positive charges on cations must equal that of the nega-

tive charges on anions. Remembering that each calcium and each carbonate ion is doubly charged, we can write an equation for electric neutrality:

$$2m_{Ca^{++}} + m_{H^+} = 2m_{CO_3^{--}} + m_{HCO_3^-} + m_{OH^-} \qquad (3.9)$$

Equations (3.8) and (3.9), in conjunction with equations (3.1)–(3.4), are then sufficient for solution of the problem, for there are 6 equations and 6 unknowns, with one stipulation: *because equations (3.1)–(3.4) are written in terms of activities, and (3.8) and (3.9) in terms of molalities, a solution of the problem is valid only if $m_i \cong a_i$, or if $\gamma_i \cong 1$.*

Many solutions of the problem in the literature ignore this qualification, so before proceeding it is well to look into the basis for making the assumption originally and also to see the procedure required for a rigorous solution. It appears at first as if the dilemma is hopeless, for γ_i values cannot be obtained until the ionic strength is determined, and the ionic strength cannot be determined until the problem is solved. This difficulty can be circumvented by a series of successive approximations, in which the problem is first solved, assuming activity coefficients are unity and determining an ionic strength. Then activity coefficients are determined, and the problem is solved again to obtain a new ionic strength, until successive approximations show no appreciable differences.

Consequently the next step is to solve the problem, assuming that $m_i = a_i$, and it is not possible to be more rigorous at the outset. Because back-substitution into six equations is a chore, it is also convenient in a first approximation to see if there are other methods of simplification. Equations (3.5) and (3.6) show that the solution will be more alkaline than the original water so that the final pH will be above 7. If it is, for example, 8, then from equation (3.2):

$$\frac{[H^+][HCO_3^-]}{[H_2CO_3]} = 10^{-6.4}$$

$$\frac{[HCO_3^-]}{[H_2CO_3]} = \frac{10^{-6.4}}{10^{-8}} = 10^{1.6}$$

Thus $[H_2CO_3]$ is small relative to $[HCO_3^-]$, and can be neglected in a first approximation. Also, if pH $\geqslant$ 8, $H^+ \leqslant 10^{-8}$, and can be temporarily ignored. This leaves:

$$[Ca^{++}][CO_3^{--}] = 10^{-8.3} \qquad (3.1)$$

$$\frac{[H^+][HCO_3^-]}{[H_2CO_3]} = 10^{-6.4} \qquad (3.2)$$

$$\frac{[H^+][CO_3^{--}]}{[HCO_3^-]} = 10^{-10.3} \tag{3.3}$$

$$[H^+][OH^-] = 10^{-14} \tag{3.4}$$

$$[Ca^{++}] = [CO_3^{--}] + [HCO_3^-] \tag{3.8 modified}$$

$$2[Ca^{++}] = 2[CO_3^{--}] + [HCO_3^-] + [OH^-] \tag{3.9 modified}$$

Multiplying $(3.8_{mod.})$ by 2 and subtracting from $(3.9_{mod.})$:

$$[HCO_3^-] = [OH^-] \tag{3.10}$$

The easiest path of substitution perhaps is to express all equilibria in terms of $[H^+]$ and substitute into $(3.8_{mod.})$. From (3.4):

$$[H^+][OH^-] = 10^{-14}$$

$$[OH^-] = \frac{10^{-14}}{[H^+]}$$

Substituting from (3.10)

$$[HCO_3^-] = \frac{10^{-14}}{[H^+]} \tag{3.11}$$

Substituting (3.11) into (3.3):

$$[CO_3^{--}] = \frac{10^{-24.3}}{[H^+]^2} \tag{3.12}$$

Substituting (3.12) in (3.1):

$$[Ca^{++}] = 10^{16}[H^+]^2 \tag{3.13}$$

Finally, by using (3.11), (3.12), and (3.13) in $(3.8_{mod.})$:

$$10^{16}[H^+]^2 = \frac{10^{-24.3}}{[H^+]^2} + \frac{10^{-14}}{[H^+]} \tag{3.14}$$

Multiplying through $[H^+]^2$ and rearranging:

$$10^{16}[H^+]^4 - 10^{-14}[H^+] = 10^{-24.3} \tag{3.15}$$

The easiest method of solution is by trial and error, and yields $[H^+] = 10^{-9.95}$.

Back-substitution into (3.13), (3.12), (3.11), and (3.10) yields:

$$[Ca^{++}] = 10^{-3.90}$$
$$[CO_3^{--}] = 10^{-4.40}$$
$$[HCO_3^-] = 10^{-4.05}$$
$$[OH^-] = 10^{-4.05}$$

It is clear that ignoring $[H^+]$ in the electric balance equation (3.9) has not led to appreciable error, and that ignoring $[H_2CO_3]$ in equation (3.8) is equally justified ($[H_2CO_3]$ from (3.2) $= 10^{-7.6}$).

Now consider the error involved in assuming $\gamma_i \cong 1$. The ionic strength of the solution is:

$$\mu = \tfrac{1}{2}([Ca^{++}] \times 2^2 + [H^+] \times 1^2 + [CO_3^{--}] \times 2^2 + [HCO_3^-] \times 1^2$$
$$+ [OH^-] \times 1^2)$$
$$= \tfrac{1}{2}(6.04 \times 10^{-4} + 1.13 \times 10^{-10} + 1.6 \times 10^{-4} + 8.9 \times 10^{-5}$$
$$+ 8.9 \times 10^{-5})$$
$$= 9.42 \times 10^{-4}$$

This ionic strength is clearly in the range where the Debye-Hückel equation can be used. For $\gamma_{Ca^{++}}$, with values from Tables 2.3 and 2.4:

$$-\log \gamma_{Ca^{++}} = \frac{0.5085 \times 4\sqrt{\mu}}{1 + 0.3281 \times 6\sqrt{\mu}} = +0.059$$

$$\gamma_{Ca^{++}} = 0.87$$

Similarly, $\gamma_{CO_3^{--}} = 0.87$, $\gamma_{HCO_3^-} = 0.97$, $\gamma_{OH^-} = 0.97$, $\gamma_{H^+} = 0.97$, $\gamma_{H_2CO_3} = 1.0$ (molecular species). These coefficients are sufficiently close to unity so that the error resulting from neglecting them is small. But for the sake of completeness in this first case, the problem will be solved by using them.

Rewriting all equations in terms of molalities and activity coefficients:

$$m_{Ca^{++}} \gamma_{Ca^{++}} m_{CO_3^{--}} \gamma_{CO_3^{--}} = 10^{-8.3} \tag{3.1}$$

$$m_{Ca^{++}} m_{CO_3^{--}} = \frac{10^{-8.3}}{\gamma_{Ca^{++}} \gamma_{CO_3^{--}}} = 10^{-8.3} \times 10^{0.1} = 10^{-8.2}$$

$$\frac{m_{H^+} \gamma_{H^+} m_{CO_3^{--}} \gamma_{CO_3^{--}}}{m_{HCO_3^-} \gamma_{HCO_3^-}} = 10^{-10.3} \tag{3.3}$$

$$\frac{m_{H^+} m_{CO_3^{--}}}{m_{HCO_3^-}} = \frac{10^{-10.3} \gamma_{HCO_3^-}}{\gamma_{H^+} \gamma_{CO_3^{--}}} = 10^{-10.3} \times 10^{0.06} = 10^{-10.2}$$

$$\frac{m_{H^+} \gamma_{H^+} m_{HCO_3^-} \gamma_{HCO_3^-}}{m_{H_2CO_3} \gamma_{H_2CO_3}} = 10^{-6.4} \tag{3.2}$$

$$\frac{m_{H^+} m_{HCO_3^-}}{m_{H_2CO_3}} = \frac{10^{-6.4} \gamma_{H_2CO_3}}{\gamma_{H^+} \gamma_{HCO_3^-}} = 10^{-6.4} \times 10^{0.03} = 10^{-6.4}$$

$$m_{H^+} \gamma_{H^+} m_{OH^-} \gamma_{OH^-} = 10^{-14} \tag{3.4}$$

$$m_{H^+} m_{OH^-} = \frac{10^{-14}}{\gamma_{H^+} \gamma_{OH^-}} = 10^{-14} \times 10^{0.03} = 10^{-14}$$

$$m_{Ca^{++}} = m_{HCO_3^-} + m_{CO_3^{--}} \tag{3.8, modified}$$

$$2m_{Ca^{++}} = 2m_{CO_3^{--}} + m_{HCO_3^-} + m_{OH^-} \tag{3.9, modified}$$

Therefore the only significant changes, inasmuch as the constants used have been assumed accurate only to the first decimal in the experiment, are in the constants of equations (3.1) and (3.3). As a result, substitution in the various equilibria would yield only two changes, and the equation parallel to (3.15) would be:

$$10^{16.1}[H^+]^4 - 10^{-14}[H^+] = 10^{-24.2} \qquad (3.15, \text{ modified})$$

This change makes the equilibrium pH slightly lower—close to 9.9—but the whole operation is essentially within the limits of the constants involved. On the other hand, the procedure used contains all the steps necessary to correct calculations for other carbonates if the activity coefficients are sufficiently small to require consideration.

In summary of Case 1, it can be said that the equilibrium pH lies between 9.9 and 10, that $m_{Ca^{++}} \cong 10^{-3.90}$; $m_{CO_3^{--}} \cong 10^{-4.4}$; $m_{HCO_3^-} \cong 10^{-4.05}$; $m_{H_2CO_3} \cong 10^{-7.6}$. These theoretical values check well against experiment; in three runs of the equilibrium pH of powdered calcite in distilled, deaerated water, the author and R. Siever obtained pH values of 9.88, 9.92, and 9.96. As previously indicated, this system has little geologic interest because it is too simple. This point is illustrated by the "defining equations"; few natural systems can be assumed to have carbonate species derived only from a single solid carbonate, nor have their ionic relations described only in terms of calcium, hydrogen, carbonate, bicarbonate, and hydroxyl ion activities.

CASE 2. CALCIUM CARBONATE–WATER, WITH EXTERNALLY FIXED PRESSURE OF CO_2

The second case, in which calcite is in equilibrium with water and with a given partial pressure of CO_2, can be derived from the first one experimentally by opening the container of calcite and water and passing air or other gas with fixed CO_2 content through the system continuously. Again the equilibria can be written:

$$[Ca^{++}][CO_3^{--}] = 10^{-8.3} \qquad (3.1)$$

$$\frac{[H^+][HCO_3^-]}{[H_2CO_3]} = 10^{-6.4} \qquad (3.2)$$

$$\frac{[H^+][CO_3^{--}]}{[HCO_3^-]} = 10^{-10.3} \qquad (3.3)$$

$$[H^+][OH^-] = 10^{-14} \qquad (3.4)$$

For this case equation (3.8) is not valid, because carbonate species are derived from the external CO_2 source as well as from the calcite. Equation (3.9), expressing electric neutrality, does hold, inasmuch as the ionic species present are still only Ca^{++}, H^+, CO_3^{--}, HCO_3^- and OH^-. Then

$$2m_{Ca^{++}} + m_{H^+} = 2m_{CO_3^{--}} + m_{HCO_3^-} + m_{OH^-} \qquad (3.9)$$

As a substitute for equation (3.8), the conditions specified—constant pressure of CO_2—can be designated.

$$P_{CO_2} = k \qquad (3.16)$$

Then from (3.7):

$$\frac{[H_2CO_3]}{P_{CO_2}} = k_{CO_2} = 10^{-1.5}$$

Rearranging:

$$[H_2CO_3] = 10^{-1.5}P_{CO_2} \qquad (3.17)$$

Then at a specified P_{CO_2}, equations (3.1)–(3.4), (3.9), and (3.17) describe the system. As a specific example, let us solve for equilibrium with the atmosphere in which $P_{CO_2} \cong 10^{-3.5}$. $\quad _{3.14 \times 10^{-4}}$
From equation (3.17):

$$[H_2CO_3] = 10^{-1.5} \times 10^{-3.5} = 10^{-5} \qquad (3.18)$$

Again substituting so as to express equation (3.9) in terms of $[H^+]$; and assuming as a first approximation that $\gamma_i \cong 1$, and $a_i \cong m_i$, equation (3.2) yields:

$$[H^+][HCO_3^-] = 10^{-6.4} \times 10^{-5} = 10^{-11.4}$$

$$[HCO_3^-] = \frac{10^{-11.4}}{[H^+]} \qquad (3.19)$$

From (3.3):

$$[CO_3^{--}] = \frac{10^{-10.3}[HCO_3^-]}{[H^+]} = \frac{10^{-21.7}}{[H^+]^2} \qquad (3.20)$$

From (3.4):

$$[OH^-] = \frac{10^{-14}}{[H^+]} \qquad (3.21)$$

From (3.1):

$$[Ca^{++}] = \frac{10^{-8.3}}{[CO_3^{--}]} = 10^{13.4}[H^+]^2 \qquad (3.22)$$

Substituting these values [equations (3.19)–(3.22)] into equation (3.9)]:

$$2 \times 10^{13.4}[H^+]^2 + [H^+] = 2 \times \frac{10^{-21.7}}{[H^+]^2} + \frac{10^{-11.4}}{[H^+]} + \frac{10^{-14}}{[H^+]}$$

Multiplying through by $[H^+]^2$ and putting all numbers in powers of ten:

$$10^{13.7}[H^+]^4 + [H^+]^3 = 10^{-21.4} + 10^{-11.4}[H^+] + 10^{-14}[H^+]$$

Collecting terms:

$$10^{13.7}[H^+]^4 + [H^+]^3 - 10^{-11.4}[H^+] = 10^{-21.4} \qquad (3.23)$$

Solving by inspection:

$$[H^+] = 10^{-8.4}$$

Then $[Ca^{++}] = 10^{-3.4}$; $[CO_3^{--}] = 10^{-4.9}$; $[HCO_3^-] = 10^{-3.0}$; $[OH^-] = 10^{-5.6}$; $[H_2CO_3] = 10^{-5}$.

Therefore the pH of a system containing $CaCO_3$ in water in equilibrium with the atmosphere is 8.4. The ionic strength is still so low that correction for the difference of molality and activity is hardly worthwhile. The molality of Ca^{++} is about $10^{-3.4}$, which is 2.5 times as great as in Case 1 in the absence of the atmosphere. Note the marked lowering of the pH because of the influence of atmospheric CO_2, showing that large errors in pH may result from permitting water samples out of contact with the atmosphere in their native state to come in contact with it before pH measurement. Experiments by the author and R. Siever again show excellent correspondence between the calculated pH and observed pH for water in equilibrium with calcite and the atmosphere.

CASE 3. FIXED TOTAL DISSOLVED CARBONATE SPECIES, pH ARBITRARILY SELECTED

Case 3 is probably that most commonly encountered by geologists and geochemists. Chemical analysis of a natural water is available, so that pH, total calcium, and total carbonate species, as well as ionic strength are known. Is the water in equilibrium with calcium carbonate, or is it oversaturated or undersaturated? The problem can be solved approximately, but in the specific instance of sea water, it has led to a long-standing and sometimes heated controversy. The sea water problem is one in which the investigators need an answer more accurate than can be provided by the data available or even procurable without extreme effort.

The procedure in Case 3 is to set up equations (3.1)–(3.4) in terms of molalities and activity coefficients:

$$m_{Ca^{++}} \, m_{CO_3^{--}} = \frac{10^{-8.3}}{\gamma_{Ca^{++}} \, \gamma_{CO_3^{--}}} \tag{3.1}$$

$$\frac{a_{H^+} m_{HCO_3^-}}{m_{H_2CO_3}} = \frac{10^{-6.4}}{\gamma_{HCO_3^-}} \tag{3.2}^3$$

$$\frac{a_{H^+} m_{CO_3^{--}}}{m_{HCO_3^-}} = \frac{10^{-10.3} \, \gamma_{HCO_3^-}}{\gamma_{CO_3^{--}}} \tag{3.3}$$

$$a_{H^+} m_{OH^-} = \frac{10^{-14}}{\gamma_{OH^-}} \tag{3.4}$$

Because total carbonate is given by analysis:

$$m_{H_2CO_3} + m_{HCO_3^-} + m_{CO_3^{--}} = k_{anal} \tag{3.24}$$

and pH is also given in the analysis:

$$a_{H^+} = k_{H^+} \tag{3.25}$$

Then the system is defined by equations (3.1)–(3.4), and (3.24) and (3.25), plus knowledge of ionic strength from the analysis, which permits calculation of approximate values of all the activity coefficients.

As an example of a specific problem of this type, let us select an analysis of a natural water at random, and attempt to determine whether or not it is in equilibrium with calcite. The analysis selected (Table 3.1) is of water from Lake Earl, California (William Back, *Geology and ground water features of the Smith River Plain, Del Norte County, California. U.S. Geol. Surv. Water Supply Paper 1254,* 1957, p. 70).

TABLE 3.1. Analysis of Water from Lake Earl (ppm)

pH	Ca	Mg	Na	K	HCO₃	CO₃	SO₄	Cl	F	NO₃	B
7.5	79	261	2110	4.0	84	0	508	3790	0.1	1.2	1.1

Recalculation of these values, ignoring F, NO₃, and B, shows that the ionic strength is 0.128; $m_{Ca^{++}}$ is 0.002 ($10^{-2.7}$); and $m_{HCO_3^-}$ is 0.0014 ($10^{-2.85}$). In analyses of this type neither CO_3^{--} nor H_2CO_3 can be determined; as will be seen the calculated values are below analytical detection. Activity coefficients for the individual ions are $\gamma_{Ca^{++}} = 0.38$; $\gamma_{HCO_3^-} = 0.76$; $\gamma_{CO_3^{--}} = 0.34$.

---

[3] Because pH is given, a_{H^+} is known, and m_{H^+} is almost never required in defining equations. Also $\gamma_{H_2CO_3}$ is so close to unity in natural solutions that it does not have to be considered, except for scrupulous work.

Substituting a_{H^+}, $m_{HCO_3^-}$, $\gamma_{HCO_3^-}$, and $\gamma_{CO_3^{--}}$ in equation (3.3):

$$\frac{10^{-7.5}m_{CO_3^{--}}}{10^{-2.85}} = \frac{10^{-10.3}10^{-0.12}}{10^{-0.47}}$$

$$m_{CO_3^{--}} = 10^{-5.3}$$

Using this value, $\gamma_{Ca^{++}}$ and $\gamma_{CO_3^{--}}$ in equation (3.1):

$$m_{Ca^{++}}10^{-5.3} = \frac{10^{-8.3}}{10^{-0.47}10^{-0.43}}$$

$$m_{Ca^{++}} = 10^{-2.1}$$

Thus calculated calcium is $10^{-2.1}$, and analytical calcium is $10^{-2.7}$, so the water is somewhat undersaturated with calcium carbonate according to these calculations.

The calculations can be continued to show that $m_{HCO_3^-}$ given by analysis is much higher than that expected at equilibrium with the atmosphere at the listed pH of 7.5. The calculated value of $m_{HCO_3^-}$ is $10^{-3.8}$, as opposed to the analyzed value of $10^{-2.8}$. If the bicarbonate present is a measure of the average conditions, the pH of the water, if in equilibrium with the atmosphere, should be higher than 8. If so, the water would be approximately saturated with calcium carbonate at this higher pH. Then we might speculate that the pH was measured at a low point in the cycle of diurnal variation.

CASE 4. SYSTEM IN EQUILIBRIUM WITH CALCITE AT A GIVEN P_{CO_2}, AND AT AN ARBITRARY pH

The greatest use of Case 4 is probably in calculation to determine the activity and molality of calcium ion in equilibrium with calcite under hypothetical conditions. For example, what are the activity and molality of calcium ion in a solution which has an ionic strength of 0.10, and has reacted to a pH of 10 because of the presence of volcanic glass, yet is open to the atmosphere and contains solid calcium carbonate?

As before, equations (3.1)–(3.4) are applicable, and the defining equations are based on the constancy of P_{CO_2} and knowledge of pH. The necessary relations are:

$$m_{Ca^{++}}\gamma_{Ca^{++}}m_{CO_3^-}\gamma_{CO_3^{--}} = 10^{-8.3} \tag{3.1}$$

$$\frac{a_H+ m_{CO_3^{--}}\gamma_{CO_3^{--}}}{m_{HCO_3^-}\gamma_{HCO_3^-}} = 10^{-10.3} \tag{3.2}$$

$$\frac{a_{H^+} m_{HCO_3^-} \gamma_{HCO_3^-}}{m_{H_2CO_3}} = 10^{-6.4} \tag{3.3}$$

$$a_{H^+} m_{OH^-} \gamma_{OH^-} = 10^{-14} \tag{3.4}$$

$$a_{H^+} = k \tag{3.25}$$

$$m_{H_2CO_3} = 10^{-1.5} P_{CO_2} \tag{3.17}$$

First activity coefficients for the individual ions must be determined. For an ionic strength of 0.1, either the Debye-Hückel or the mean activity coefficient method can be used (Chapter 2).

Using Debye-Hückel, taking advantage of the values for A and B and for $\mathring{a}$ in Tables 2.3 and 2.4, and substituting in

$$-\log \gamma_i = \frac{A z_i^2 \sqrt{\mu}}{1 + \mathring{a} B \sqrt{\mu}}$$

the following values are obtained: $\gamma_{Ca^{++}} = 0.40$; $\gamma_{CO_3^{--}} = 0.37$; $\gamma_{HCO_3^-} = 0.77$; $\gamma_{OH^-} = 0.76$. As before, $\gamma_{H_2CO_3}$ can be considered to be unity, without serious error. Substitution of these γ values in equations (3.1)–(3.4) and the conditions that pH = 10 and that the system is in equilibrium with the atmosphere ($P_{CO_2} = 10^{-3.5}$) in equations (3.25) and (3.17) then provide relations all in terms of molalities, with the exception of a_{H^+}, which is known directly by measurement of the solution.

$$m_{Ca^{++}} m_{CO_3^{--}} = \frac{10^{-8.3}}{\gamma_{Ca^{++}} \gamma_{CO_3^{--}}} = 10^{-7.5} \tag{3.1}$$

$$\frac{a_{H^+} m_{CO_3^{--}}}{m_{HCO_3^-}} = \frac{10^{-10.3} \gamma_{HCO_3^-}}{\gamma_{CO_3^{--}}} = 10^{-10.0} \tag{3.2}$$

$$\frac{a_{H^+} m_{HCO_3^-}}{m_{H_2CO_3}} = \frac{10^{-6.4}}{\gamma_{HCO_3^-}} = 10^{-6.3} \tag{3.3}$$

$$a_{H^+} m_{OH^-} = \frac{10^{-14}}{\gamma_{OH^-}} = 10^{-13.9} \tag{3.4}$$

$$a_{H^+} = 10^{-10} \tag{3.25}$$

$$m_{H_2CO_3} = 10^{-1.5} P_{CO_2} = 10^{-5.0} \tag{3.17}$$

The solution is then easy. Putting $m_{H_2CO_3} = 10^{-5.0}$ and $a_{H^+} = 10^{-10}$ from equations (3.17) and (3.25) into (3.3):

$$\frac{10^{-10} m_{HCO_3^-}}{10^{-5}} = 10^{-6.3}; \quad m_{HCO_3^-} = 10^{-1.3}$$

Substituting this value into (3.2):

$$\frac{10^{-10}m_{CO_3^{--}}}{10^{-1.3}} = 10^{-10.0}; \quad m_{CO_3^{--}} = 10^{-1.3}$$

Then, from (3.1):

$$m_{Ca^{++}}10^{-1.3} = 10^{-7.5}; \quad m_{Ca^{++}} = 10^{-6.2}$$

Finally,

$$m_{Ca^{++}}\gamma_{Ca^{++}} = a_{Ca^{++}}$$

$$10^{-6.2}10^{-0.40} = 10^{-6.6} = a_{Ca^{++}}$$

In the particular ground water considered, the molality of calcium ion is thus calculated to be vanishingly low—a few hundredths of a part per million. The order of magnitude is certainly trustworthy for $m_{Ca^{++}}$. If actual analysis of the water yields high values for dissolved calcium, additional ionic or molecular species containing calcium must be present.

CASE 5. EQUILIBRIUM IN A SYSTEM OF WATER ORIGINALLY OPEN TO ATMOSPHERIC CO$_2$, THEN CLOSED BEFORE ADDITION OF CaCO$_3$

Case 5 is actually a combination of Cases 1 and 2, but it has peculiar geologic interest because it represents the situation where rainwater, which is roughly equivalent to pure water in equilibrium with atmospheric CO_2, descends through a nonreactive soil or rock layer and comes in contact with calcite-bearing material. How much carbonate is leached per unit of descending solution? The question is a fundamental one in the attempt to determine the leaching action of rainwater quantitatively.

The basic equilibria are as before, but with a slight difference in the defining equations. Considering the rainwater first, only the relations for dissolved carbonate species, plus knowledge of atmospheric P_{CO_2} and an electric neutrality equation are necessary:

$$\frac{[H^+][HCO_3^-]}{[H_2CO_3]} = 10^{-6.4} \tag{3.2}$$

$$\frac{[H^+][CO_3^{--}]}{[HCO_3^-]} = 10^{-10.3} \tag{3.3}$$

$$[H_2CO_3] = 10^{-1.5}P_{CO_2} \tag{3.17}$$

$$P_{CO_2} = 10^{-3.5} \tag{3.26}$$

$$[H^+] = [HCO_3^-] + 2[CO_3^{--}] \tag{3.27}$$

From (3.26) and (3.17), $[H_2CO_3] = 10^{-5.0}$. Also, inasmuch as the reaction of CO_2 with water alone results in production of H^+, the concentration of carbonate ion must be negligible ($k_{HCO_3^-} = 10^{-10.3}$), so from equations (3.27) and (3.2):

$$[H^+] = [HCO_3^-] \qquad \text{(3.27, modified)}$$

$$\frac{[H^+]^2}{[H_2CO_3]} = 10^{-6.4} \qquad \text{(substitution in 3.2)}$$

$$[H^+]^2 = 10^{-11.4} \qquad \begin{array}{l}\text{(using value of } [H_2CO_3] \\ \text{from (3.17) and (3.26))}\end{array}$$

$$[H^+] = 10^{-5.7}$$

$$[HCO_3^-] = 10^{-5.7} \qquad \text{(3.27 modified)}$$

Then the total dissolved carbonate in rainwater is $[H_2CO_3] + [HCO_3^-] = 10^{-5} + 10^{-5.7} = 10^{-4.9}$. Again the difference between activities and molalities can be ignored, inasmuch as the ionic strength is very low.

When the rainwater reaches the calcite and reacts with it, the original dissolved carbonate species are augmented by carbonate from the calcite. Every carbonate or bicarbonate ion or H_2CO_3 molecule from the calcite also produces a calcium ion, so one defining equation is:

$$[Ca^{++}] + 10^{-4.9} = [H_2CO_3] + [HCO_3^-] + [CO_3^{--}] \qquad \text{(3.28)}$$

From electric neutrality relations:

$$2[Ca^{++}] + [H^+] = [HCO_3^-] + [OH^-] + 2[CO_3^{--}] \qquad \text{(3.9)}$$

Then we can proceed, using the other relations:

$$[Ca^{++}][CO_3^{--}] = 10^{-8.3} \qquad \text{(3.1)}$$

$$\frac{[H^+][HCO_3^-]}{[H_2CO_3]} = 10^{-6.4} \qquad \text{(3.2)}$$

$$\frac{[H^+][CO_3^{--}]}{[HCO_3^-]} = 10^{-10.3} \qquad \text{(3.3)}$$

$$[H^+][OH^-] = 10^{-14} \qquad \text{(3.4)}$$

The procedure follows that used in Case 1, and yields:

$$[Ca^{++}] = 10^{-3.85}$$

$$[H^+] = 10^{-9.9}$$

$$[H_2CO_3] = 10^{-7.5}$$

$$[HCO_3^-] = 10^{-4.0}$$

$$[CO_3^{--}] = 10^{-4.4}$$

It is of interest that these values deviate only slightly (hardly more than the error of calculation) from those of Case 1 (p. 50), in which the reaction is entirely between $CaCO_3$ and H_2O. In fact, the increase in solubility is only about 10 percent over that in pure water. The reason for this emerges when we note that the total dissolved carbonate in the rainwater is only $10^{-4.9}$ moles per liter, so that its reacting value is low. On the other hand, if there are rootlets in the soil through which the rainwater passes, or other sources of CO_2, there will be a corresponding increase in calcite solubility and a lowering of the equilibrium pH. On the other hand, the very high value of pH achieved by the reaction of rainwater on calcite has perhaps not been appreciated in consideration of reactions in the weathering zone. In summary it can be said that the role of dissolved CO_2 in ground-waters in dissolving carbonates may be overrated, and that of hydrolysis alone—the reaction with pure water—underrated.

THE EFFECT OF TEMPERATURE ON CARBONATE EQUILIBRIA

It is not the purpose of this text to consider pressure-temperature relations, on the assumption that the techniques necessary to change the equilibria illustrated here at 25°C and 1 atmosphere total pressure to those at other P-T conditions are readily available in textbooks on

TABLE 3.2. Carbonate Equilibria[a]

Temperature (°C)	pK_1	pK_2	pK_S
0	6.577	10.625	8.023
5	6.517	10.557	8.087
10	6.465	10.490	8.150
15	6.420	10.430	8.215
20	6.382	10.377	8.280
25	6.351	10.329	8.342
30	6.327	10.290	8.395
40	6.296	10.220	8.515
50	6.287	10.172	8.625
80	(6.315)	(10.122)	8.975

[a] Protolysis Constants of Carbonic Acid, Solubility Product of $CaCO_3$. *J. Am. Chem. Soc.*, 67, 1026 (1945); 63, 1706 (1941).

thermodynamics. But in this specific and important case of carbonate equilibria values of the constants for the reactions at temperatures in the vicinity of 25°C are so useful in handling water analyses that they are portrayed in Table 3.2. The equilibrium constant values at the

temperature conditions of the ground water can be substituted for those at 25°C used in the text. Pressure effect also becomes important at total pressures of more than 25 atmospheres, but attempts to correct for such effects become so complicated that change of equilibrium constant with pressure is not listed. For discussion of the pressure effect the reader is referred to Owen and Brinkley (B. B. Owen and S. R. Brinkley, Jr., Calculation of the effect of pressure upon ionic equilibria in pure water and in salt solutions. *Chem. Revs.*, *29*, 461–474 (1941)).

SUMMARY

Five situations, corresponding to those most frequently encountered by the geochemist in attempting to deduce the interactions of carbonates in natural solutions, have been discussed and the detailed procedures for solution of the problems described. In the examples cited, values of the constants for 25°C and 1 atmosphere total pressure were used, and the calculations were made for calcite, with the recognition that the same procedures apply to any other metal carbonate. The last case considered was a combination of two of the more fundamental situations, and was illustrated to suggest that a great many real problems can be handled adequately by such combinations. Values of equilibrium constants at temperatures other than 25°C have been listed for convenience.

SELECTED REFERENCES

Revelle, Roger, and Rhodes Fairbridge, Carbonates and carbon dioxide, in *Treatise on Marine Ecology and Paleoecology*, Vol. 1, *Geol. Soc. Am. Memoir 67*, 1957, pp. 239–295.
   Summary discussion of carbonates, including many data on solubility in the marine environment.

Sverdrup, H. U., Martin W. Johnson, and R. H. Fleming, The Oceans: Prentice-Hall, Inc., Englewood Cliffs, N.J., 1942, pp. 192–211.
   Detailed discussion of chemistry of CO_2 in sea water. Illustrates the complexities of the natural system, and the mechanical difficulties resulting from use of empirical constants for equilibria.

Schoeller, H., Geochemie des eaux souterraines: Revue de l'Institut Français du Pétrole et Annales des Combustibles Liquides, Paris, 1956, pp. 21–28.
   Development of equations representing solubility of $CaCO_3$ in natural waters. Concise, useful.

Harned, H. S., and S. R. Scholes, The ionization constant of HCO_3^- from 0–50°. *J. Am. Chem. Soc.*, *63*, 1706–1709 (1941).

Harned, H. S., and F. T. Bonner, The first ionization constant of carbonic acid in aqueous solutions of sodium chloride. *J. Am. Chem. Soc.*, *67*, 1026–1031 (1945).

Turner, R. C., A theoretical treatment of the pH of calcareous soils. *Soil Science*, *86*, 32–34 (1958).

4

Measurement of Eh and pH

Mᴇᴀsᴜʀᴇᴍᴇɴᴛ of Eh and pH has become a routine procedure in many branches of chemistry and biology. Many different companies produce the necessary equipment, and a variety of instruments and electrodes is available for measurements in the laboratory and in the field.

pH *MEASUREMENT*

Measurement of pH is accomplished today almost exclusively by use of a glass electrode in combination with a reference electrode. The glass electrode consists of an acid solution inside a special glass bulb. When the bulb is immersed in a solution an EMF is developed between the inner and outer solutions that is proportional to the logarithm of the activity of hydrogen ions in the external solution. The reference electrode necessary to complete the circuit is commonly a mercury-mercurous chloride electrode in saturated KCl solution connected to the solution to be measured by a salt bridge of KCl. Thus the reference electrode has a constant EMF, whereas that of the glass electrode varies regularly with the activity of hydrogen ions, so that the overall voltage can be calibrated in terms of pH.

For details of the theory and practice of pH measurement the reader is referred to such excellent books as those of Gold and of Bates (Victor Gold, *pH Measurement*: John Wiley and Sons, New York, 1956, 125 pp.; R. G. Bates, *Electrometric pH Determinations*: John Wiley and Sons,

New York, 1954, 331 pp.). Here emphasis is on the mechanics of measurement and on the precautions to observe in geological application.

THE GLASS ELECTRODE

Modern glass electrodes can be obtained in a variety of shapes and sizes. The "general purpose" electrode is designed for most efficient operation in the pH range 0–11. For measurements above a pH of about 11, special electrodes must be used for accurate work. In high pH solutions the hydrogen ion activity is so low, and the activity of alkali metal ions usually so high that pH is no longer proportional to the EMF of ordinary electrodes. Correction tables for this effect on general purpose electrodes are available, but use of the special electrodes is preferable. Fortunately few natural solutions have pH values as high as 11.

Although the change in EMF of various glass electrodes for a given change in pH is the same, it is rare that two electrodes exhibit the same EMF in a given solution. Thus it is necessary to calibrate every electrode used against standard buffer solutions. It is common practice to calibrate against a single buffer solution, usually at pH 7, but experience shows that many unsatisfactory results would be avoided by calibration with two buffers. In this way one can be sure that $\Delta EMF/\Delta pH$ is correct. For various reasons electrodes may respond erratically, and calibration at a single pH will not reveal unsatisfactory behavior. Furthermore, use of two buffers provides a check on the probable error of measurement for a given instrumental set up.

THE REFERENCE ELECTRODE

Various electrodes can be used in conjunction with the glass electrode in the measurement of pH; the chief requisite is that they provide a constant EMF at a given temperature. Currently the *saturated calomel electrode* is in most general use. It consists of mercury in contact with mercurous chloride, in turn in contact with a saturated solution of potassium chloride. Thus the half-cell reaction is:

$$2Hg_l + 2Cl^-_{aq} = Hg_2Cl_{2c} + 2e$$

Because the activity of Hg_l and Hg_2Cl_{2c} are constant, as well as that

of Cl^-_{aq} because the KCl solution is in equilibrium with solid KCl, the equation of the half-cell is:

$$Eh = E° + \frac{0.059}{2} \log \frac{a_{Hg_2Cl_2}}{a^2_{Hg} \times a^2_{Cl^-}}$$

and

$$Eh = E° + \frac{0.059}{2} \log \frac{1}{1^2 \times k^2}$$

Then

$$Eh = E° + \text{constant} = 0.245 \text{ volt}$$

Therefore the saturated calomel half-cell has an EMF of 0.245 volt positive relative to the standard hydrogen electrode at 25°C.

In practice the standard calomel is connected to the solution to be measured by a variety of devices. Some electrodes are contained in a glass tube which is immersed in the solution, and connection is by an asbestos fiber sealed through the base of the electrode. Diffusion of KCl through the fiber provides electric connection. In others a hole in the side of the electrode is covered by a ground-glass sleeve fitted to the electrode, so that connection is by a thin film of KCl solution between the sleeve and the electrode. In still others the calomel electrode is maintained externally to the solution, and connection is through a salt bridge. The most commonly used electrodes are designed for immersion in the solution to be measured, and a small amount of KCl inevitably diffuses into the solution from the electrode, so that measurements of solutions containing ingredients sensitive either to K^+ or Cl^- may be affected. If so, the use of a salt bridge containing a nonreacting electrolyte is indicated.

If an electrode is immersed in a solution for hours or days, not only will KCl contamination of the solution become serious, but diffusion of solution ions into the electrode will also occur, and may change its EMF. Thus it is good practice to replace the KCl solution after each 24 hours or so of immersion.

pH *MEASUREMENT PRECAUTIONS*

Directions for operation of various types of pH equipment are available with the apparatus, but some remarks about the limitations of readings may be helpful.

Because the glass electrode has a high resistance, the instrument to measure the EMF between the glass and calomel electrodes is a high-gain amplifier. In making direct measurements in the field long

electrode leads are required, and unless the lead from the glass electrode is carefully shielded, erratic pH values may result. Most glass electrode leads are provided with a shield, so that the chief precaution necessary is to maintain shielding if an external connection must be made.

A thermometer is an important part of field equipment, for the error involved in assuming that all solutions are at 25°C may be several tenths of a pH unit. Most instruments have a temperature compensator that can be set at the temperature of the solution to be measured. Also, the pH of buffers changes during calibration of the electrodes. The "instrument zero" of pH meters is temperature sensitive, so that it is important to check before and after each reading to be sure that no instrument drift has occurred. This is particularly important in outdoor work. In high mountains, for example, early morning readings may be made at an instrument temperature of 10°C, whereas in the early afternoon instrument temperatures may be close to 40°C. This change has a marked effect on battery and amplifier performance; if frequent zero checks are not made, the error in pH may be as much as 0.5 unit, and corrections cannot be made because of the erratic nature of the drift.

In general, electrode response to homogeneous solutions is rapid, but the glass electrode should be rinsed several times with distilled water between readings to remove adsorbed ions. Because equilibrium is reached with a decreasing rate of pH change on the instrument, readings should be made at regular intervals until drift has ceased. A small change in pH with time should never be accepted as an approximation of the final value; in all too many instances the reaction of the electrodes to a new environment is rapid at first, and then changes to a slow steady drift over a considerable pH range before final equilibrium with the solution takes place.

pH *READINGS IN NATURAL MEDIA*

The major problem of obtaining satisfactory pH readings from earth surface environments is that of introducing electrodes into the environment without changing it significantly. Good results can be obtained from open waters such as streams, lakes, and oceans, which are already in intimate contact with the atmosphere. On the other hand, values for environments not open to the atmosphere are difficult to obtain because of contamination during or after emplacement of the electrodes.

Entry of the electrodes commonly introduces gases or permits them to escape.

Little has been done in the development of special electrodes and techniques for sampling natural waters *in situ*. The tendency has been to bring the water to the instrument, which usually permits exchange with the atmosphere. This is reflected by a steady drift in the pH readings, and the operator is in the unenviable position of attempting to guess what the reading would have been without exchange. Also, the practice of bringing the sample to the machine allows temperature change, which promotes gain or loss of volatiles. Carbon dioxide and hydrogen sulfide are two of the most important volatile constituents, and both tend to be the constituent of the system controlling the pH, so that extraordinary precautions have to be taken in protecting any sample collected and brought to the meter.

The difficulties of sampling homogeneous solutions are considerable, but they are minor compared with the problems related to measuring and interpreting the results of pH determinations on mineral suspensions or pore waters of rocks. For example, the pH of stirred suspensions may be different from that of the supernatant after settling, indicating an effect on the electrodes of particles with adsorbed hydrogen ion [E. A. Hauser and C. E. Reed, Studies in thixotropy. II. Effect of drying and of certain cations and anions on the cation-exchange capacity of soils. *Soil Sci.*, *59*, 175–190 (1937)]. The electrodes "see" only their immediate environment, so that great care must be exercised to be sure that the medium adjacent to the electrodes is that the operator wishes to measure. There is a tendency to use pH measurements made in muds or similar environments in chemical calculations valid only for homogeneous solutions; the results are highly suspect.

Innumerable determinations of "soil pH" are available in the literature. The usual practice is to suspend a given weight of soil sample in a given weight of water, and then to determine the pH of the slurry. The results are useful only in a highly qualitative sense, inasmuch as they represent the complex contribution of the hydrogen ions in the original water plus those released by the soil sample plus effects of soil colloids on the electrodes. If the suspension used is open to the atmosphere, and the sample uses up hydrogen ions from the added water the original reaction may be to give a high pH, followed by a downward drift as CO_2 is adsorbed.

A good example of the kinds of changes that can occur is represented

by the addition of excess finely ground calcite to deaerated water.
The original pH is about 9.9.   On opening the system to the atmosphere a downward drift sets in, with a final pH at equilibrium of 8.4.
Thus the difference with and without air is 1.5 pH units!   Differences
of the same order of magnitude can be observed by measuring the pH
of synthetic brines first in a nitrogen atmosphere and then in equilibrium with air (R. Siever, personal communication).

Lest too dark a picture be painted, it should be said that the pH
values measured on soil samples suspended in water probably do
represent fairly accurately the pH of the interstitial solution, except at
pH values of 4 or lower, where colloidal effects on the glass electrode
become important.   If techniques are used to insert electrodes directly
into the natural system to be measured without contamination, the
results are a satisfactory characterization of pore waters in most cases.
The electrodes must go to the environment—too many dangers
accompany attempts to bring the environment to the electrodes.

Eh *MEASUREMENT*

Oxidation potential is measured with an electrode pair consisting
of an inert electrode and a reference electrode.   The same reference
electrode is used for most Eh measurements as for pH measurements—
the saturated calomel.

The inert electrode used most is bright platinum, although the gold
electrode has a fair number of applications.   As in pH measurements,
the role of the calomel electrode is to supply a known EMF and to
make electric connection with the system to be measured.   The inert
electrode acts as an electron acceptor or donor to the ions in the
measured solution.   When connected to the calomel electrode, the
platinum electrode can accept electrons from dissolved ionic species,
or it can give them up, depending on whether the potential of the dissolved species is greater or less than that of the calomel reference
electrode.   Therefore the reactions involved when a platinum and a
calomel electrode are placed in a solution with 0.01 $a_{Fe^{++}}$ and 0.01
$a_{Fe^{+3}}$ is:

$$Pt_{(inert)} \left| \begin{array}{ll} Fe^{+++}_{aq} & 0.01 \\ Fe^{++}_{aq} & 0.001 \end{array} \right| \left| \begin{array}{l} Hg_2Cl_{2c} \\ KCl_{aq\,sat} \end{array} \right| Hg_1$$

The reaction at the left is:

$$2Fe^{++}_{aq} = 2Fe^{+++}_{aq} + 2e \qquad\qquad (4.1)$$

And the reaction on the right is:

$$2Hg_l + 2Cl_{aq}^- = Hg_2Cl_2 + 2e \qquad (4.2)$$

As shown before (p. 63), the EMF of reaction (4.2) is 0.245 volt at 25°C. For reaction (4.1) the potential is:

$$Eh = E^\circ_{Fe^{+++}/Fe^{++}} + \frac{0.059}{2} \log \frac{a^2_{Fe^{+++}}}{a^2_{Fe^{++}}}$$

Simplifying:

$$Eh = E^\circ_{Fe^{+++}/Fe^{++}} + 0.059 \log \frac{a_{Fe^{+++}}}{a_{Fe^{++}}}$$

Substituting numerical values for E° and for the activities of the ferric and ferrous ions:

$$Eh = 0.771 + 0.059 \log \frac{0.01}{0.001} = 0.830 \text{ volt} \qquad (4.3)$$

Therefore, subtracting (4.2) from (4.1):

$$2Fe_{aq}^{++} \qquad = 2Fe_{aq}^{3+} + 2e \qquad Eh = 0.830 \text{ volt}$$
$$2Hg_l + 2Cl_{aq}^- \quad = Hg_2Cl_{2c} + 2e \qquad Eh = 0.245 \text{ volt}$$
$$\overline{\text{Measured potential} = E = 0.585} \qquad (4.4)$$

Because the calomel reference electrode has a constant Eh at any given temperature and pressure, the potential of the half-cell at the platinum electrode is the measured EMF plus that of the calomel cell:

$$Eh_{(Pt)} = E_{measured} + Eh_{calomel}$$

As shown above, the measured potential of the calomel-ferrous-ferric pair is 0.585 volt (4.4), and the potential of the saturated calomel electrode is 0.245 volt, so that the Eh of the ferrous-ferric pair should be:

$$Eh_{(Pt)} = 0.585 + 0.245 = 0.830 \text{ volt}$$

Thus in practice the measured voltage of the inert electrode reference electrode pair is added algebraically to the potential of the reference electrode to get the Eh of the half-cell reaction occurring at the platinum electrode.

The change of potential of the saturated calomel electrode with temperature in the vicinity of 25°C is given by Glasstone (Samuel Glasstone, *An Introduction to Electrochemistry*. D. Van Nostrand Co., Princeton, N.J., 1942, p. 232) as:

$$Eh = 0.245 - 0.00076(t - 25)$$

$$0.2415 - 0.00076 (t - 25)$$

Use of Eh measurements in the calculation of activity ratios of ion pairs is predicated upon the following assumptions:

1. All dissolved species for which calculations are made are in internal equilibrium; that is, the measured EMF indicates the tendency of any such pairs to oxidize or reduce. For example, if a solution containing ferric ion is added to one containing vanadous ion, it is assumed that they will interact: $Fe^{3+} + V^{3+} + H_2O = Fe^{++} + VO^{++} + 2H^+$; and that the resulting proportions of ions are equilibrium proportions. In general this assumption is satisfactory for simple dissolved species, with the notable inorganic exceptions of sulfate or bisulfate ions and dissolved oxygen.

2. The platinum or gold electrode functions as an inert electrode. In some solutions the platinum or gold may react and become coated with another substance, in which case readings are useless for calculations involving dissolved species. Notable offenders are solutions containing divalent sulfur, in which platinum electrode behavior may become erratic. Fortunately the worst offenders in causing reaction of gold or platinum are strong oxidizing agents not encountered in nature.

THE PLATINUM ELECTRODE

The platinum electrode functions best if it has a large surface, so that "thimble type" electrodes generally are more satisfactory than "button type" or single platinum wires. As indicated before, the platinum electrode may become coated by reaction with the solution to be measured or by precipitates from the solution. Various cleaning techniques have been employed, but the most satisfactory seems to be mechanical cleaning with fine emery paper. Drastic chemical cleaning may in many instances simply lead to the formation of a new reaction coating.

The platinum-calomel pair is usually checked against ZoBell solution (C. E. ZoBell, 1946, Occurrence and activity of bacteria in marine sediments. *Recent Marine Sediments.* American Association of Petroleum Geologists, 1946, p. 495), a solution of $0.003M$ potassium ferrocyanide and $0.003M$ potassium ferricyanide in $0.1M$ KCl solution. This solution has an Eh of 0.428 volt at 25°C, or an observed potential of 0.183 volt when measured against a saturated calomel. The temperature coefficient in the range near 25° is expressed by the relation:

$$Eh = 0.428 - 0.0022(t - 25)$$

Thus the observed potential between the saturated calomel and the platinum electrode, when they are immersed in ZoBell solution is:

$$E_{\text{calomel-ZoBell (Pt)}} = \text{Eh}_{\text{ZoBell}} - \text{Eh}_{\text{calomel}} = [0.428 - 0.0022(t - 25)]$$
$$-[0.245 - 0.00076(t - 25)] = 0.183 - 0.00144(t - 25)$$

THE REFERENCE ELECTRODE

A saturated calomel electrode is the usual reference electrode, and the preceding remarks under "pH Measurement" are applicable. In addition it appears that contamination of the calomel electrode by diffusion of solution into the electrode is even more serious in the case of Eh measurements than it is for pH, and electrodes must be cleaned after every few hours of use.   When the calomel electrode is dipped into a solution 5 to 10 degrees above the initial temperature of the electrode, as much as half an hour may be necessary for equilibration of the electrode.

Eh *MEASUREMENT PRECAUTIONS*

Eh measurement is subject to most of the precautions applicable to pH measurement in terms of instrumentation, except that the measuring circuit has relatively low resistance, and fewer difficulties are experienced in the shielding of electrode leads.

In Eh measurements, most of the difficulties result from contamination of the platinum electrode, so it is a useful experimental device to have two platinum electrodes available so that they can be alternated in the circuit.   The poisoning of the platinum electrode is usually an erratic process, so that any such effects show up as differences in potential from the two electrodes.   It is the writer's experience that even careful work cannot be duplicated closer than about 5 millivolts, and that differences in replication of measurements on natural media may be of the order of 10–20 millivolts.   The most satisfactory method of Eh-pH measurement, although it does not lend itself easily to field studies, is by use of commercial continuous recording equipment.   In such setups the amplifiers are on continuously, which tends toward stability of measurement.   Also, grounding of instruments and solutions and shielding of leads is far better than for "spot" measurement instruments, which leads to smaller fluctuations of potentials from extraneous EMF's and capacitance effects. Finally, continuous recording permits observation and accurate determination of "drifts"

over long periods of time that might easily escape notice in the course of collection of individual readings. Under laboratory conditions pH values can be determined ± 0.01 pH unit, and changes of pH of as little as 0.01 pH unit per hour can be discerned easily.

Eh *READINGS IN NATURAL MEDIA*

The number of Eh readings that have been made in natural media is but a small fraction of the number of pH measurements. It can be fairly said at the time of this writing that there are few useful readings available from systems not in equilibrium with the atmosphere.

The values available from systems in equilibrium with the atmosphere have been disappointing in the sense that they show little range of Eh. The readings are in accord with the "irreversible oxygen potential" as discussed by Merkle (F. G. Merkle, Oxidation-reduction processes in soils, in *Chemistry of the Soil*, Firman E. Bear, editor. Reinhold Publishing Corporation, New York, 1955, pp. 200–218). Dissolved oxygen does not exert the potential expected if it is functioning at equilibrium; instead it acts like a much weaker oxidizing agent. Apparently there is a slow oxidation step of low potential in the action of dissolved oxygen on dissolved ionic species. As a result the effect of the oxygen of the atmosphere is to provide a relatively mild oxidizing effect, with an Eh of about 0.650 to 0.700 volt at pH $= 0$, and of 0.300 to 0.350 volt at pH $= 8$. Although this effect is far less than theoretical, admission of air into systems of originally low Eh is followed by rapid reaction to the "irreversible" potential. Also, there seems to be some tendency for direct action of dissolved oxygen on the platinum electrode, so that the potential observed in systems containing dissolved air is to a certain extent independent of the oxidation state of the dissolved components. In short, systems exposed to air show potentials according to the approximate relation:

$$Eh = 0.70 - 0.06pH$$

This is in contrast to the expected value at equilibrium of:

$$Eh = 1.22 - 0.06pH$$

It is difficult to measure natural systems out of equilibrium with air because of the problem of introducing electrodes without simultaneously introducing air. The general technique of bringing samples to the instrument is even more unsatisfactory in making Eh measurements than it is for pH measurements because of the rapid and homo-

genizing effect of oxygen. On the other hand, careful work can yield results of great utility, as shown by the excellent study of environmental relations in aerated and water-logged soils by Starkey and Wight (R. L. Starkey and K. M. Wight, Anaerobic Corrosion of Iron in Soils. American Gas Association, New York, 1946). They designed a sealed probe that could be driven into water-logged soils and then opened to permit the soil slurry to come into contact with pH and Eh electrodes. Some of their measurements and correlations with iron corrosion are given in Table 4.1.

TABLE 4.1. Eh-pH Measurements of Water-Logged Soils

Eh	pH	Corrosion Effects on Iron Pipe
0.046	6.5	Crust of FeS, corrosion severe
− 0.293	6.7	Crust of FeS, corrosion moderate
0.206	6.5	No corrosion observed
0.370	6.2	Slight corrosion
0.563	7.7	No corrosion
0.544	7.6	Small amount iron oxides, little corrosion

Most of the other trustworthy Eh measurements of natural conditions come from studies of deoxygenated bottom environments of lakes and seas. They indicate that the extreme range of reducing environments can be attained, for the lowest potentials are those of waters containing dissolved hydrogen, inasmuch as analyses show the presence of hydrogen gas. Just as for pH, many measurements have been made of the Eh of soils and sediments, in which a given weight of the sample is suspended in a given quantity of water. The significance of such Eh measurements is not at all clear. Most results apparently indicate the fact that the experimenter did not preclude air from the suspension. In others, in which air was excluded (except for that already in the sample?) the readings apparently measure the relative proportions of various oxidation-reduction ion pairs that happen to be soluble in water. It certainly is questionable whether the readings bear any relation either to the bulk composition of the sediment or to what might have been expected from a pore water originally in contact with the sediment.

The great unexplored region is the Eh of pore waters in natural contact with rocks. The experimental difficulties of placing electrodes so that they will not permit access of foreign materials to the environment, nor inhibit natural circulation, are great, but solution of the

problem will tell us much about oxygen loss from migrating waters, and about rates at which pore waters equilibrate with their surroundings.

Summary.   Eh and pH readings on free waters and on the pore waters of sediments and rocks are difficult to obtain.   Most measurements to date leave much to be desired in terms of values truly representative of the environment that is of interest to determine.   However, some excellent work has been done, and indicates how more useful values might be obtained.   If such results are not overinterpreted, they can be of great geochemical interest.

MEASUREMENT OF INDIVIDUAL ION ACTIVITIES

An aspect of EMF measurement that has been little used in geologic environments, in terms of its potentialities, is the determination of individual ion activities by use of suitable electrodes.   In theory the activity of almost any individual ion can be measured by use of an appropriate electrode; in practice there are many restrictions.   For any aqueous solution containing a cation, symbolized as Me^{++}, the activity of the ion at equilibrium is related to the EMF of an electrode of the same metal by:

$$\text{Eh} = E^{\circ}_{\text{metal ion/metal}} + \frac{RT}{2\mathcal{F}} \ln a_{Me^{++}}$$

It is beyond the scope of this text to attempt to assess the advantages and disadvantages of all the possible electrodes that could be used, but it is important to point out that methods are available, or perhaps can be developed, to measure the activities of a great many ions in their natural habitat.

There are two major barriers to the use of metallic electrodes to measure activities of their ions in natural environments.   One is the lack of reproducibility, owing largely to the presence of strains in all but the softest metals.   The second difficulty lies in the sensitivity of most metals to oxygen, which reacts with them to coat the electrode with an adherent oxide or hydroxide film.   In this circumstance the electrode becomes reactive to hydrogen ions, instead of the metal ion. In fact some metal-metal oxide pairs (i.e., As/As_2O_3, Bi/Bi_2O_3) can be used as pH electrodes.

Lack of reproducibility of the native metal electrode can be overcome for some metals by methods of preparation, that yield a fine-grained material, or by using an amalgam (i.e., Pb/Hg, Cu/Hg), but the

necessity for excluding oxygen is a severe limitation. Not only does it prevent measurements in environments open to the atmosphere, but also stringent precautions must be used to protect the electrode before and during insertion into a low potential natural environment.

On the other hand, several satisfactory electrodes are available for measurement of anion activities. Among them are the Ag/AgCl electrode for determination of chloride ion activity:

$$Ag_c + Cl^-_{aq} = AgCl_c + e$$

$$Eh = E° + \frac{RT}{\mathscr{F}} \ln \frac{1}{a_{Cl^-}}$$

and the silver-silver sulfide electrode for measurement of sulfide ion:

$$2Ag_c + S^{--}_{aq} = Ag_2S_c + 2e$$

$$Eh = E° + \frac{RT}{2\mathscr{F}} \ln \frac{1}{a_{S^{--}}}$$

Marshall [cf. C. E. Marshall and W. E. Bergman. The electrochemical properties of mineral membranes. II. Measurement of potassium-ion activities in colloidal clays. *J. Phys. Chem.*, *46*, 52–61 (1942)] has developed electrodes of another type for measurement of alkali metal ion activities in simple solutions. These are fundamentally concentration cells in which an inert electrode dips into an alkali salt solution of known activity enclosed in a porous clay membrane. The clay container dips into the unknown solution, and the difference in activity between the alkali salt inside and outside the membrane sets up an EMF that can be calibrated in terms of the activity of the alkali metal salt in the external solution. This device is similar in principle to the glass electrode. The EMF-activity relations are:

$$E = \frac{RT}{\mathscr{F}} \ln a_{standard} - \frac{RT}{\mathscr{F}} \ln a_{unknown}$$

These brief descriptions are intended only to suggest some general limitations and possible applications of electrode potentials in field and laboratory applications to geologic problems. Standard texts on electrochemistry are easily available and provocative sources of information on cell types and uses.

SUMMARY

Measurement of Eh and pH for geologic purposes is set about with many difficulties, and numerous precautions must be taken. A number of the difficulties attending measurement itself are described,

and an attempt is made to stress aspects not covered in the general directions that are supplied at the time of purchase of the instrument and electrodes. Most values for Eh and pH in the literature are for soil and water systems that are either in intimate contact with the atmosphere in their original state, or are subjected to the atmosphere after collection but prior to and during measurement. Techniques for introduction of electrodes into natural environments without contamination of the environments appear to be the most pressing need today.

SELECTED REFERENCES

Starkey, R. L., and K. M. Wight, *Anaerobic Corrosion of Iron in Soil.* American Gas Association, New York, 1945.

ZoBell, Claude E., Studies on redox potentials of marine sediments: *Bull. Am. Assoc. Petrol. Geol.*, 30, 477–513 (1946).

5

Partial Pressure Diagrams

A_T 25°C and 1 atmosphere total pressure, equilibrium relations for reactions of type 1, solid-solid reactions, are essentially impossible to represent, inasmuch as the mineral relations are functions only of temperature and pressure. It is mere chance if the free energy of such a reaction happens to be zero under these arbitrarily chosen conditions. On the other hand, reactions of type 2, involving a gas phase of variable activity, can be shown as a function of the gas phase activity. At the low temperature and pressure conditions of interest, the activity of the gas phase is measured directly by its partial pressure, for almost all gases behave nearly ideally under these conditions.

STABILITY OF WATER

The most fundamental chemical relation of geologic interest is the stability of water. If we assume equilibrium between water and its dissociation products hydrogen and oxygen, we can write:

$$2H_2O_l = 2H_{2\,g} + O_{2\,g} \qquad (5.1)$$

The equilibrium constant is:

$$\frac{P^2_{H_2}P_{O_2}}{[H_2O]^2} = k \qquad (5.2)$$

for nearly pure water $[H_2O] \cong 1$, and:

$$P^2_{H_2}P_{O_2} = k \qquad (5.3)$$

The free energy relations for equation (5.1) are:

$$2\Delta F^\circ_{f\,H_2} + \Delta F^\circ_{f\,O_2} - 2\Delta F^\circ_{f\,H_2O} = \Delta F^\circ_R \qquad (5.4)$$

Mineral Equilibria

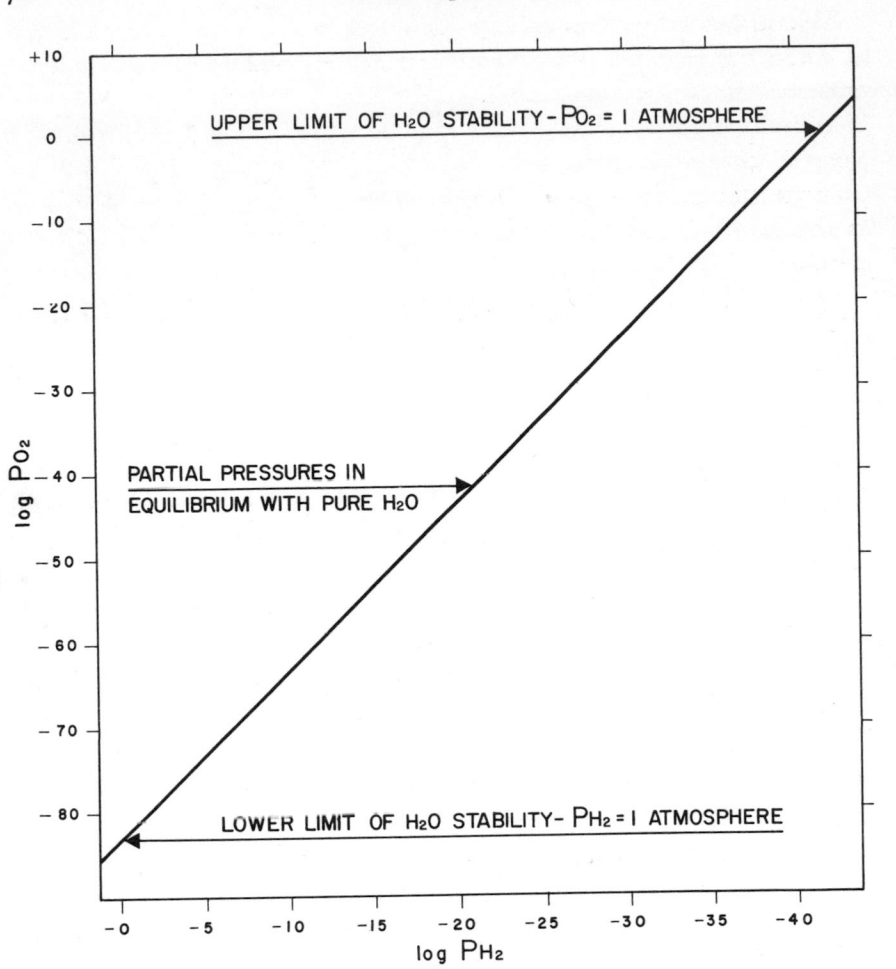

FIGURE 5.1. Partial pressures of oxygen and hydrogen in equilibrium with water at 25°C and approximately 1 atmosphere total pressure.

Substituting numerical values and solving:

$$0 + 0 + 113.4 = \Delta F_R^\circ$$

$$\Delta F_R^\circ = 113.4 \text{ kcal} \qquad (5.5)$$

Then, from the relation between standard free energy of reaction and the equilibrium constant, $\Delta F_R^\circ = -1.364 \log k$:

$$113.4 = -1.364 \log k$$

$$k = 10^{-83.1}$$

From (5.3):

$$P_{H_2}^2 P_{O_2} = 10^{-83.1} \qquad (5.6)$$

Thus the degree of dissociation of water into hydrogen and oxygen at room temperature is extremely small, but nonetheless the partial pressure can be used, assuming equilibrium, to characterize the range of stability of water. If the partial pressure of either hydrogen or oxygen exceeds 1 atmosphere at earth surface conditions, the gas pressure will exceed that of the atmosphere, and oxygen or hydrogen, as the case may be, will be released from the water, which will decompose to yield more oxygen or hydrogen. When $P_{O_2} = 1$, then

$$P_{H_2}^2 = 10^{-83.1}; \quad P_{H_2} = 10^{-41.5} \tag{5.7}$$

When $P_{H_2} = 1$, then

$$P_{O_2} = \frac{10^{-83.1}}{1} = 10^{-83.1} \tag{5.8}$$

If an arbitrary value is given to either oxygen or hydrogen partial pressure, the equilibrium is fixed. It is convenient for further reference to make a plot of P_{H_2} against P_{O_2} so that if either gas pressure is known the other can be obtained without calculation (Figure 5.1).

STABILITY OF IRON OXIDES

The stability relations among the various iron oxides of mineralogic interest can be handled in the same way. The first step is to write the reactions in terms of the iron compounds and gaseous oxygen, being careful to include all permutations and combinations:

$$Fe_c + \tfrac{1}{2}O_{2g} = FeO_c \tag{5.9}$$

$$3Fe_c + 2O_{2g} = Fe_3O_{4c} \tag{5.10}$$

$$2Fe_c + \tfrac{3}{2}O_{2g} = Fe_2O_{3c} \tag{5.11}$$

$$3FeO_c + \tfrac{1}{2}O_{2g} = Fe_3O_{4c} \tag{5.12}$$

$$2FeO_c + \tfrac{1}{2}O_{2g} = Fe_2O_{3c} \tag{5.13}$$

$$2Fe_3O_4 + \tfrac{1}{2}O_{2g} = 3Fe_2O_{3c} \tag{5.14}$$

Because the activities of the crystalline solids are unity, each reaction is at equilibrium at a particular partial pressure of oxygen. The calculations necessary are illustrated by solving for P_{O_2} for equilibrium in reaction (5.14):

$$\frac{[Fe_2O_3]^3}{[Fe_3O_4]^2 P_{O_2}^{1/2}} = k; \quad \frac{1}{P_{O_2}^{1/2}} = k \tag{5.15}$$

The standard free energy of the reaction is:

$$3\Delta F^\circ_{f\,Fe_2O_3} - 2\Delta F^\circ_{f\,Fe_3O_4} - \tfrac{1}{2}\Delta F^\circ_{f\,O_2} = \Delta F^\circ_R \tag{5.16}$$

Substituting numbers:

$$3(-177.1) - 2(-242.4) - \tfrac{1}{2}(0) = \Delta F_R^{\circ}$$

$$\Delta F_R^{\circ} = -46.5 \text{ kcal} \qquad (5.17)$$

Then

$$\Delta F_R^{\circ} = -1.364 \log \frac{1}{P_{O_2}^{1/2}}$$

$$-46.5 = -1.364 \log \frac{1}{P_{O_2}^{1/2}}$$

$$P_{O_2} = 10^{-68.2} \text{ atm} \qquad (5.18)$$

Table 5.1 gives the results of the calculations for the various equations:

TABLE 5.1. Partial Pressure of Oxygen for Equilibrium Between Iron-Oxygen Compounds at 25°C and 1 atm Total Pressure

Reaction	P_{O_2}	$\log P_{O_2}$
$Fe_c + \tfrac{1}{2}O_{2g} = FeO_c$	$10^{-85.6}$	-85.6
$3Fe_c + 2O_{2g} = Fe_3O_{4c}$	$10^{-89.0}$	-89.0
$2Fe_c + \tfrac{3}{2}O_{2g} = Fe_2O_{3c}$	$10^{-85.0}$	-85.0
$3FeO_c + \tfrac{1}{2}O_{2g} = Fe_3O_{4c}$	$10^{-113.0}$	-113.0
$2FeO_c + \tfrac{1}{2}O_{2g} = Fe_2O_{3c}$	$10^{-85.4}$	-85.4
$2Fe_3O_{4c} + \tfrac{1}{2}O_{2g} = 3Fe_2O_{3c}$	$10^{-68.2}$	-68.2

The relations among these compounds are better illustrated by showing the P_{O_2} pressure on a bar graph, as in Figure 5.2. Then, starting at the bottom, it is possible to follow the sequence of events that should occur if metallic iron is exposed to increasing partial pressures of oxygen, with pressure increased so slowly that equilibrium is approximated. The actual experiment, at 25°C, is not possible to perform directly as indicated by the incredibly low oxygen pressures. The calculated pressures are a useful yardstick, but cannot be translated into a real oxidation experiment.

The first reaction encountered, from FeO to Fe_3O_4, is clearly metastable, inasmuch as FeO cannot oxidize to Fe_3O_4 before iron has oxidized at all. Thus iron would be stable until a P_{O_2} of 10^{-89} was attained, at which value Fe_c and Fe_3O_{4c} would be in equilibrium. If $P_{O_2} = 10^{-88}$, Fe will convert to Fe_3O_4. Consequently the next

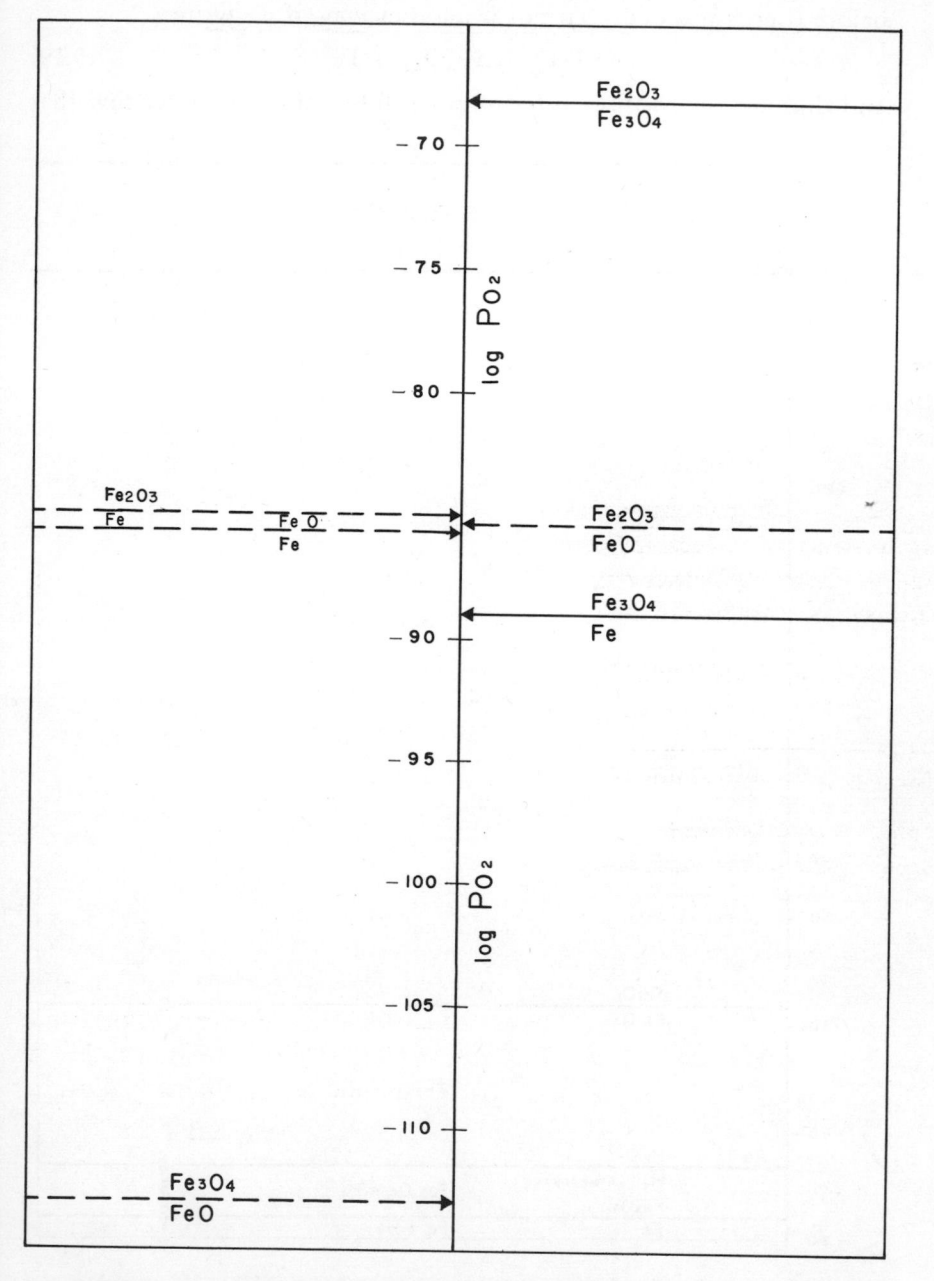

FIGURE 5.2. Bar graph showing P_{O_2} in equilibrium with various iron compounds at 25°C and 1 atmosphere total pressure. Dashed lines indicate metastable reactions.

reaction, Fe to FeO, is metastable, because iron converts to magnetite before it goes to FeO. To put it another way, if we write:

$$4FeO_c \rightleftharpoons Fe_3O_{4\,c} + Fe_c \qquad (5.19)$$

and thus put the relation in terms of a solid-solid reaction, we find that

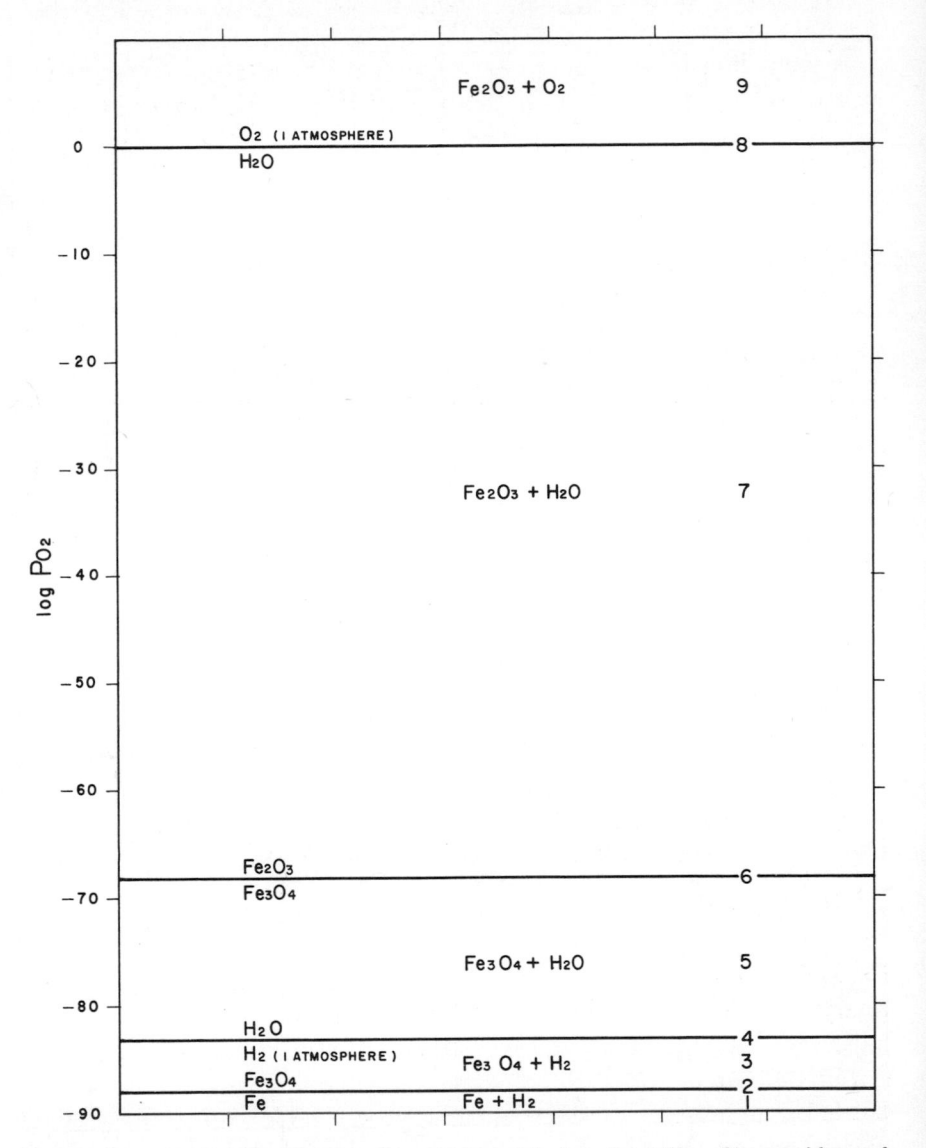

FIGURE 5.3. Composite diagram showing interrelation of stability of iron oxides and water at 25 °C and 1 atmosphere total pressure. Numbers correspond to tie lines and 3-phase fields on Figure 5.4.

ΔF_R° is negative, and that FeO will disproportionate into magnetite and metallic iron at equilibrium at room temperature, and hence has no field of stability. There are numerous ways of checking metastable relations, but the use of the P_{O_2} yardstick is as convenient as most.

Continuing upward P_{O_2}-wise along the bar graph, it is found that the next reaction to occur is from Fe_3O_4 to Fe_2O_3.

A simplified bar graph of the stable phases Fe, Fe_3O_4, and Fe_2O_3 can now be constructed, and the first dividend accruing from use of

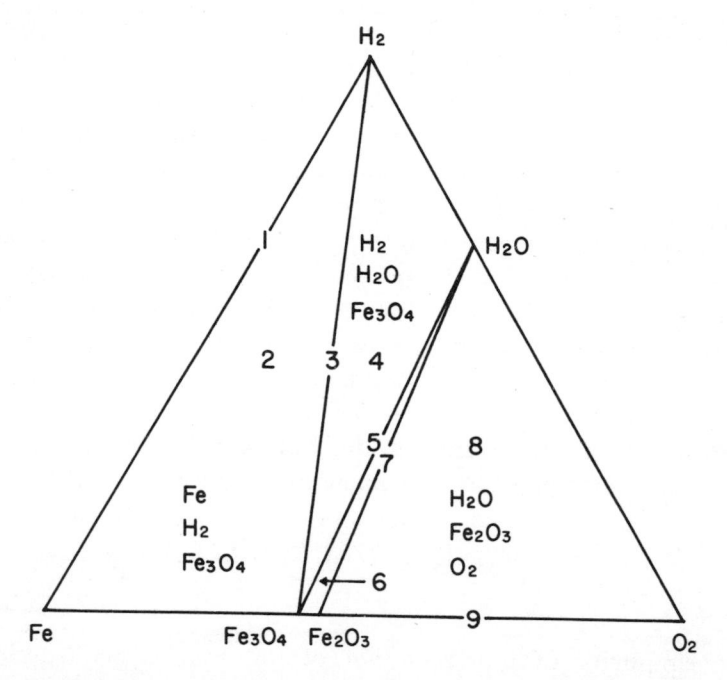

FIGURE 5.4. Composition diagram of the 3-component system Fe–O_2–H_2 at 25°C and 1 atmosphere total pressure. Numbers correspond to fields and boundaries on Figure 5.3. Compositions are on atomic % basis.

P_{O_2} can be realized, for direct comparison can be made with the P_{O_2} relations for water (Figure 5.3). Although a P_{O_2} value of 10^{-89} perhaps has little physical significance by itself, comparison with the stability limits of water shows immediately that metallic iron is not stable in the presence of water at earth surface conditions, and furthermore that magnetite oxidizes to hematite near the lower limit of water stability. Therefore hematite, although a compound of ferric iron and oxygen, is clearly a poor environmental indicator, inasmuch as it is

stable over such a large range of oxidation conditions. On the other hand, magnetite, which might be thought of as an oxidized compound because two-thirds of its iron is in the ferric state, is stable only under strongly reducing conditions, and is not reduced itself even in the presence of water and hydrogen under 1 atmosphere pressure.

RELATION OF PARTIAL PRESSURE DIAGRAMS TO COMPOSITION DIAGRAMS

Figure 5.3 shows the interrelations of iron, hydrogen, and oxygen, and can be translated into the 3-component composition diagram $Fe-O_2-H_2$. Figure 5.4 shows such a diagram, with the tie lines deduced from Figure 5.3. At the bottom of Figure 5.3 iron and hydrogen coexist, and water is unstable. Thus this field corresponds to the tie line from iron to hydrogen on Figure 5.4. The field on Figure 5.3 is independent of the amount of iron present, so long as there is any at all, and this is reflected in the range of compositions indicated by the tie line of Figure 5.4. The 3-phase field $Fe-H_2-Fe_3O_4$ similarly is reflected by the line in Figure 5.3, showing that the pressures of oxygen and hydrogen are invariant during the coexistence of 3 phases. Note that the combination of Figures 5.3 and 5.4 conveniently provides specific values for gas pressures in the 3-phase fields and also gives the ranges of pressures possible for 2-phase associations.

P_{O_2}-P_{CO_2} DIAGRAMS

$Fe-O_2-CO_2$

The simplicity of representation of the iron-oxygen species, in which a bar graph can be used, suggests immediately the possibility of representing reactions with two gas partial pressures as variables. Of the minerals involving iron, the obvious gases to use are CO_2 and S_2. Using CO_2 first and writing the reactions from native iron and the oxides to the lone carbonate mineral species siderite:

$$Fe_c + CO_{2g} + \tfrac{1}{2}O_{2c} = FeCO_{3c} \tag{5.20}$$

$$Fe_3O_{4c} + 3CO_{2g} = 3FeCO_{3c} + \tfrac{1}{2}O_{2g} \tag{5.21}$$

$$Fe_2O_{3c} + 2CO_{2g} = 2FeCO_{3c} + \tfrac{1}{2}O_{2g} \tag{5.22}$$

For reaction (5.20):

$$\Delta F^\circ_{f\,FeCO_3} - \Delta F^\circ_{f\,Fe} - \Delta F^\circ_{f\,CO_2} - \tfrac{1}{2}\Delta F^\circ_{f\,O_2} = \Delta F^\circ_R$$
$$-161.06 - (0) - (-94.26) - (0) = -66.80 \text{ kcal}$$

Then

$$-66.80 = -1.364 \log k$$

$$\log k = 48.2 = \log \frac{1}{P_{O_2}^{1/2} P_{CO_2}}$$

and

$$-\tfrac{1}{2} \log P_{O_2} - \log P_{CO_2} = 48.2$$

$$\log P_{CO_2} = -48.2 - \tfrac{1}{2} \log P_{O_2}$$

Similar calculations for reactions (5.21) and (5.22) yield the following relations:

Equation	Stability Boundary	Defining Equation in Terms of P_{O_2} and P_{CO_2}
(5.20)	Fe-FeCO$_3$	$\log P_{CO_2} = -48.2 - \tfrac{1}{2} \log P_{O_2}$
(5.21)	Fe$_3$O$_4$-FeCO$_3$	$\log P_{CO_2} = 10.3 + \tfrac{1}{6} \log P_{O_2}$
(5.22)	Fe$_2$O$_3$-FeCO$_3$	$\log P_{CO_2} = 15.6 + \tfrac{1}{4} \log P_{O_2}$

In a plot of $\log P_{O_2}$ versus $\log P_{CO_2}$, the boundaries between these three pairs are straight lines with slopes of $-1/2$, $+1/6$, and $+1/4$ respectively. Figure 5.5 shows these boundaries, plus those for the iron oxides and water. A simple method of plotting is to substitute an arbitrary value for P_{CO_2}, obtain a corresponding value for P_{O_2}, and then draw a line of proper slope from the point obtained.

From the relations of Figure 5.5, the metastability of the various reaction pairs in various regions of the diagram can be deduced by inspection. For example, a boundary between Fe and FeCO$_3$ at oxygen pressures above 10^{-88} is clearly metastable, because Fe is unstable relative to the oxides above this oxygen pressure. After elimination of metastable relations, a final diagram is obtained as shown in Figure 5.6. Here the fields of stability can be designated. Comparison of Figures 5.5 and 5.6 shows that the free energy values used are at least internally consistent. Note on Figure 5.5 how equations (5.14), (5.21), and (5.22) intersect, and how (5.21), (5.20), and (5.10) also intersect. A hiatus at either of these points would indicate an error in the free energy values used for one of the equations. On Figure 5.6 the boundary between Fe$_2$O$_3$ and FeCO$_3$ is dashed at P_{CO_2} values above 10^0 to indicate the upper limit of the validity of the partial pressure calculated from data valid only at 25°C and 1 atmosphere total pressure.

A diagram of this type is valid *only for the species considered*; it does not reveal whether species not considered might not be stable relative to

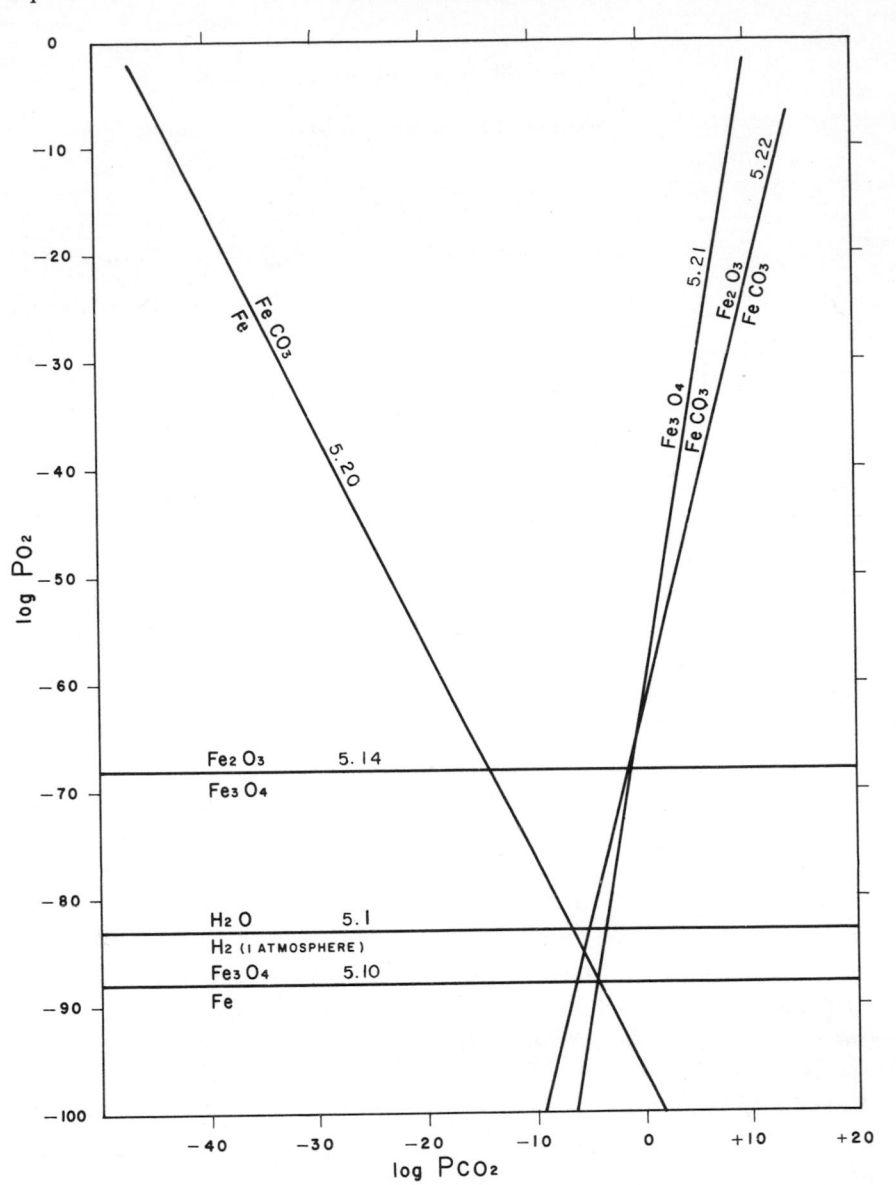

FIGURE 5.5.   Plot of equations representing stability relations of iron compounds as functions of P_{O_2} and P_{CO_2} at 25°C.

those used.   Specifically, the diagram as shown is a superimposition of Fe-O_2-CO_2 relations on H_2O-H_2 relations, and it is not impossible that Fe_2O_3 and H_2O might be unstable with respect to the reaction $Fe_2O_{3\,c} + H_2O_l = 2FeOOH_c$.   If so, the hematite-water field would

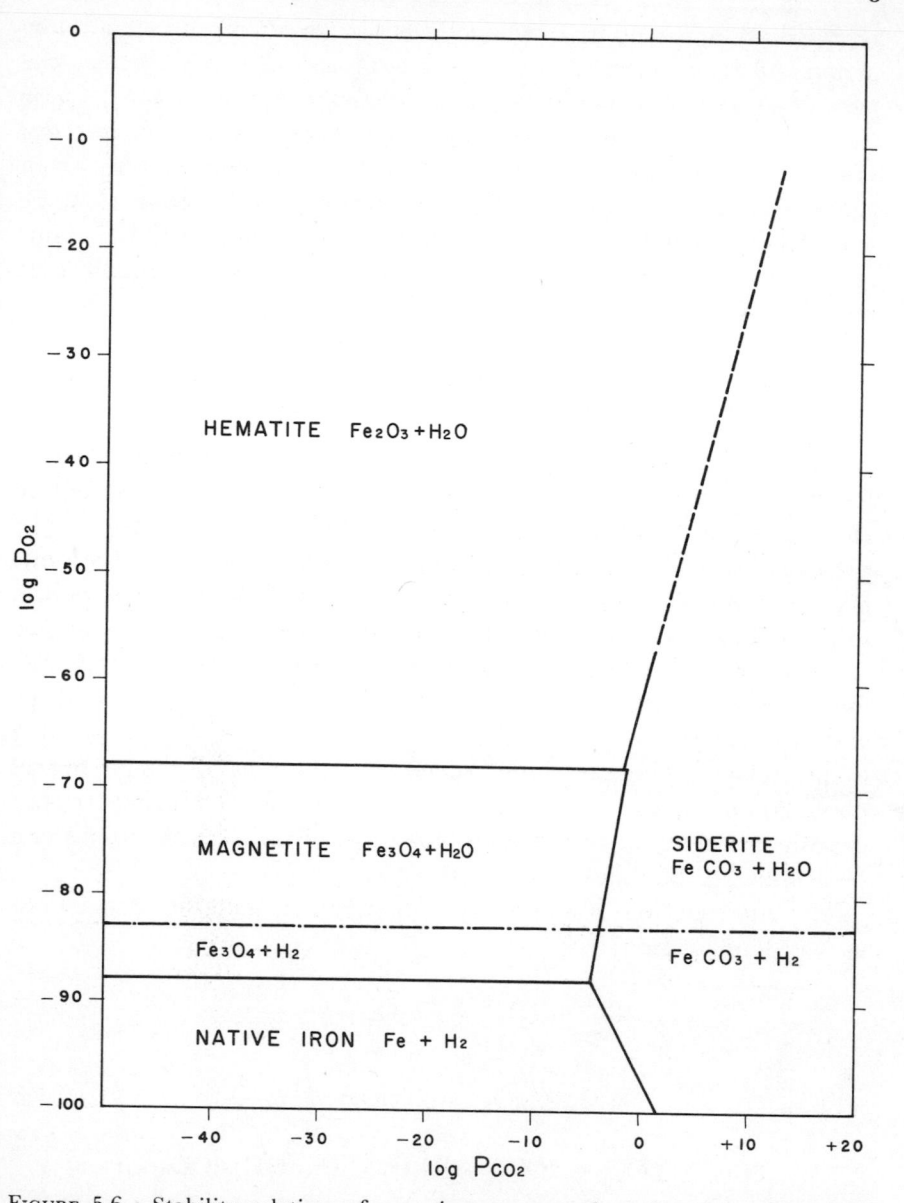

FIGURE 5.6. Stability relations of some iron compounds as functions of P_{O_2} and P_{CO_2} at 25°C and a few atmospheres maximum total pressure. Stability relations for water are superimposed.

disappear in favor of a goethite-water field, and the goethite-water field could be larger than the hematite-water field as shown. Simple superimposition of stability relations, using the same coordinates for

representation, should always be followed by an attempt to see if inter-action will occur to form new species. *It is difficult to overemphasize that the methods used here provide reasonably satisfactory stability relations among the species examined, but does not guarantee that they are the only ones that should have been considered.* As always, a better answer can be given concerning those relations that cannot occur at equilibrium (i.e., Fe and H_2O), rather than those that can (i.e., Fe_2O_3 and H_2O?). Thus the safest method of use is to ask questions concerning the equilibrium relations of actual mineral associations.

$Cu-CO_2-O_2$

The number of diagrams of this type that could be constructed is limited only by the investigator's interest in oxide-carbonate relations for the elements in the periodic table (as well as the availability of free energy data). The copper minerals are of special significance to the geologist because of the economic importance of oxidation and second-ary enrichment. Also they are a convenient demonstration of the results of interaction with water. The major species are native copper (Cu), cuprite (Cu_2O), tenorite (CuO), malachite ($Cu_2(OH)_2CO_3$), and azurite ($Cu_3(OH)_2(CO_3)_2$). If we restrict P_{O_2} values to those within the field of water stability ($P_{O_2} = 10^{-83.1} - 10^0$), it is possible to interrelate the various copper species by equations containing nearly pure liquid water. In nature the solutions in oxidizing copper deposits are commonly dilute, so that the activity of the solutions can be assumed to be that of pure water.

The interrelating reactions are (eliminating metastable reactions as was done for iron):

$$2Cu_c + \tfrac{1}{2}O_{2g} = Cu_2O_c; \quad k = \frac{1}{P_{O_2}^{1/2}} \tag{5.23}$$

$$Cu_2O_c + \tfrac{1}{2}O_{2g} = 2CuO_c; \quad k = \frac{1}{P_{O_2}^{1/2}} \tag{5.24}$$

$$3Cu_c + \tfrac{3}{2}O_{2g} + 2CO_{2g} + H_2O_1 = Cu_3(OH)_2(CO_3)_{2c};$$
$$k = \frac{1}{P_{O_2}^{3/2}P_{CO_2}^2} \tag{5.25}$$

$$3Cu_2O_c + 4CO_{2g} + \tfrac{3}{2}O_{2g} + 2H_2O_1 = 2Cu_3(OH)_2(CO_3)_{2c};$$
$$k = \frac{1}{P_{CO_2}^4 P_{O_2}^{3/2}} \tag{5.26}$$

$$Cu_2O_c + \tfrac{1}{2}O_{2g} + CO_{2g} + H_2O_l = Cu_2(OH)_2CO_{3c};$$

$$k = \frac{1}{P_{O_2}^{1/2} P_{CO_2}} \tag{5.27}$$

$$2CuO_c + CO_{2g} + H_2O_l = Cu_2(OH)_2CO_{3c};$$

$$k = \frac{1}{P_{CO_2}} \tag{5.28}$$

$$3Cu_2(OH)_2CO_{3c} + CO_{2g} = 2Cu_3(OH)_2(CO_3)_2 + H_2O_l;$$

$$k = \frac{1}{P_{CO_2}} \tag{5.29}$$

The corresponding equations are:

Equation	Stability Boundary	Defining Equations in Terms of P_{O_2} and P_{CO_2}
(5.23)	Cu-Cu$_2$O	$\log P_{O_2} = -51.30$
(5.24)	Cu$_2$O-CuO	$\log P_{O_2} = -37.6$
(5.25)	Cu-Cu$_3$(OH)$_2$(CO$_3$)$_2$	$\log P_{CO_2} = -36.9 - \tfrac{3}{4}\log P_{O_2}$
(5.26)	Cu$_2$O-Cu$_3$(OH)$_2$(CO$_3$)$_2$	$\log P_{CO_2} = -17.6 - \tfrac{3}{8}\log P_{O_2}$
(5.27)	Cu$_2$O-Cu$_2$(OH)$_2$CO$_3$	$\log P_{CO_2} = -22.7 - \tfrac{1}{2}\log P_{O_2}$
(5.28)	CuO-Cu$_2$(OH)$_2$CO$_3$	$\log P_{CO_2} = -3.8$
(5.29)	Cu$_2$(OH)$_2$CO$_3$-Cu$_3$(OH)$_2$(CO$_3$)$_2$	$\log P_{CO_2} = -2.5$

The results of the plotting of the equations are shown in Figure 5.7. The general relations are strikingly similar to those of the iron oxides and carbonate, as shown in Figure 5.6, with the added feature of an extra carbonate species. The plot leads to some interesting speculations; under surface conditions of high P_{O_2} and P_{CO_2} of $10^{-3.5}$ malachite is stable relative to azurite; azurite can exist stably only by increasing P_{CO_2} or by decreasing the activity of water (equation 5.29). Thus it is quite possible that in the dry air of semi-arid climates the relative humidity is low enough to permit azurite to form stably, but when specimens are brought to regions of higher humidity, azurite transforms into malachite. This is the explanation of the green skies of so many pictures removed from a homeland where azurite is a stable pigment.

P_{O_2}-P_{S_2} DIAGRAMS

Fe-O$_2$-S$_2$

The interrelations of metal oxides and sulfides are also handled conveniently by partial pressure diagrams. To depict their relations diatomic sulfur gas is chosen here. The stable molecular species of

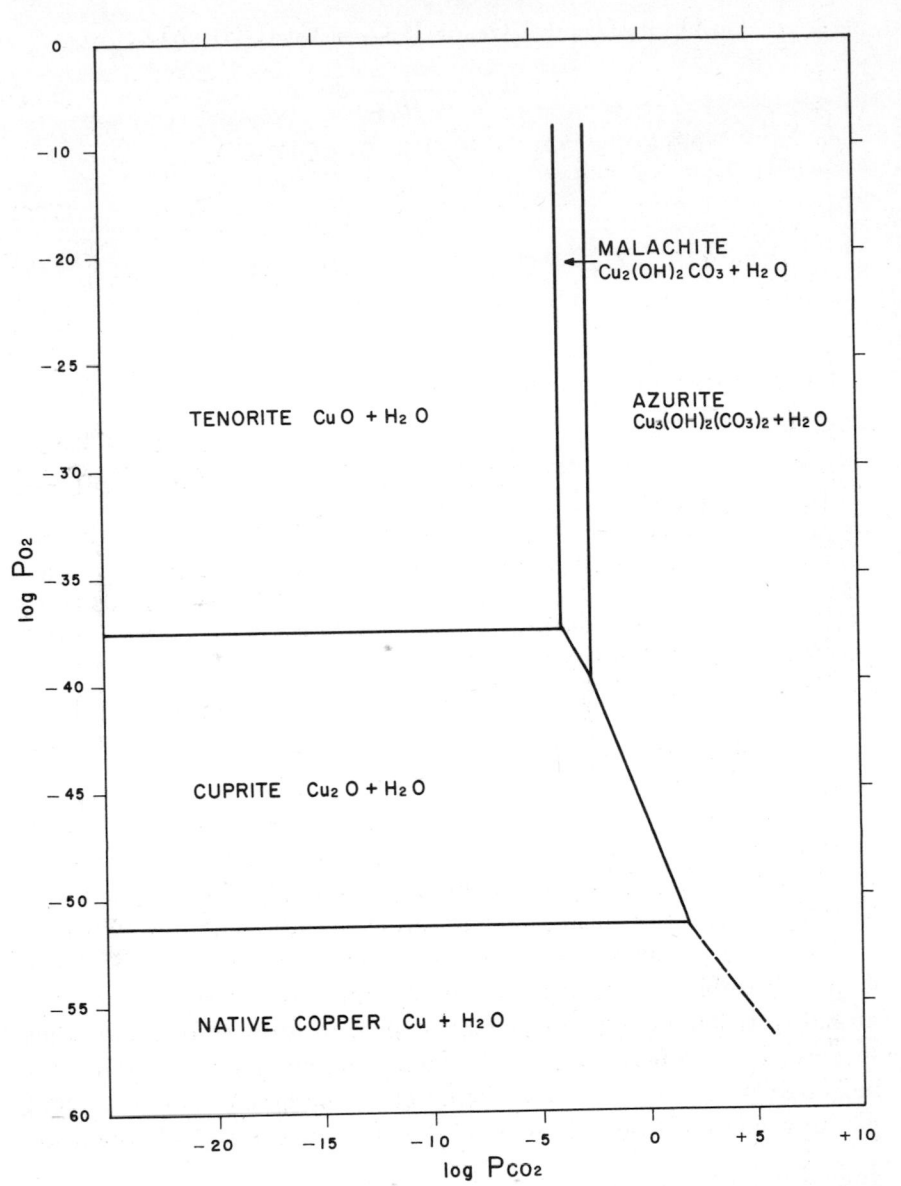

FIGURE 5.7. Stability of copper compounds as functions of P_{O_2} and P_{CO_2} at 25°C and 1 atmosphere total pressure.   Pure liquid water is assumed present in all cases.

sulfur gas is in doubt at 25 °C; it is very likely a more condensed species than S_2, but the species chosen is not important, inasmuch as it is to be used only as a yardstick for comparison of iron mineral reactions with reactions among other minerals.   Also, after obtaining stability rela-

tions in terms of any convenient pair of variables such as P_{O_2} and P_{S_2}, we can translate the relations into functions of other gases, if we wish, by writing reactions interrelating the original variables to the new ones.

As before, the first step is to write the reactions in terms of the minerals and the gases. A pattern of procedure begins to emerge: first we write the equations for the reactions involving only one variable:

$$3Fe_c + 2O_{2g} = Fe_3O_{4c} \qquad (5.10)$$

$$2Fe_3O_{4c} + \tfrac{1}{2}O_{2g} = 3Fe_2O_{3c} \qquad (5.14)$$

$$2Fe_c + S_{2g} = 2FeS_c \qquad (5.30)$$

$$Fe_c + S_{2g} = FeS_{2c} \qquad (5.31)$$

Then the reactions involving both:

$$Fe_3O_{4c} + \tfrac{3}{2}S_{2g} = 3FeS_c + 2O_{2g} \qquad (5.32)$$

$$Fe_3O_{4c} + 3S_{2g} = 3FeS_{2c} + 2O_{2g} \qquad (5.33)$$

$$Fe_2O_{3c} + 2S_{2g} = 2FeS_{2c} + \tfrac{3}{2}O_{2g} \qquad (5.34)$$

Note that we can use previous experience with the iron oxide relations (see Figure 5.2) to eliminate consideration of all but the stable reactions for iron-oxygen interplay. In writing the iron-sulfur and iron-oxygen-sulfur set for the first time, all possible reactions should be considered as guided by known mineral species. Only one has been left out here, the reaction of Fe_2O_3 with S_2 to produce FeS. If included and plotted, it would have been discovered to be metastable, as might have been surmised from mineral relations. Furthermore, we have restricted our interest to *sulfides*—sulfates and other sulfur-oxygen compounds could appear as a result of the interaction of iron, sulfur, and oxygen. But we have arbitrarily decided to limit our attention to the sulfides, recognizing all the while that we are not attempting to discover all the possible interactions at this juncture.

One final word of caution, which will be repeated from place to place. The calculations are made for FeS_c, which is in fact not FeS, but $Fe_{1-x}S$. Therefore the free energy value used is for a particular composition ($Fe_{0.95}S$ as given by the free energy tables in the Appendix), and is not valid for other compositions. The error, however, is *generally* slight for deviations of this order of magnitude from strict stoichiometry, but should always be considered and assessed before taking a calculated boundary too seriously.

Figure 5.8 shows the result of obtaining the equilibrium constants for equations (5.10), (5.14), and (5.30)–(5.34). Even though this is a

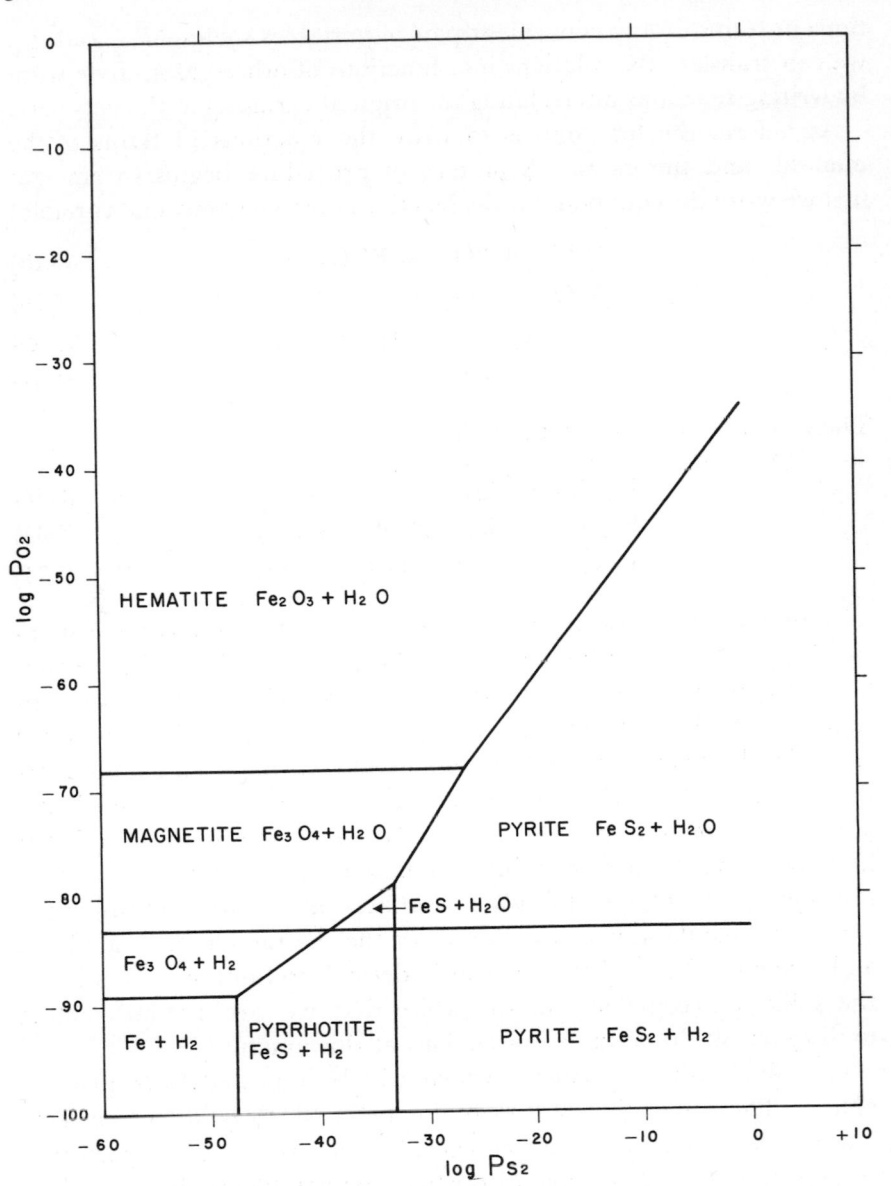

FIGURE 5.8.   Stability of some iron oxides and sulfides as functions of P_{O_2} and P_{S_2} at 25°C and 1 atmosphere total pressure.   Stability relations for water are super-imposed.

25°C diagram, some of the associations and impossible associations have a familiar ring to the geologist.   The 3-phase association of pyrrhotite, pyrite, and magnetite is one such, and the incompatibility

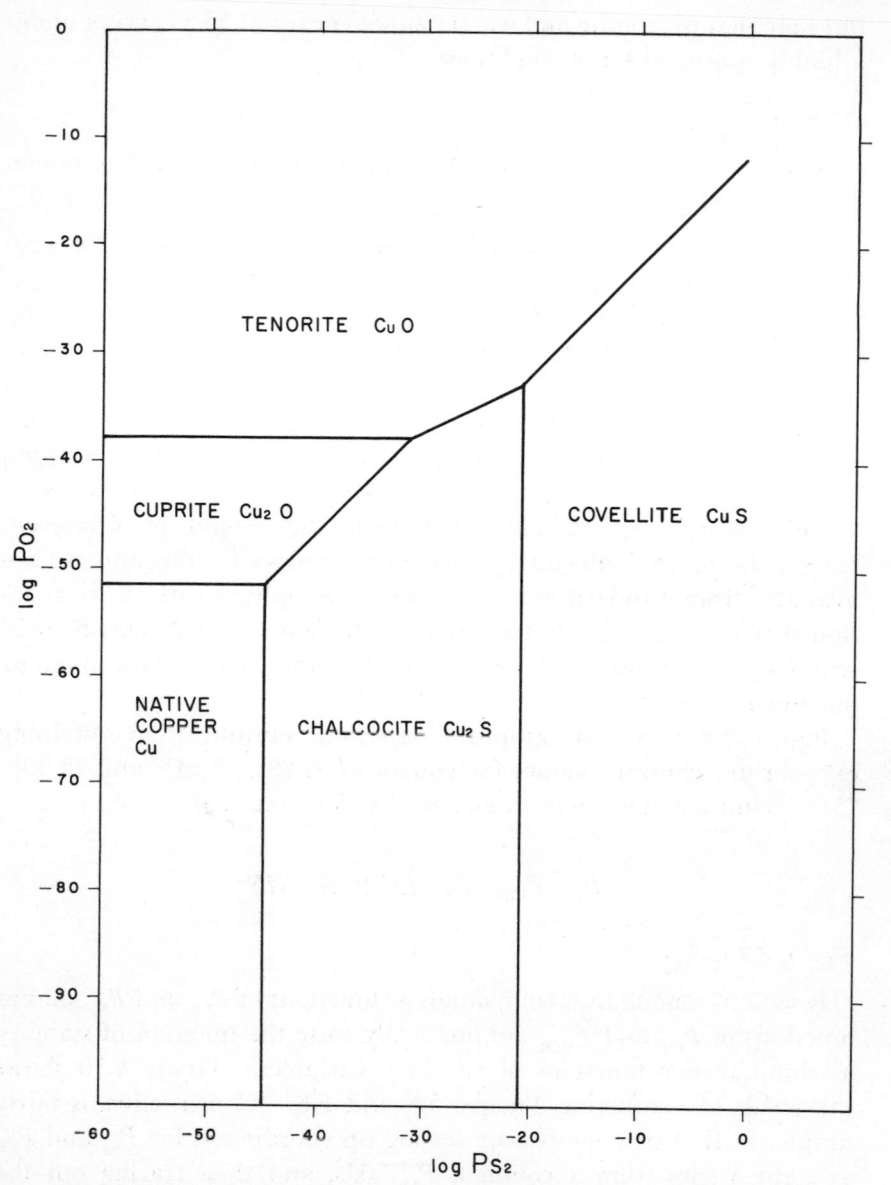

FIGURE 5.9. Stability relations among some copper oxides and sulfides at 25°C and 1 atmosphere total pressure as functions of P_{O_2} and P_{S_2}.

of pyrrhotite and hematite is another. The overlay of the boundaries of water also tells a story. The equilibria plotted are independent of water, and water is not a necessary companion to the iron minerals,

but note that pyrrhotite and water cannot coexist at $25\,^\circ$C except under a highly restricted set of conditions.

Cu-S_2-O_2

Again the treatment of iron can be paralleled with that for copper. The reactions are:

$$2Cu_c + \tfrac{1}{2}O_{2g} = Cu_2O_c \tag{5.23}$$
$$Cu_2O_c + \tfrac{1}{2}O_{2g} = 2CuO_c \tag{5.24}$$
$$2Cu_c + \tfrac{1}{2}S_{2g} = Cu_2S_c \tag{5.35}$$
$$Cu_2S_c + \tfrac{1}{2}S_{2g} = 2CuS_c \tag{5.36}$$
$$Cu_2O_c + \tfrac{1}{2}S_{2g} = Cu_2S_c + \tfrac{1}{2}O_{2g} \tag{5.37}$$
$$2CuO_c + \tfrac{1}{2}S_{2g} = Cu_2S_c + O_2 \tag{5.38}$$
$$CuO_c + \tfrac{1}{2}S_{2g} = CuS_c + \tfrac{1}{2}O_{2g} \tag{5.39}$$

This list does not include a compound that would be of interest, Cu_9S_5, the mineral digenite. Free energy values for digenite are not available from standard sources, so it will be omitted with the recognition that we would like to include it. The same caution must be used with Cu_2S as was used with FeS, for the mineral chalcocite is commonly not stoichiometric.

Figure 5.9 shows the graphical relations resulting from obtaining equilibrium constant values for equations (5.23), (5.24), and (5.35)–(5.39), and making a plot similar to that for iron.

P_{O_2}-P_{CO_2}-P_{S_2} DIAGRAMS

Fe-O_2-CO_2-S_2

Relations among iron compounds as functions of P_{O_2} and P_{S_2}, and as functions of P_{O_2} and P_{CO_2} automatically raise the question of stability as simultaneous functions of all three variables. Figure 5.10 shows the result of combining Figures 5.8 and 5.6. Construction is fairly simple, in that it involves only setting up coordinates for P_{S_2} and P_{O_2} at right angles from a common P_{O_2} axis, and then tracing out the intersection of the planes. Only one new equation is needed, that for pyrite to siderite:

$$FeS_{2c} + CO_{2g} + \tfrac{1}{2}O_{2g} = FeCO_{3c} + S_{2g} \tag{5.40}$$

This is the only stability boundary that makes an angle with all three axes, that is to say, includes P_{S_2}, P_{O_2}, and P_{CO_2} in its equation.

Cu-O_2-CO_2-S_2

The relations among some of the copper oxides, hydroxycarbonates, and sulfides also can be delineated in terms of all three partial pressures, as shown in Figure 5.11. The figure portrays relations at CO_2 pressures far above those for which the data are applicable, but the

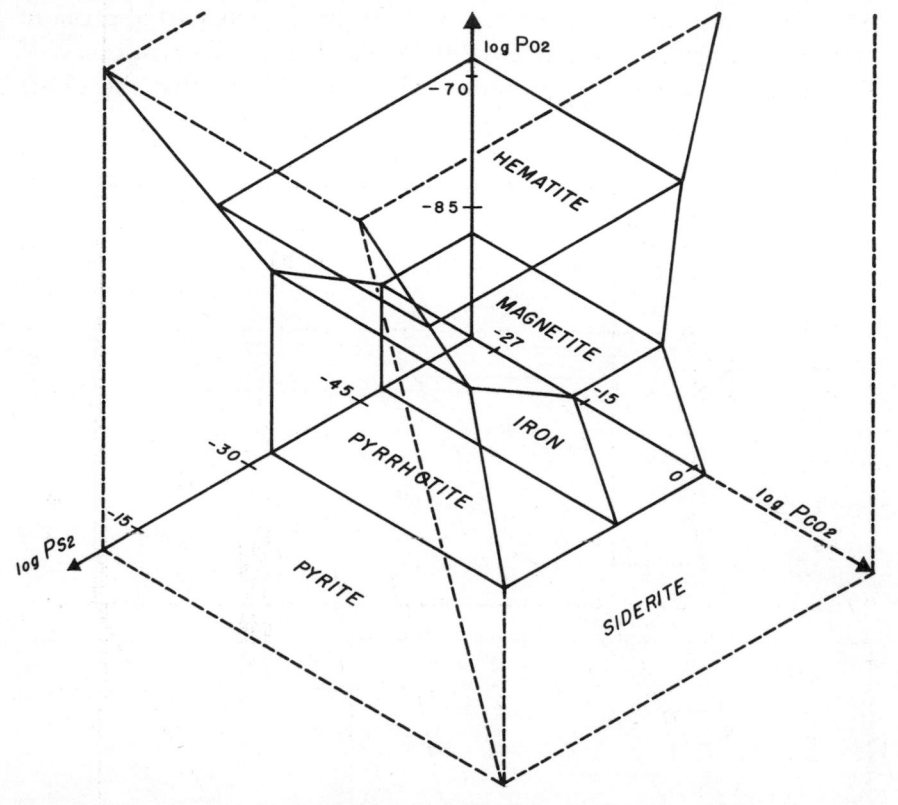

FIGURE 5.10. Stability relations of some iron compounds as functions of P_{O_2}, P_{CO_2}, and P_{S_2} at 25°C and 1 atmosphere total pressure.

diagram still serves to show the very high pressures necessary to convert the sulfides to hydroxycarbonates at low oxygen pressures. Except for these equilibria, the diagram is well within the range of useful values of the partial pressures.

SUPERIMPOSITION OF DIAGRAMS

Because partial pressure diagrams for minerals of different elements can be expressed in terms of the same variables, it is often of interest to

overlay diagrams to compare stability relations of various metal sulfides, oxides, and carbonates.

Fe-Mn-O_2-S_2

In Figure 5.12 the P_{O_2}-P_{S_2} diagram for manganese has been overlaid on the iron diagram (Figure 5.8). In addition to the combination plot, a new restraint has been put on the system. The partial pressure of S_2 in equilibrium with alabandite, MnS, rises to values in excess of 1 atmosphere at low P_{O_2} pressures, which reminds us that the vapor

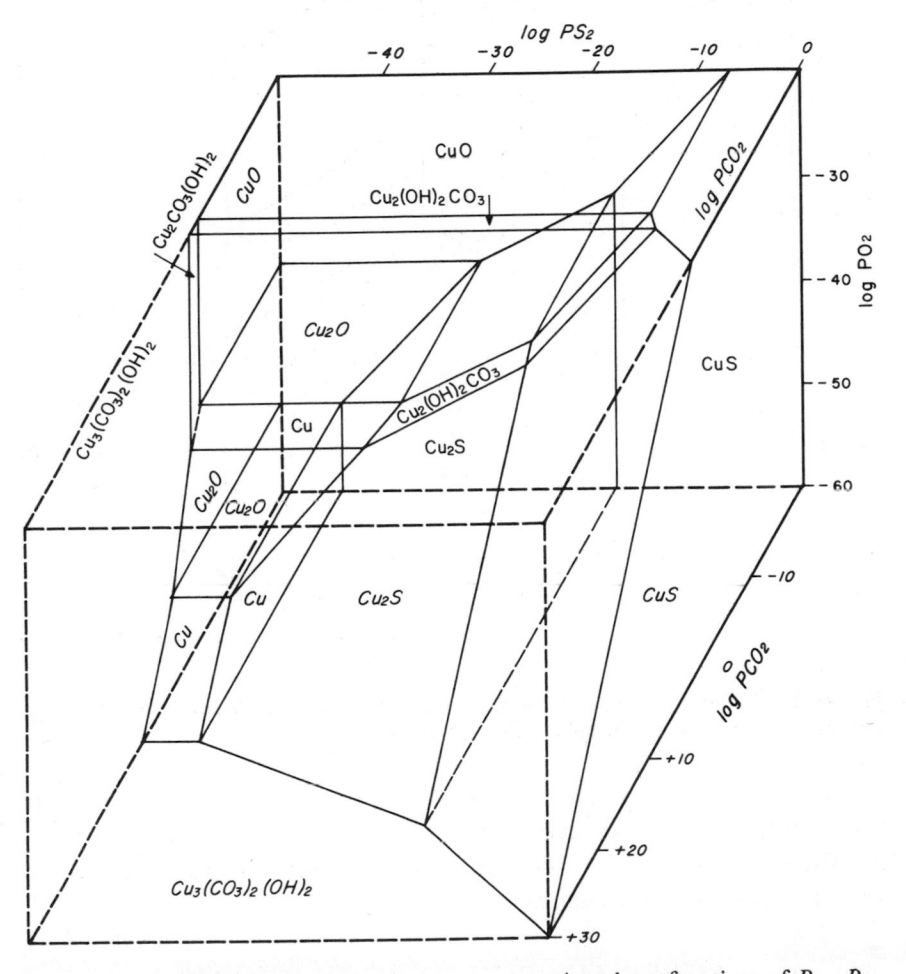

FIGURE 5.11. Stability relations of some copper minerals as functions of P_{O_2}, P_{CO_2} and P_{S_2} in the presence of pure water at 25°C and 1 atmosphere total pressure. Values for P_{CO_2} are extrapolated beyond the range of validity of the data. (Courtesy J. Anderson, Department of Geology, Harvard University Graduate School, 1958.)

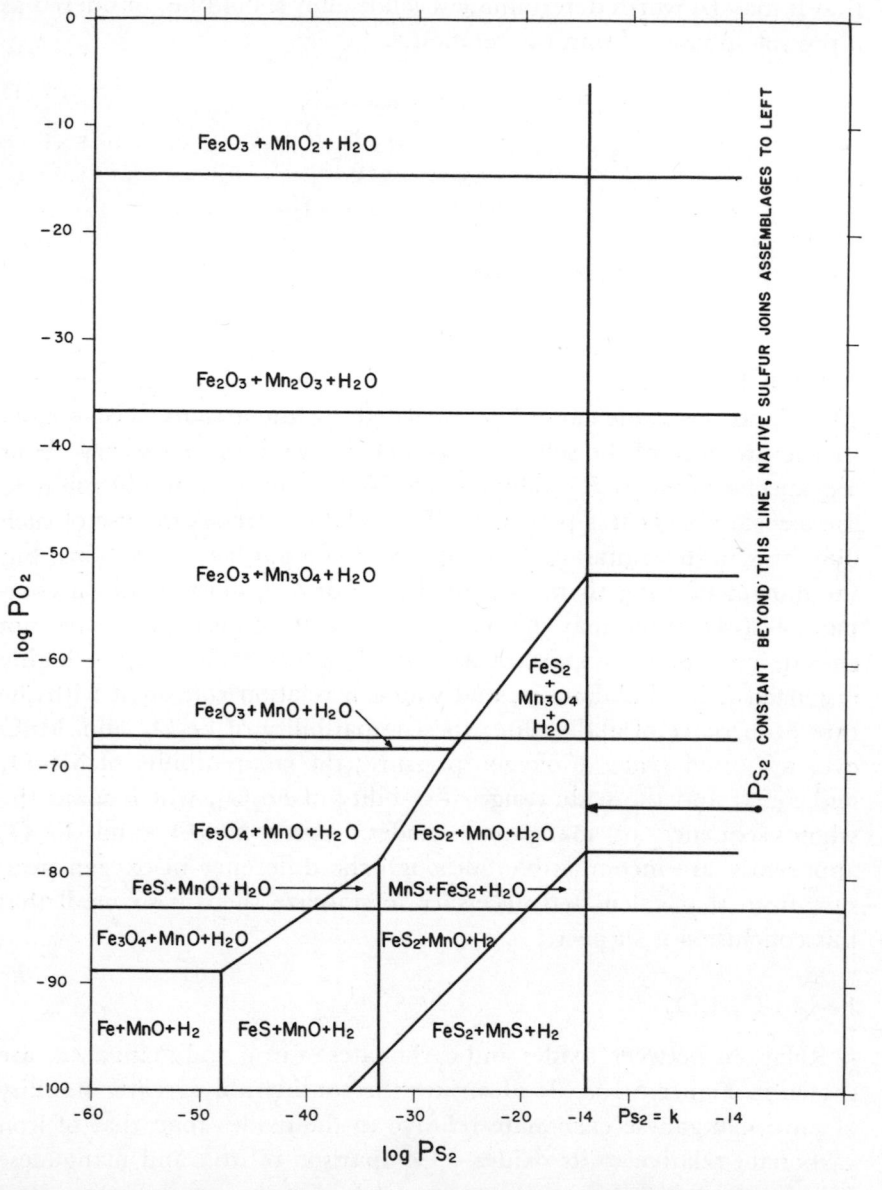

FIGURE 5.12. Stability of some iron and manganese compounds as functions of P_{S_2} and P_{O_2} at 25 °C and 1 atmosphere total pressure. Consideration of stability of native sulfur and of water shows limiting effect on P_{O_2} and P_{S_2} values that can be achieved. (Courtesy J. Reitzel, Department of Geology, Harvard University Graduate School, 1958.)

pressure of solid sulfur at low temperature is probably pretty low, so that it may be worth determining if solid sulfur should be considered as a possible phase. From the relation:

$$S_{2g} = 2S_{c,\,rhombic} \tag{5.41}$$
$$2\Delta F^{\circ}_{f\,Sc} - \Delta F^{\circ}_{f\,S2g} = \Delta F^{\circ}_{R}$$
$$0 - 19.13 = -19.13$$
$$-19.13 = -1.364 \log k$$
$$\log k = 14 = \log \frac{1}{P_{S_2}}$$
$$\log P_{S_2} = -14$$

Thus the vapor pressure of S_2 in equilibrium with native sulfur is 10^{-14}, and this value cannot be exceeded, for the activity of S_2 is fixed by the presence of the solid. Consequently we need not worry about any species stable at P_{S_2} values above 10^{-14}, and we can add sulfur to the associations at this pressure. This relation stresses the use of such diagrams to determine incompatible and compatible associations, but the danger of using them as a predictive device, inasmuch as a compatible association may be metastable with respect to species not considered. Some important aspects of the diagram are the highly restricted field of alabandite and water, a relation consistent with the rare occurrence of alabandite; the compatibility of Fe_2O_3 and MnO over a limited range of oxygen pressure; the compatibility of Mn_3O_4 and FeS_2; and the wide range of stability of Fe_2O_3, which spans the whole sequence of manganese oxides. Also, Mn_3O_4 and Fe_3O_4 apparently are incompatible, although the difference in oxygen pressure from that calculated necessary to stabilize them is so small that this conclusion is suspect.

Fe-Mn-O$_2$-CO$_2$

Relations between oxides and carbonates of iron and manganese are shown in Figure 5.13. It illustrates the considerably greater stability of pure manganese carbonate relative to the oxides than that of iron carbonate relative to its oxides. Comparison of iron and manganese behavior in this fashion serves to remind us of the possibility of interaction, such as the formation of $(Fe_xMn_y)CO_3$, and that we are looking at two separate diagrams in which interactions have not been considered. In general, however, solid solution is least under the conditions being considered.

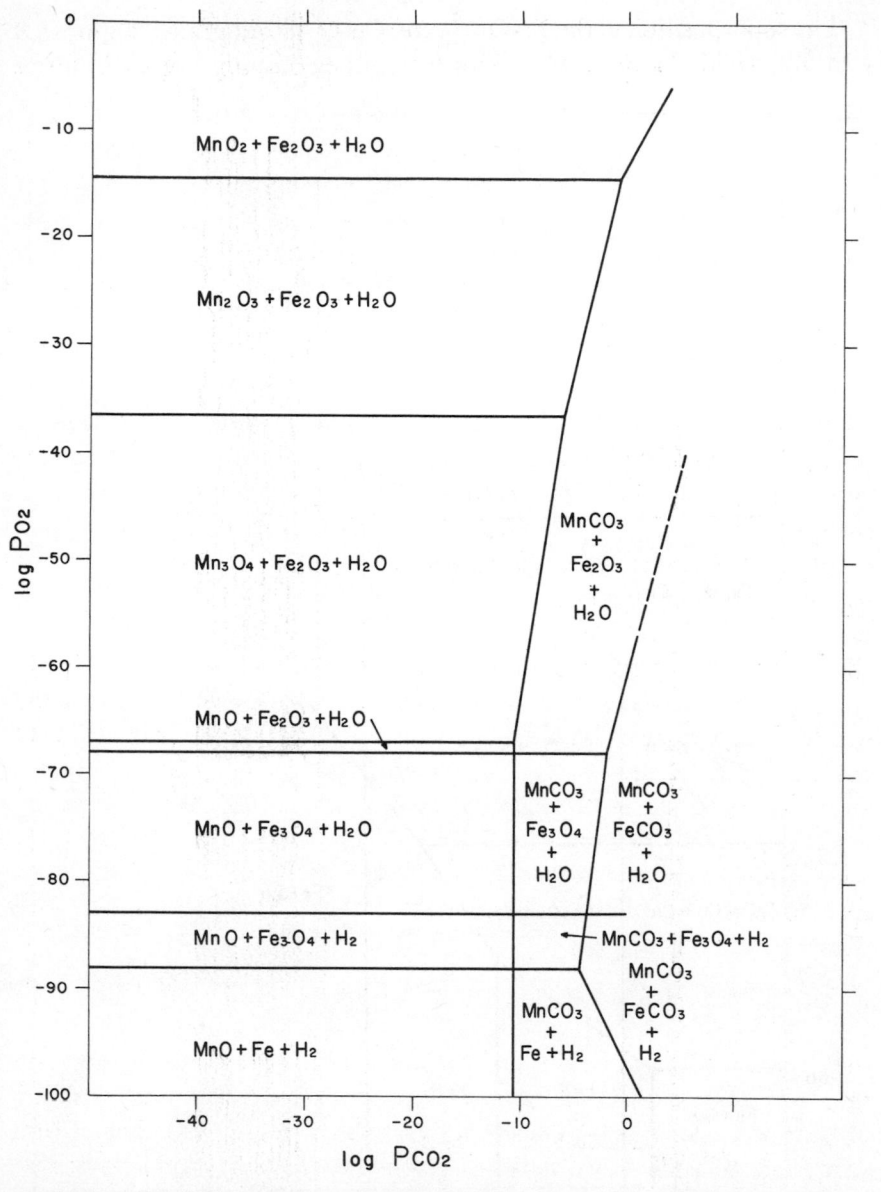

FIGURE 5.13.   Stability relations among iron and manganese oxides and carbonates as functions of P_{O_2} and P_{CO_2} at 25°C and 1 atmosphere pressure.   Stability range of water also shown.   No interactions between Fe and Mn compounds are considered. (Courtesy J. Reitzel, Department of Geology, Harvard University Graduate School, 1958.)

Mineral Equilibria

Fe-Cu-O$_2$-S$_2$

The superposition of the Fe-O$_2$-S$_2$ and Cu-O$_2$-S$_2$ diagrams (Figures 5.8 and 5.9) yields Figure 5.14. This figure is eloquently barren in terms

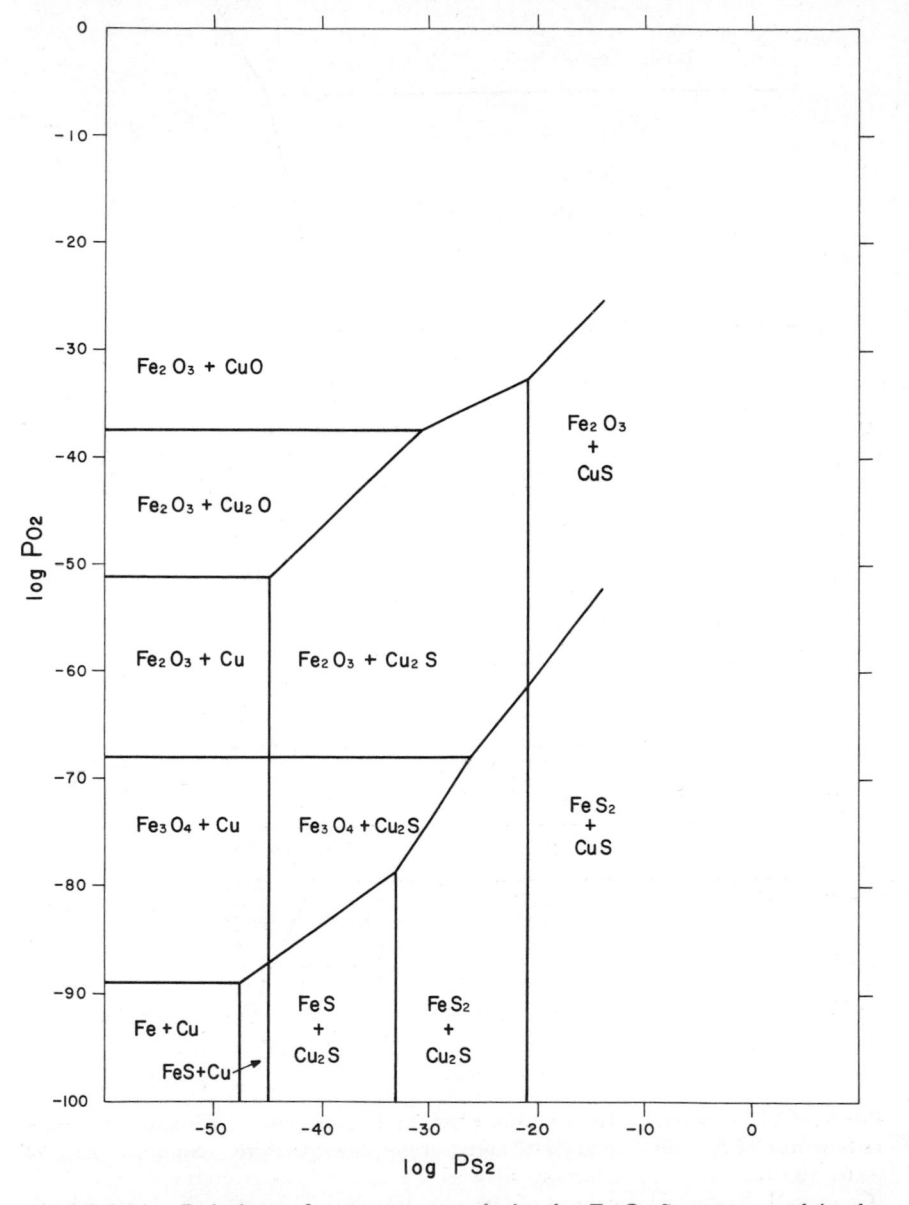

FIGURE 5.14. Relations of some compounds in the Fe-O$_2$-S$_2$ system and in the Cu-O$_2$-S$_2$ system plotted simultaneously as functions of P_{O_2} and P_{S_2} at 25°C and 1 atmosphere total pressure. No interactions are considered.

of compounds containing both iron and copper, such as chalcopyrite ($CuFeS_2$) and bornite (Cu_5FeS_4). R. Natarajan (unpublished manuscript, Department of Geology, Harvard University, 1958) has attempted to take into account such interactions, basing his interpretation of the position of the compounds on the diagrams of McKinstry and Kennedy [H. E. McKinstry and G. C. Kennedy, Some suggestions

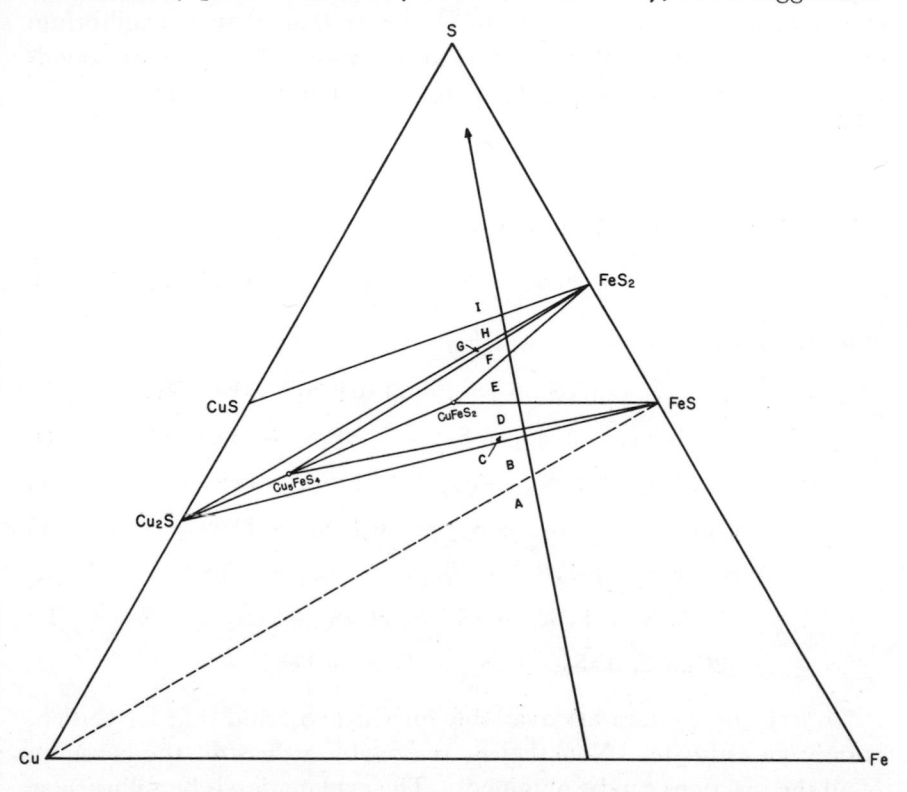

FIGURE 5.15. Stability relations in the system Cu-Fe-S at 25°C and 1 atmosphere total pressure, as deduced by R. Natarajan. There is some uncertainty concerning the composition of Cu_2S and FeS at this temperature.

concerning the sequence of certain ore minerals. *Econ. Geol.*, *52*, 379–390 (1957)], and McKinstry [H. E. McKinstry, Phase assemblages in sulfide ore deposits. *N.Y. Acad. Sci.*, Ser. II, *20*, 15–26 (1957)], who have assembled data on the natural associations in this system. For the 25°C relations, Natarajan studied the mineralogy of the zone of oxidation and secondary sulfide enrichment. The composition diagram for Cu-Fe-S_2 at 25°C, as deduced by Natarajan, is shown in Figure 5.15. The reactions involved in following the heavy arrow

through the diagram (increasing sulfur content) can be written as follows, with the equation letters keyed to the tie lines in the composition diagram.

Starting from the Cu-Fe tie line, the 3-phase field Cu-Fe-FeS is encountered, then the tie line Cu-FeS. (The Cu-FeS association is not known to occur in nature, probably because of the low S_2 pressure required, as well as a pressure of O_2 lower than that in equilibrium with water.) The 3-phase field is at a constant P_{S_2} and corresponds to a vertical line on the P_{O_2}-P_{S_2} diagram. The line is defined by the reaction:

$$Fe_c + Cu_c + \tfrac{1}{2}S_{2g} = FeS_c + Cu_c \tag{A}$$

The next reaction is from Cu + FeS to Cu_2S + FeS:

$$2Cu_c + FeS_c + \tfrac{1}{2}S_{2\,g} = Cu_2S_c + FeS_c \tag{B}$$

and, in sequence:

$$5Cu_2S_c + 3FeS_c + \tfrac{1}{2}S_{2g} = 2Cu_5FeS_{4\,c} + FeS_c \tag{C}$$

$$Cu_5FeS_{4\,c} + 5FeS_c + S_{2g} = 5CuFeS_{2\,c} + FeS_c \tag{D}$$

$$CuFeS_{2\,c} + FeS_c + \tfrac{1}{2}S_{2g} = CuFeS_{2\,c} + FeS_{2\,c} \tag{E}$$

$$5CuFeS_{2\,c} + FeS_{2\,c} + S_{2g} = Cu_5FeS_{4\,c} + 5FeS_{2\,c} \tag{F}$$

$$2Cu_5FeS_{4\,c} + FeS_{2\,c} + \tfrac{1}{2}S_{2g} = 5Cu_2S_c + 3FeS_{2\,c} \tag{G}$$

$$Cu_2S_c + FeS_{2\,c} + \tfrac{1}{2}S_{2g} = 2CuS_c + FeS_{2\,c} \tag{H}$$

$$2CuS_c + FeS_{2\,c} + \tfrac{1}{2}S_{2g} = CuS_c + FeS_{2\,c} + S_c \tag{I}$$

No free energy data are available for Cu_5FeS_4, and that for $CuFeS_2$ is only an estimate. Nonetheless, reasonable values for the constants of all the reactions can be obtained. The explanation is best illustrated by reference to Figure 5.16, which shows the stability relations as deduced. The base from which the diagram was started is Figure 5.14 (heavy lines on Figure 5.16), which shows the stability fields for which free energy data are available. Reactions (A)–(H) then give the sequence in which the minerals occur as P_{S_2} increases, and serves to place the light lines in correct positions relative to known equilibria across the lower part of the diagram. By adding information concerning mineral associations from the ternary system Cu-Fe-O_2-S_2, it becomes necessary to adjust further the position of the light line representing the new equilibria. To obtain the mineral associations $CuFeS_2$-Fe_3O_4 and $CuFeS_2$-Fe_2O_3, both of which are common, the

line for the boundary $Cu_5FeS_4 + FeS = CuFeS_2 + FeS$ (D) cannot be placed on the diagram unless it is within 1 or 2 log units of P_{S_2}. Furthermore, because the *slopes* of all equilibria are known, irrespective

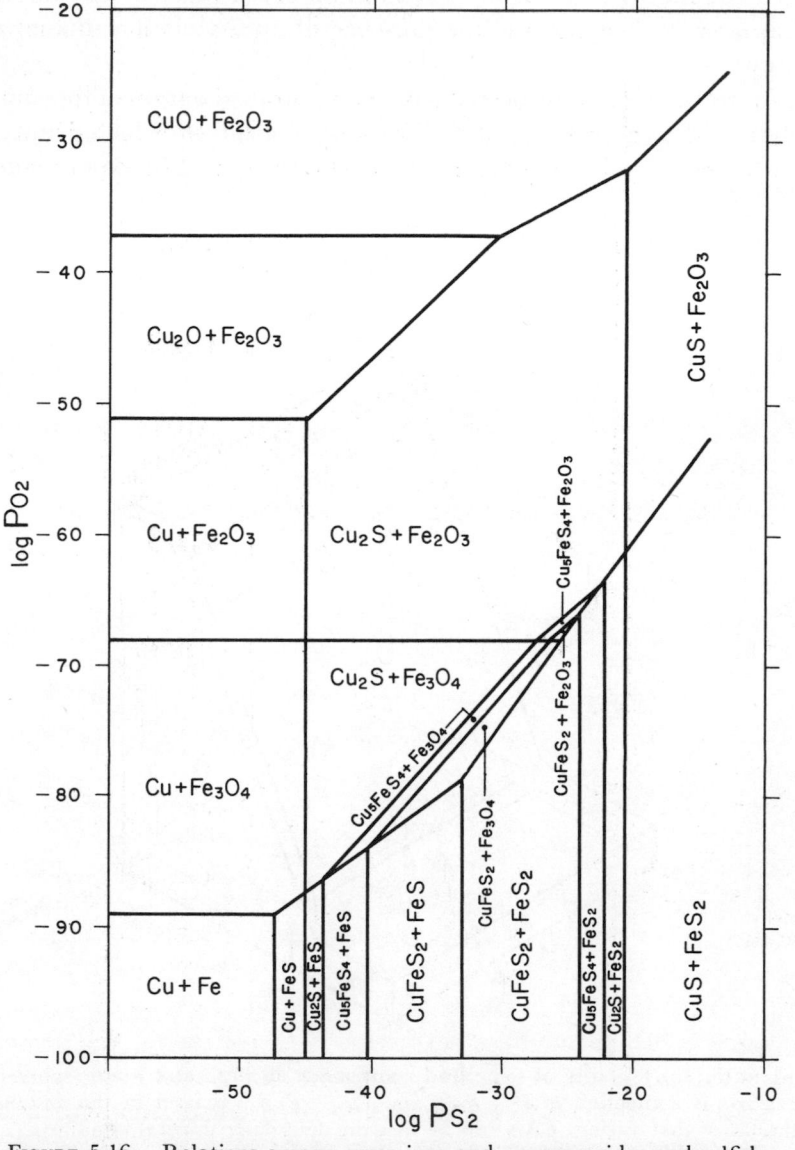

FIGURE 5.16. Relations among some iron and copper oxides and sulfides at 25°C and 1 atmosphere total pressure. Heavy lines are from superposition of iron and copper P_{O_2}-P_{S_2} diagrams; lighter lines are relations deduced from mineral associations. (R. Natarajan and R. Garrels, unpublished manuscript, 1958.)

of their absolute values, once a position for P_{S_2} of equation (D) is chosen, the position for the boundary $CuFeS_2 + FeS_2 = Cu_5FeS_4 + FeS_2$ (F) also is fixed.   It will thus be noted that any significant change in the boundaries shown will cause an observed mineral association to disappear, or it will cause the presence of an association unknown in nature.

Figure 5.16 is not purported to be an accurate diagram of the mineral relations shown, but it is a useful working model from which deductions can be made and tested against natural occurrences or experiment.

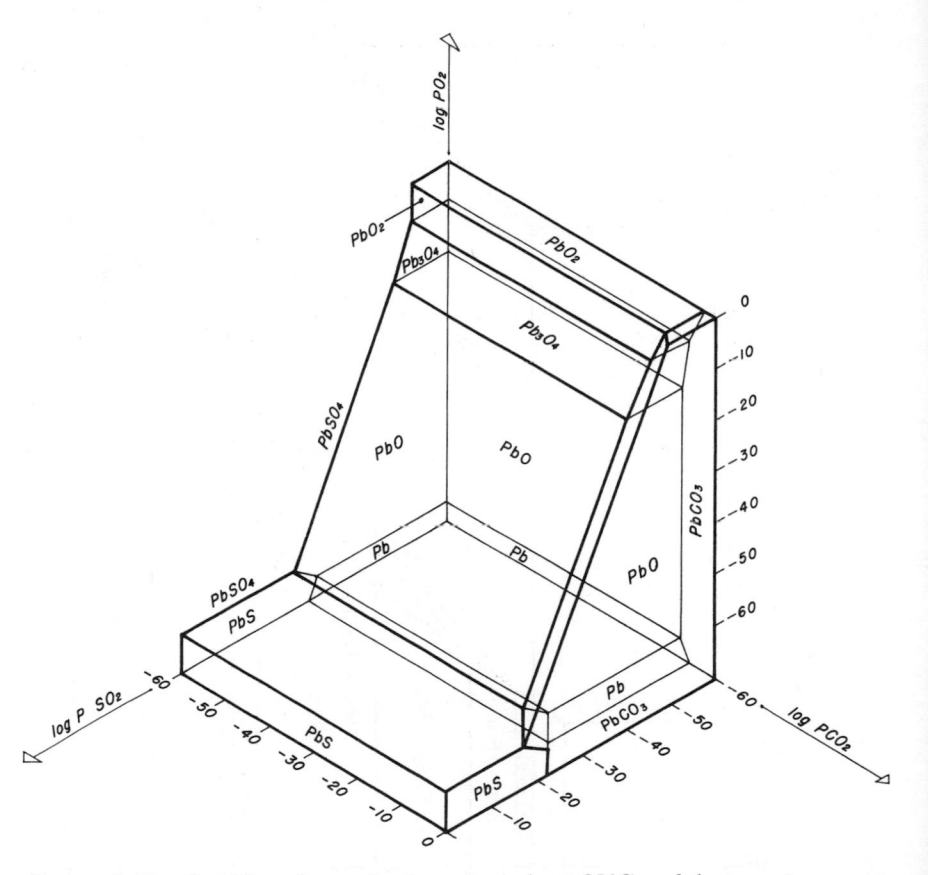

FIGURE 5.17.   Stability of some lead compounds at 25°C and 1 atmosphere total pressure as a function of P_{O_2}, P_{CO_2}, and P_{SO_2}. P_{SO_2} was used in this instance to emphasize that various gases can be used in describing mineral equilibria.   Note that PbS, PbSO$_4$, and PbCO$_3$ are the phases expected at near-surface conditions. (Courtesy J. Anderson, Department of Geology, Harvard University Graduate School, 1958.)

SUMMARY

In this chapter a variety of diagrams has been developed to illustrate the utility of expressing mineral relations in terms of the common denominators of partial pressures of gases. The gases of greatest geologic interest are O_2, CO_2, and S_2. Relations among the oxides, carbonates, and sulfides of various metals can be expressed as individual plots, or they can be superimposed for purposes of comparison. Such superimposition permits only comparison of the minerals considered in the individual systems, and is not to be construed as a representation of all stable phases that may occur. There are three chief limitations of such diagrams: (1) Data are not yet available to take into consideration compositional variation of real minerals. (2) Interactions to form new mineral species should be considered to achieve relations of geologic interest, and simple superposition of diagrams is not sufficient in many cases to be of great utility. (3) Although partial pressures of gases are convenient for comparison of mineral relations, the calculated values, with the exception of P_{CO_2}, are so low as to have little physical significance. The calculated values are not verifiable by direct experiment, and they are not easy to translate into the environmental conditions that can be observed in the field.

SELECTED REFERENCE

Darken, L. S., and R. W. Gurry, *The Physical Chemistry of Metals*. McGraw-Hill Book Co., New York, 1953, 535 pp.

6

Eh–pH Diagrams

THE current rapid increase in use of Eh-pH diagrams to show mineral stability relations is a little surprising because the ingredients necessary to manufacture them have been known for a long time. The development of the concept of pH and its extensive application to the interpretation of the chemistry of soils and natural waters dates back several decades, and the Nernst equation relating Eh to $E°$ and to the activities of reactants and products of half-cells is of even more ancient derivation.

It would be impossible to attempt a complete bibliography of all papers of geologic interest that have made significant use of Eh or pH or both, but the answer to the enigma concerning the late development of mineral stability diagrams perhaps can be given in part by citing some key publications in chronological sequence. As early as 1923 Clark (cf. W. M. Clark and Barnett Cohen, An analysis of the theoretical relations between reduction potentials and pH. *Public Health Reports, Reprint 826, 1923*) discussed at length the interrelation of Eh and pH, but his interests were to a large extent in the field of biochemistry, and his attention was directed to equilibria among dissolved species, rather than among solids. Thus his work created little stir in geochemistry.

One of the first papers in geology devoted to the stability relations of minerals, as well as those of dissolved ions, was Scerbina's discussion of the role of oxidation potential as applied to mineral paragenesis [V. V. Scerbina, Oxidation-reduction potentials as applied to the study of the paragenesis of minerals. *Compte. rend. acad. sci. U.R.S.S., 22*, 503–506 (1939)]. He considered the effect of pH in his discussion, but

made no plots involving the two variables. On the other hand, he suggested groups of minerals that could coexist under given Eh conditions.

The next milestone was the publication of ZoBell's classic work on Eh values for marine sediments [Claude E. ZoBell, 1946, Studies on redox potentials of marine sediments. *Bull. Am. Assoc. Petrol. Geol.*, *30*, 477–513 (1946)]. He made available in a widely circulated geological journal a comprehensive treatment of the theory and practice of Eh and pH measurement, and the interpretation of such measurements in terms of the natural environment. The scope of the article is greater than indicated by the title, for it is a critical résumé of most of the previous work. The one aspect missing is the depiction of the stability fields of solids as functions of Eh and pH. His paper, plus one a year older, by Starkey and Wight (R. L. Starkey and K. M. Wight, *Anaerobic Corrosion of Iron in Soil*. American Gas Association, New York, 1945, 108 pp.) stand as basic references for anyone interested in practicing the profession of Eh and pH.

Attention was further directed toward the use of pH and potential by Mason [Brian Mason, Oxidation and reduction in geo-chemistry. *J. Geol.*, *57*, 62–72 (1949)], who discussed mineral stability relations as functions of Eh and pH, but did not use any clear-cut mineral stability-field diagrams.

In 1946, M. Pourbaix published a book on the thermodynamics of dilute solutions; in 1949 it was translated into English. (M. J. N. Pourbaix, *Thermodynamics of Dilute Aqueous Solutions*. Edward Arnold & Co., London, 1949, 136 pp.) Because of the title, it was missed by geochemists at first, although the methods are ideally suited to the treatment of mineral equilibria. In fact the author of this text is embarrassed to have published a paper on the Eh-pH stability relations in 1953 without being aware of Pourbaix's work. Pourbaix's book is the summary of a decade of development of methods of representing the stability of solids and dissolved species as functions of pH and Eh. Much of the following development is based on Pourbaix's work, with slight adaptation and extension of some of his methods.

Since the publication of his book, Pourbaix, as director of the Belgian Institute for the Study of Corrosion, has published, with his co-workers, numerous technical reports, each concerned with equilibria of a given element in oxygenated water. A complete list of the reports of interest is given at the end of this chapter. The reports, although aimed primarily at metallurgists, can be used without modification by anyone

interested in mineral stability relations, insofar as pure chemical compounds resemble minerals.

Largely through the impact of Pourbaix's work, use of Eh-pH stability diagrams has ramified rapidly through the geochemical literature. A bibliography and discussion of some of the publications of geologic interest is given in Chapter 7.

CONSTRUCTION OF Eh-pH DIAGRAMS

The mechanics of constructing Eh-pH diagrams is illustrated in this text by a detailed development of diagrams showing relations among iron minerals. The calculations and equations are presented with a degree of elaboration not entirely necessary if the text were limited to a discussion of iron alone, in the anticipation that readers may want to make similar calculations for other elements. The complexities that may be encountered in such attempts are most likely to be demonstrated if all aspects of the calculations for iron are treated with comparable thoroughness.

The two basic equations for Eh-pH relations have been developed in Chapter 1. The first is:

$$E_R^\circ = \frac{\varDelta F_R^\circ}{n \mathscr{F}} \tag{1.7}$$

which related the standard potential, E°, to the standard free energy of reaction, $\varDelta F_R^\circ$, the number of electrons involved, n, and the faraday $\mathscr{F}$. The second equation is:

$$\text{Eh} = E^\circ + \frac{0.059}{n} \log \frac{[D]^d [E]^e}{[B]^b [C]^c} \tag{1.12}$$

in which Eh is the potential of the half-cell relative to the hydrogen electrode, n is the number of electrons, as before, and D, E, B, and C are the activities of the products and reactants.

The following discussion relates entirely to 25°C and 1 atmosphere total pressure. Insofar as possible the pattern of Chapter 5 will be followed to show the interrelation of partial pressure diagrams to Eh-pH diagrams.

THE STABILITY OF WATER

In Chapter 5 the stability of water was expressed as a function of hydrogen and oxygen partial pressures by obtaining the equilibrium constant for the reaction:

$$2H_2O_l = 2H_{2\,g} + O_{2\,g}$$

The upper limit of water stability was determined as the equilibrium between water and oxygen at 1 atmosphere pressure. These relations are shown in Figure 5.1.

If we wish to show these same limits as functions of Eh and/or pH, the method is to write a reaction between water and oxygen in terms of hydrogen ions and/or electrons, so that representation of the relation can be plotted with Eh and pH as ordinate and abscissa.

For the upper limit of water stability ($P_{O_2} = 1$ atmosphere):

$$2H_2O_l = O_{2g} + 4H^+_{aq} + 4e \qquad (6.1)$$

Then from equation (1.20):

$$Eh = E^\circ + \frac{0.059}{4} \log \frac{P_{O_2}[H^+]^4}{[H_2O]^2} \qquad (6.2)$$

Under the conditions chosen, P_{O_2} is unity, as is the activity of pure liquid water, so:

$$Eh = E^\circ + \frac{0.059}{4} \log [H^+]^4$$

Substituting $-$pH for [H$^+$]:

$$Eh = E^\circ - 0.059 \, pH \qquad (6.3)$$

Therefore the equilibrium between water and oxygen at a partial pressure of 1 atmosphere is a straight line in an Eh-pH plot, with a slope of -0.059 volt per pH unit, and has an intercept of E°. To obtain a numerical value of E° for the reaction, the standard free energy is obtained, and is substituted in equation (1.15):

$$E^\circ_R = \frac{\Delta F^\circ_R}{n\mathscr{F}} \qquad (1.15)$$

First, ΔF°_R is obtained:

$$2H_2O_l = O_{2g} + 4H^+_{aq} + 4e \qquad (6.1)$$

$$\Delta F^\circ_{fO_2} + 4\Delta F^\circ_{fH^+} - 2\Delta F^\circ_{fH_2O} = \Delta F^\circ_R$$

$$0 + (4 \times 0) - (2 \times -56.69) = +113.4 \, kcal$$

Substituting in (1.15):

$$E^\circ_R = \frac{113.4}{4 \times 23.06} = 1.23 \text{ volts}$$

The final equation is:

$$Eh = 1.23 - 0.059 \, pH \qquad (6.4)$$

The line representing this relation is shown on Figure 6.1. Note that this line must represent a fixed oxygen pressure, so that in a sense

a change from a representation in terms of P_{O_2} to one involving Eh and pH has resulted in the splitting of a single variable into two. In general this is the reverse of the usual procedure, which is to use as few

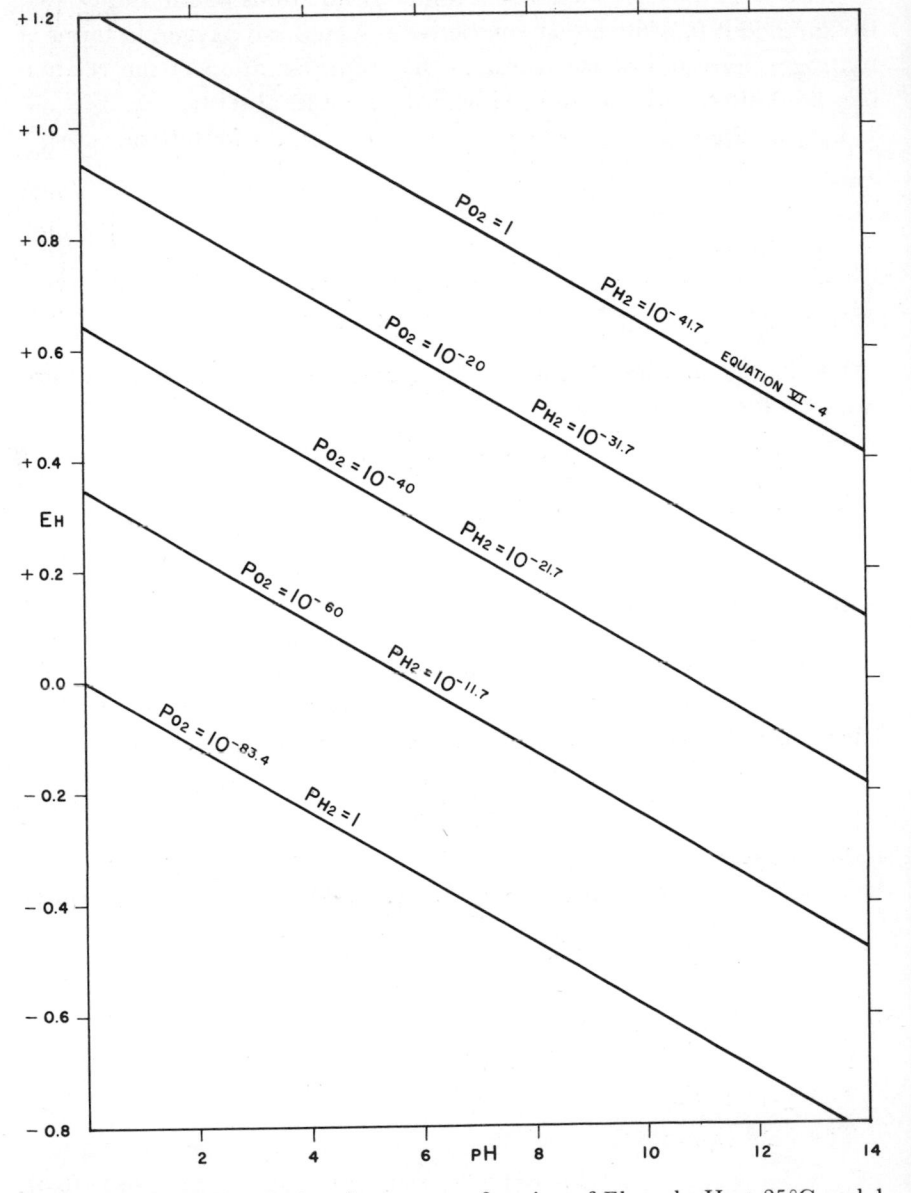

FIGURE 6.1.   Stability limits of water as a function of Eh and pH at 25°C and 1 atmosphere total pressure.   Contours show partial pressures of hydrogen and oxygen at intermediate Eh values.

variables as possible, but because Eh and pH are both easily measure-able, and because much of our thinking is in terms of acidity, alkalinity, reduction, and oxidation, the representation is useful.

If we reexamine equation (6.2) we see that it can be rewritten with the numerical value obtained for $E°$:

$$\text{Eh} = 1.23 + \frac{0.059}{4} \log P_{O_2} - 0.059 \text{ pH} \qquad (6.5)$$

At a partial pressure of oxygen of 1 atmosphere, the P_{O_2} term disappears, but evidently the equation can be used to plot a line on an Eh-pH diagram for any chosen pressure of oxygen. Therefore isobaric oxygen contours on an Eh-pH diagram (in equilibrium with water!) are parallel straight lines with a slope of -0.059 volt/pH.

Also, because of the relation shown in equation (5.1):

$$2H_2O_l = 2H_{2\,g} + O_{2\,g}$$

the partial pressure of hydrogen is also fixed if that of oxygen is stipulated, and P_{H_2} contours must also be straight lines with the same slope. However, values for P_{H_2} can also be derived by writing the half-cell reaction:

$$H_{2\,g} = 2H^+_{aq} + 2e \qquad (6.6)$$

This half-cell reaction does not include liquid water, but its presence is implicit in the term H^+_{aq}. The Eh equation is:

$$\text{Eh} = E° + \frac{0.059}{2} \log \frac{[H^+]^2}{P_{H_2}}$$

Substituting $-$pH for log $[H^+]$, and rearranging:

$$\text{Eh} = E° - \frac{0.059}{2} \log P_{H_2} - 0.059\text{pH} \qquad (6.7)$$

As before, the numerical value of $E°$ is obtained by calculating ΔF_R° and substituting into the relation $E_R^\circ = \Delta F_R^\circ / n\mathscr{F}$:

$$2\Delta F_{fH^+}^\circ - \Delta F_{fH_2}^\circ = \Delta F_R^\circ$$
$$0 \qquad -0 \qquad = 0$$

$$E_R^\circ = \frac{0}{2 \times 23.06} = 0$$

The final equation, since $E° = 0$, is:

$$\text{Eh} = -\frac{0.059}{2} \log P_{H_2} - 0.059\text{pH} \qquad (6.8)$$

Figure 6.1 is the result of plotting equations (6.5) and (6.8). The heavy lines at top and bottom are for $P_{O_2} = 1$ atmosphere and $P_{H_2} =$

1 atmosphere respectively, and show the equilibrium limits of the existence of water under earth surface or near-surface conditions.

Under experimental conditions, water can exist for long periods of time at higher and lower Eh values than those shown. Overvoltages of about 0.5 volt are generally necessary to achieve water decomposition at rates easily observed in the laboratory. However, the reaction can be catalyzed, and inasmuch as bacteria function well in this regard, it is probably unlikely that natural waters maintain Eh values much above or below the limits shown on Figure 6.1 for appreciable time intervals.

THE STABILITY OF IRON OXIDES

As derived in Chapter 5, the stable iron compounds are native iron, magnetite, and hematite. The stability relations were determined as functions of the partial pressure of oxygen. These can be converted to reactions expressible as functions of Eh and pH by adding the water dissociation half-cell to the reactions expressed in terms of oxygen partial pressure. For the oxidation of iron to magnetite:

$$3Fe_c + 2O_{2g} = Fe_3O_{4c} \qquad (5.10)$$

$$4H_2O_l = 8H^+_{aq} + 2O_{2g} + 8e \qquad (6.1)$$

$$\overline{3Fe_c + 4H_2O_l = Fe_3O_{4c} + 8H^+_{aq} + 8e} \qquad (6.9)$$

The addition serves to eliminate oxygen gas and to substitute for it H^+ and electrons as variables.

The standard free energy of reaction 6.9 is:

$$\Delta F^\circ_{fFe_3O_4} + 8\Delta F^\circ_{fH^+} - 3\Delta F^\circ_{fFe} - 4\Delta F^\circ_{fH_2O} = \Delta F^\circ_R$$

$$-242.4 + (8 \times 0) - (3 \times 0) - (4 \times -56.69) = -15.6 \text{ kcal}$$

From the relation $E^\circ_R = \dfrac{\Delta F^\circ_R}{n\mathscr{F}}$:

$$E^\circ_R = \frac{-15.6}{8 \times 23.06} = -0.084 \text{ volt}$$

The half-cell represented by reaction 6.9 can then be expressed by the Eh equation:

$$Eh = -0.084 + \frac{0.059}{8} \log \frac{[Fe_3O_4][H^+]^8}{[Fe]^3[H_2O]^4} \qquad (6.10)$$

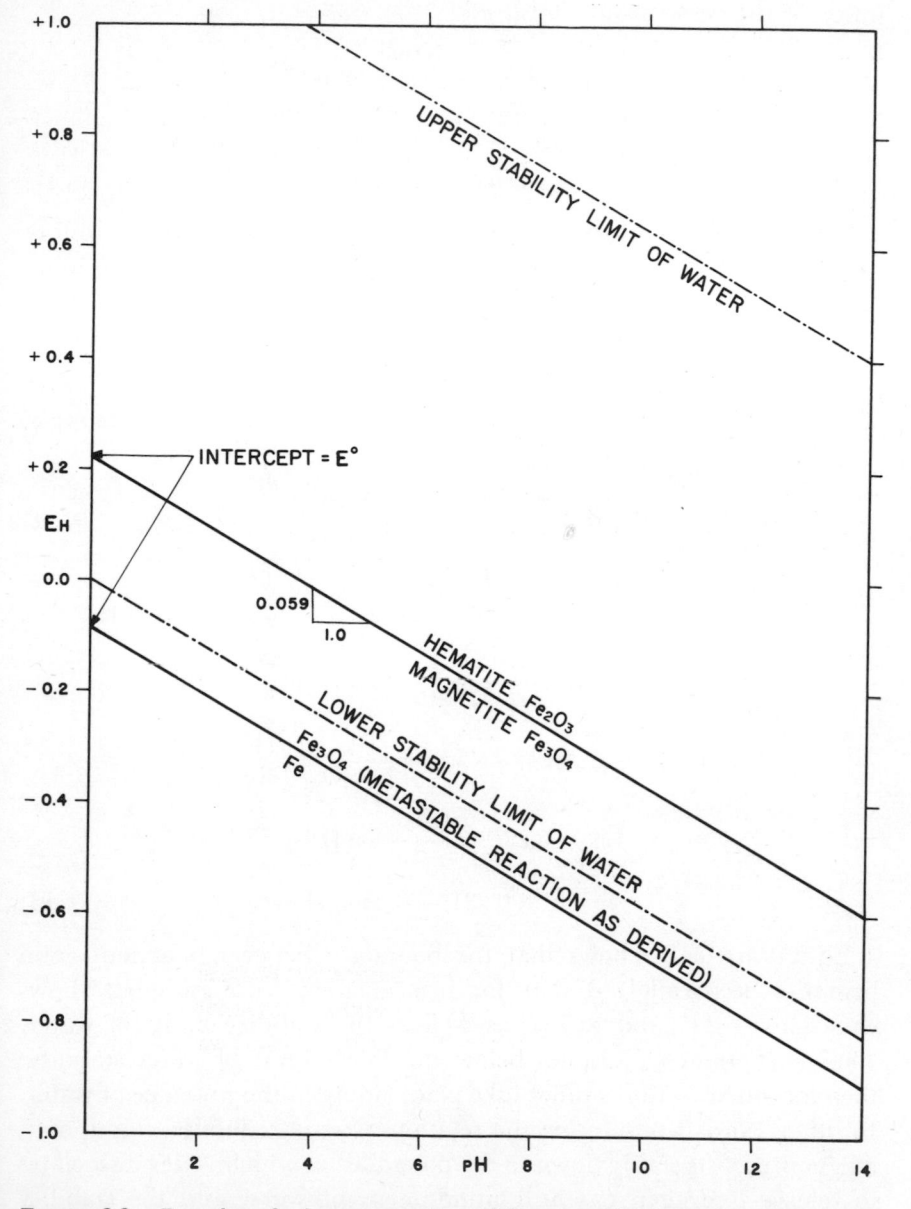

FIGURE 6.2. Boundary for iron-magnetite and for magnetite-hematite as a function of Eh and pH at 25°C and 1 atmosphere total pressure. Because the Fe-Fe$_3$O$_4$ boundary is below the lower stability limit for water, the reaction is metastable, and metallic iron cannot exist at equilibrium in the presence of water at any pH.

Remembering that the activities of Fe_3O_{4c}, Fe_c, and H_2O_l are unity (if the water is nearly pure!):

$$Eh = -0.084 + \frac{0.059}{8} \log [H^+]^8$$

Substituting $-pH$ for $\log [H^+]$:

$$Eh = -0.084 - 0.059 \, pH \tag{6.11}$$

The reaction between iron and magnetite is therefore a straight line on the Eh-pH plot, and has the same slope as the water stability boundary lines.

For the oxidation of magnetite to hematite the derivation of the Eh-pH equation is similar and is shown without explanatory steps.

$$2Fe_3O_{4\,c} + \tfrac{1}{2}O_{2\,g} = 3Fe_2O_{3\,c} \tag{5.14}$$

$$\underline{H_2O_l \qquad\qquad\quad = 2H^+_{aq} + \tfrac{1}{2}O_{2\,g} + 2e} \tag{6.1}$$

$$2Fe_3O_{4\,c} + H_2O_l = 3Fe_2O_{3\,c} + 2H^+ + 2e \tag{6.12}$$

$$3\Delta F^{\circ}_{f Fe_2O_3} + 2\Delta F^{\circ}_{f H^+} - 2\Delta F^{\circ}_{f Fe_3O_4} - \Delta F^{\circ}_{f H_2O} = \Delta F^{\circ}_R$$

$$(3 \times - 177.1) + (2 \times 0) - (2 \times - 242.4) - (-56.69) = +10.2 \text{ kcal}$$

$$E^{\circ} = \frac{+10.2}{2 \times 23.06} = 0.221 \text{ volt}$$

$$Eh = 0.221 + \frac{0.059}{2} \log \frac{[Fe_2O_3]^3[H^+]^2}{[Fe_3O_4]^2[H_2O]}$$

$$Eh = 0.221 + \frac{0.059}{2} \log [H^+]^2$$

$$Eh = 0.221 - 0.059 \, pH \tag{6.13}$$

Equation (6.13) shows that the boundary between magnetite and hematite is parallel to that for iron-magnetite. Figure 6.2 shows equations (6.11) and (6.13), as well as the stability limits of water. The reaction Fe-Fe$_3$O$_4$ lies below the lower limit of water stability, therefore the reaction cannot take place stably in the presence of water. In other words, considering the relations from a reduction standpoint, magnetite exists stably down to the potentials at which water dissociates to release hydrogen gas at 1 atmosphere pressure, and the stability field of iron cannot be reached in the presence of water, if equilibrium is maintained. The position of the line as drawn, then, is the boundary between iron and magnetite under the condition that liquid water is present metastably.

Figure 6.3 summarizes the stability relations of the iron oxides and water as functions of Eh and pH and will be used as the base for determining ionic activities.

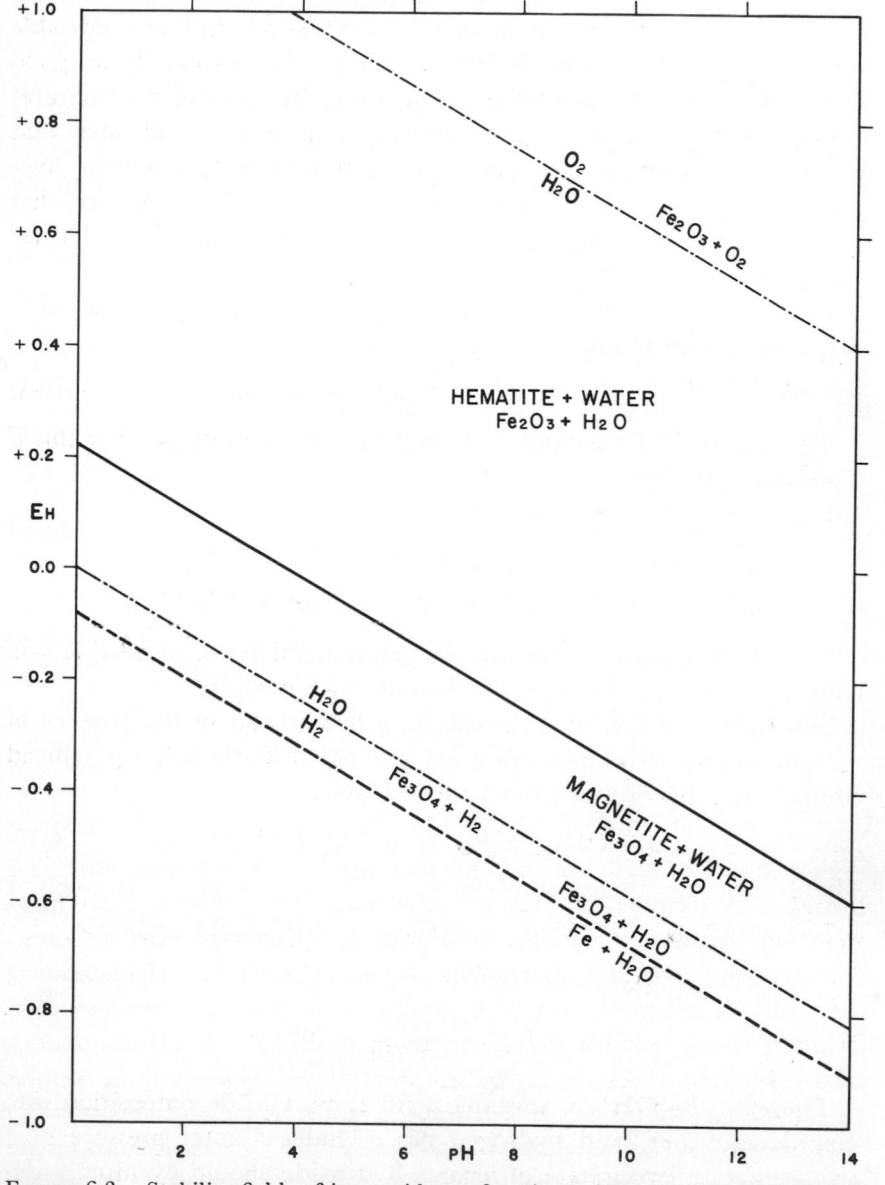

FIGURE 6.3. Stability fields of iron oxides as functions of Eh and pH at 25°C and 1 atmosphere total pressure. Dashed line indicates lower stability limit of magnetite in presence of metastable water.

STABILITY RELATIONS OF IRON HYDROXIDES

When a ferric salt in solution is precipitated by addition of hydroxide, the first precipitate is a hydrous oxide of indeterminate water content, often referred to as ferric hydroxide.   This first precipitate is unstable with respect to both hematite and goethite.   Unfortunately no good free energy data are available for goethite, but its intimate natural association with hematite in sedimentary iron ores indicates that hematite and goethite are very nearly equally stable in natural low-temperature aqueous solutions.   We shall assume henceforward that a stability field for hematite in water is essentially identical to that for goethite.

For the relation between freshly precipitated "ferric hydroxide" and hematite we can write:

$$2Fe(OH)_{3\,pptd} \rightleftharpoons Fe_2O_{3\,c} + 3H_2O_l \qquad (6.14)$$

The activities of reactants and products are all unity, so that this is a go-no-go relation.

From the free energies of formation:

$$\Delta F^\circ_{f Fe_2O_3} + 3\Delta F^\circ_{f H_2O} - 2\Delta F^\circ_{f Fe(OH)_3} = \Delta F^\circ_R$$

$$-177.1 + (3\times -56.69) - (2\times -166.0) = \mp 15.17 \text{ kcal}$$

Thus with sufficient time freshly precipitated ferric hydroxide will convert to the much more stable hematite (or goethite).

Similarly, addition of hydroxide to a ferrous salt in the absence of oxygen yields ferrous hydroxide—in this case a fairly well crystallized compound.   But if we consider the reaction:

$$3Fe(OH)_{2\,c} = Fe_3O_{4\,c} + H_{2\,g} + 2H_2O_l \qquad (6.15)$$

Then

$$\Delta F^\circ_{f Fe_3O_4} + \Delta F^\circ_{f H_2 g} + 2\Delta F^\circ_{f H_2O} - 3\Delta F^\circ_{f Fe(OH)_2} = \Delta F^\circ_R$$

$$-242.4 + 0 + (2\times -56.69) - (3\times -115.57) = -11.1 \text{ kcal}$$

$$k = P_{H_2} = \frac{-11.1}{-1.364} = 10^{8.1}$$

Therefore $Fe(OH)_2$ is unstable with respect to decomposition into magnetite, water, and hydrogen gas.   Under a total pressure of 1 atmosphere, a precipitate of ferrous hydroxide should eventually decompose to yield magnetite, and hydrogen would bubble from the system until the conversion was complete.

Yet both ferric and ferrous hydroxides are compounds of more than transitory existence. Although they clearly are not stable relative to hematite and magnetite, we can show their fields of temporary stability

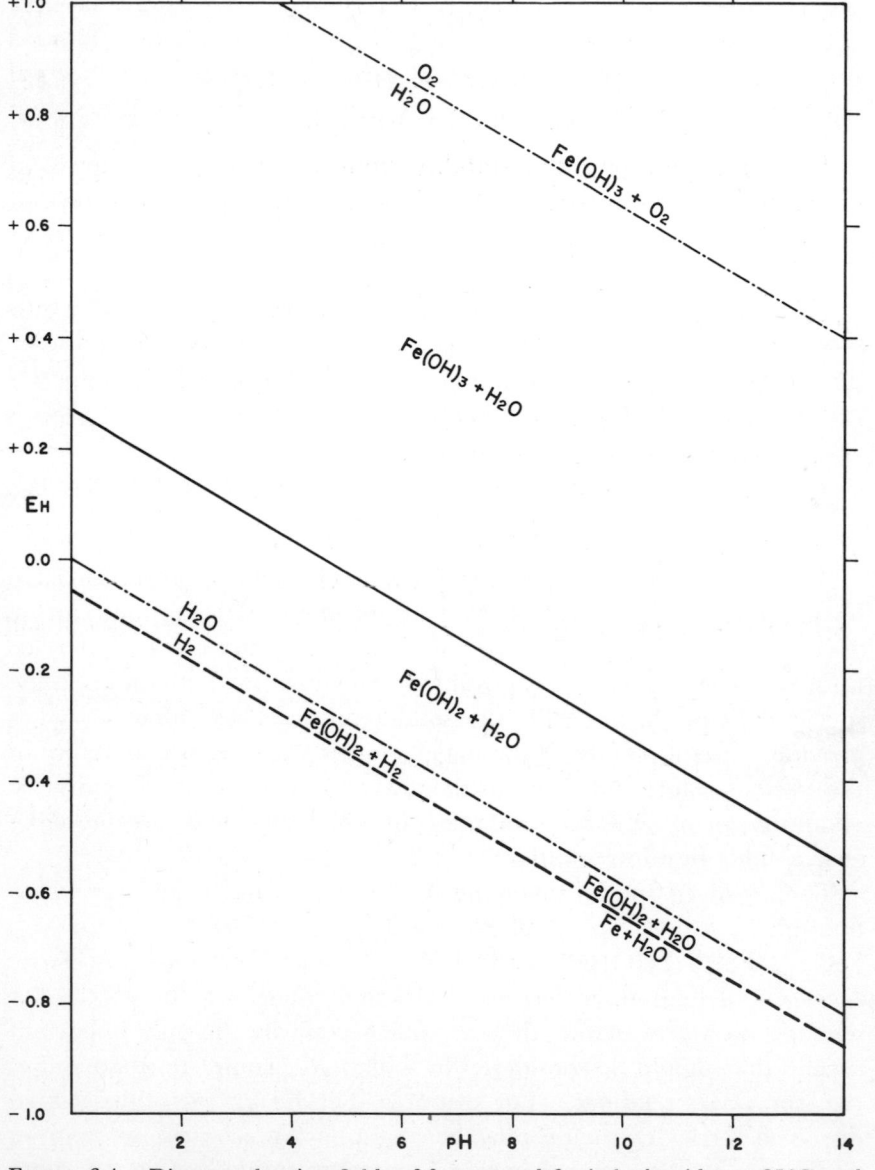

FIGURE 6.4. Diagram showing fields of ferrous and ferric hydroxides at 25°C and 1 atmosphere total pressure. Stability limits of water also shown. Dashed line is metastable boundary of Fe and $Fe(OH)_2$ in water.

just as well as if they were permanent products, if it suits our purpose to examine short-lived equilibria.

For the reaction:

$$Fe_c + 2H_2O_l = Fe(OH)_{2c} + 2H^+ + 2e \qquad (6.16)$$

$$Eh = -0.047 - 0.059\,pH \qquad (6.17)$$

Similarly:

$$Fe(OH)_{2c} + H_2O_l = Fe(OH)_{3c} + H^+_{aq} + e \qquad (6.18)$$

$$Eh = 0.271 - 0.059\,pH \qquad (6.19)$$

The equations, plus the stability limit for water, are shown in Figure 6.4. The similarity to the relations among the oxides shown in Figure 6.3 is obvious; the chief difference is that $Fe(OH)_2$ oxidizes to $Fe(OH)_3$ at a higher potential than Fe_3O_4 oxidizes to Fe_2O_3.

This diagram of the relations among metastable iron compounds serves to illustrate again that the calculations throughout are valid for the species considered, but have no guarantee attached that the species considered are the truly stable ones.

ACTIVITIES OF IONS IN EQUILIBRIUM WITH IRON OXIDES

After diagrams showing the stability fields of the iron oxides have been prepared, the aspect of chief utility of Eh-pH diagrams can be developed. Because free energy of formation values are available for numerous ionic species, it is possible to calculate the activities of these species in equilibrium with the solid oxides. These ionic activities provide a useful picture of the major contributions to the solubility of the various solids and serve to delineate the conditions of acidity or alkalinity, or of oxidation potential, in which the solids are probably least soluble in dilute solution.

The dissolved species involving iron, oxygen, and water, for which free energy values are available are Fe^{+++}_{aq}, $Fe(OH)^{++}_{aq}$, $Fe(OH)^+_{2\,aq}$, $FeO^-_{2\,aq}$, Fe^{++}_{aq}, $Fe(OH)^+_{aq}$, and $HFeO^-_{2\,aq}$. The first four are ferric species, the final three ferrous. Although these are the species for which data are available, they are not necessarily the only important species that should be considered in a relatively complete treatment of the iron-water relations. For example, $Fe(OH)_{3\,aq}$, or undissociated dissolved ferric hydroxide may be an important contributor to iron solubility (J. Winchester, personal communication). On the other hand, we progress if we prepare diagrams showing the relations of known species to the stable solids.

Reference to Figure 6.3 shows that the relations needed to show the activities of the dissolved species are reactions expressing relations between magnetite and hematite, the stable solids in water, and the dissolved species, written in such a way as to be expressible in terms of Eh and pH. There are certain general relations that are helpful in calculation if recognized prior to the attempt to write the reactions.

For example, reactions involving hematite and any dissolved species containing ferric iron will be Eh independent, inasmuch as no oxidation or reduction is required. Similarly, reactions involving hematite and dissolved species containing ferrous iron will certainly be Eh dependent, and may be pH dependent as well. Consequently, as a general rule, derivation of relations between dissolved species and solids is easier if reactions involving only one valence state are considered first.

The pattern of procedure used here is to calculate the activities of each dissolved species in equilibrium with hematite and magnetite and to contour the activities within the Eh-pH framework of solid stability. After individual diagrams have been prepared, the final step is to superimpose them all, and emerge with a composite diagram showing all information concerning dissolved species for which data are available. Thus the individual diagrams are reasonably permanent records, whereas the composite diagram can be considered a progress report, in the sense that it can be added to at any time that more data become available on additional species.

Ferric Ion. Let us first calculate in detail the relations among magnetite, hematite, and the activity of ferric ion. Observing the rule previously stated, the first step is to write the reaction of ferric ion with ferric oxide, always trying to keep it in terms of water and hydrogen ions:

$$Fe_2O_{3c} + 6H^+_{aq} = 2Fe^{+++}_{aq} + 3H_2O_l \qquad (6.20)$$

The standard free energy of the reaction is:

$$2\Delta F^\circ_{fFe^{+++}} + 3\Delta F^\circ_{fH_2O} - \Delta F^\circ_{fFe_2O_3} - 6\Delta F^\circ_{fH^+} = \Delta F^\circ_R$$

$$(2 \times -2.53) + (3 \times -56.69) - (-177.1) - 6(0) = +2.0\,\text{kcal}$$

The equilibrium constant is:

$$\log k = \frac{\Delta F^\circ_R}{-1.364} = \frac{2.0}{-1.364} = -1.45$$

Eliminating Fe_2O_{3c} and H_2O_l from the constant because their activity is unity:

$$\log \frac{[Fe^{+++}]^2}{[H^+]^6} = -1.45$$

Rearranging, and substituting $-\text{pH}$ for $\log[\text{H}^+]$:

$$2\log[\text{Fe}^{+++}] = -1.45 - 6\,\text{pH}$$

$$\log[\text{Fe}^{+++}] = -0.72 - 3\,\text{pH} \tag{6.21}$$

The log of the activity of ferric ion in equilibrium with $\text{Fe}_2\text{O}_{3\,c}$ is seen to be a linear function of pH. If pH is stipulated, $[\text{Fe}^{+++}]$ is fixed; and vice versa. The usual method is to assume convenient values of $[\text{Fe}^{+++}]$, and solve for pH. Because Eh is not involved, such contours of $[\text{Fe}^{+++}]$ will lie parallel to the Eh axis. Table 6.1 shows pairs of values of $\log[\text{Fe}^{+++}]$ and pH. The values chosen for $[\text{Fe}^{+++}]$ or other ions usually range from about 10^{-1} to 10^{-8} or 10^{-10}. Values higher than 10^{-1} fall in such a high concentration range that activities can be expected to depart markedly from molalities, for one thing, and also we are rarely interested in geology in activities greater than 10^{-1} for a given species. On the other hand, when values for a given ion become less than 10^{-8} (about 1 part Fe^{+++} per 10 billion) the activity or molality of the ion can be considered insignificant.

TABLE 6.1. Solution of Equation (6.21) to Yield Values of pH for Activities of Fe^{+++} in Equilibrium with Hematite

$\log[\text{Fe}^{+++}]$	pH
-1	0.09
-2	0.43
-3	0.76
-4	1.09
-5	1.43
-6	1.76
-7	2.09
-8	2.43

Figure 6.5a shows contours of $\log[\text{Fe}^{+++}]$ plotted from the table.

Next we can consider the equilibrium between ferric ions and magnetite:

$$\text{Fe}_3\text{O}_{4\,c} + 8\text{H}^+_{aq} = 3\text{Fe}^{+++}_{aq} + 4\text{H}_2\text{O}_l + e \tag{6.22}$$

In this case an oxidation is involved, so that this half-cell reaction is described by (eliminating substances of unit activity):

$$\text{Eh} = E^\circ + \frac{0.059}{1}\log\frac{[\text{Fe}^{+++}]^3}{[\text{H}^+]^8}$$

Obtaining ΔF_R° as before, and from it a numerical value of E°; and substituting $-$pH for log $[H^+]$:

$$Eh = 0.337 + 0.177 \log [Fe^{+++}] + 0.472 \, pH \qquad (6.23)$$

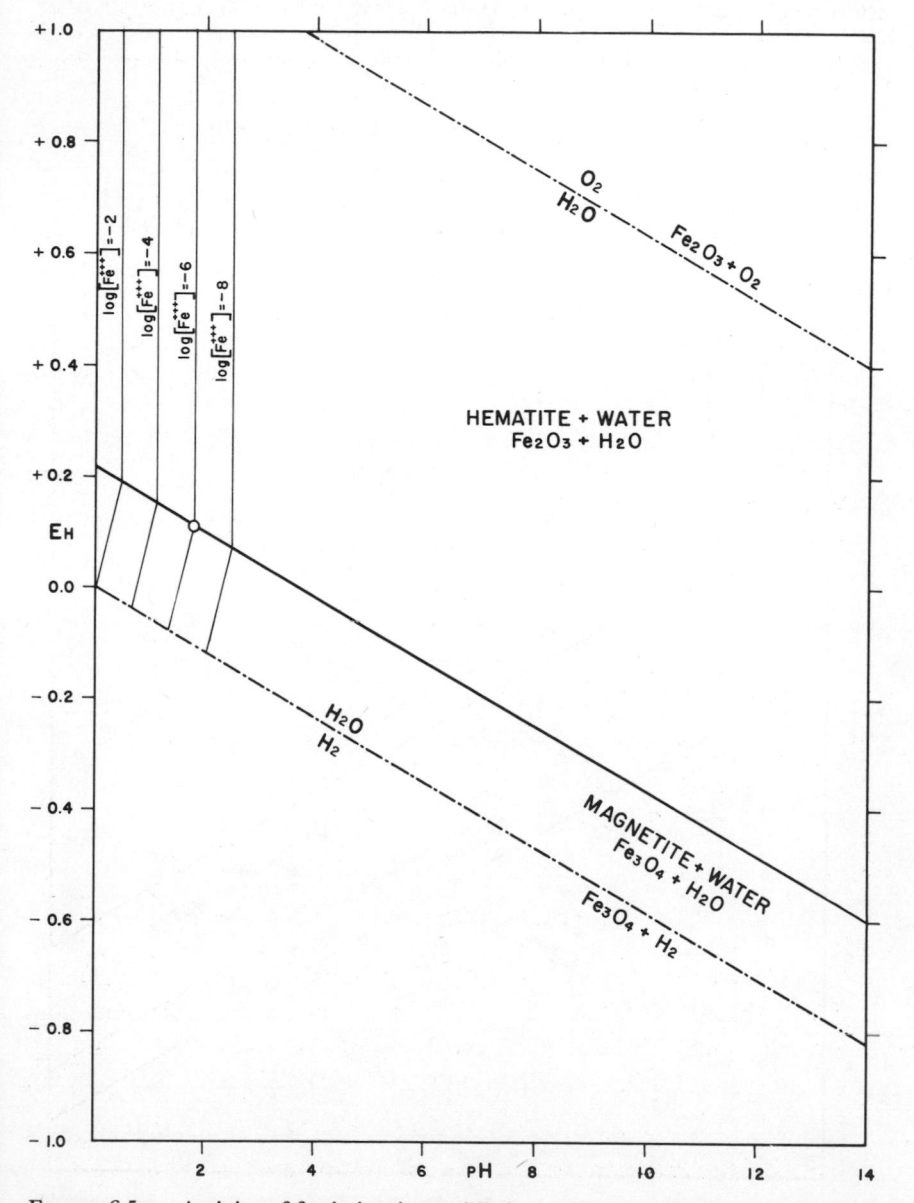

FIGURE 6.5a.   Activity of ferric ion in equilibrium with hematite and magnetite at 25°C and 1 atmosphere total pressure.   Contours are log $[Fe^{+++}]$.   Note that values become vanishingly small at low pH in the fields of both solids.

Mineral Equilibria

Here we are faced with a new problem—it is not enough to stipulate [Fe^{+++}] to define the equation—a pH or an Eh value must also be chosen. However, this does in fact provide us with a test of the consistency of the thermodynamic data. If we choose a value such as

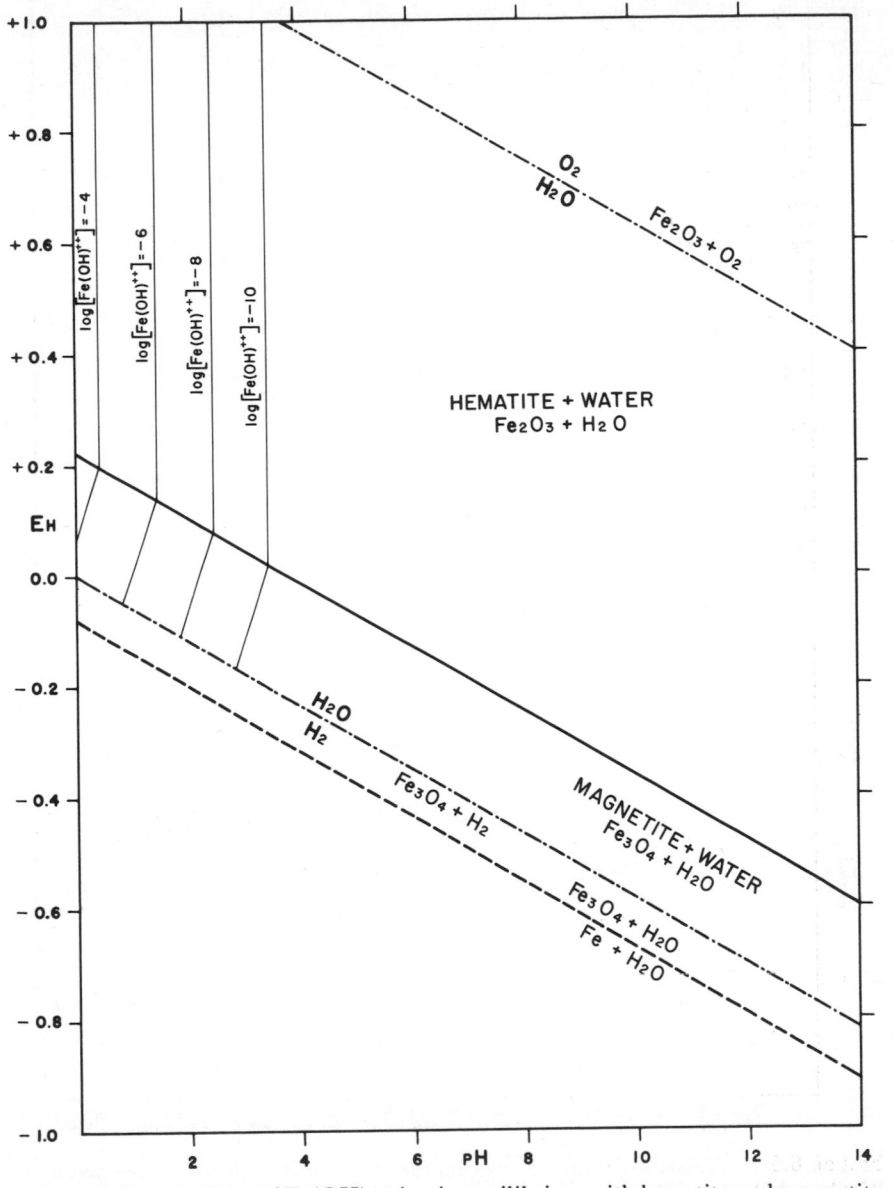

FIGURE 6.5b. Activity of Fe(OH)$^{++}$ ion in equilibrium with hematite and magnetite at 25°C and 1 atmosphere total pressure, within the stability field of water.

10^{-6} for [Fe^{+++}], and the corresponding pH value for [Fe^{+++}] in equilibrium with *hematite*, then the Eh we obtain should be that of the hematite-magnetite boundary at the appropriate [Fe^{+++}] and pH, inasmuch as at a given point on the boundary the two solids are in

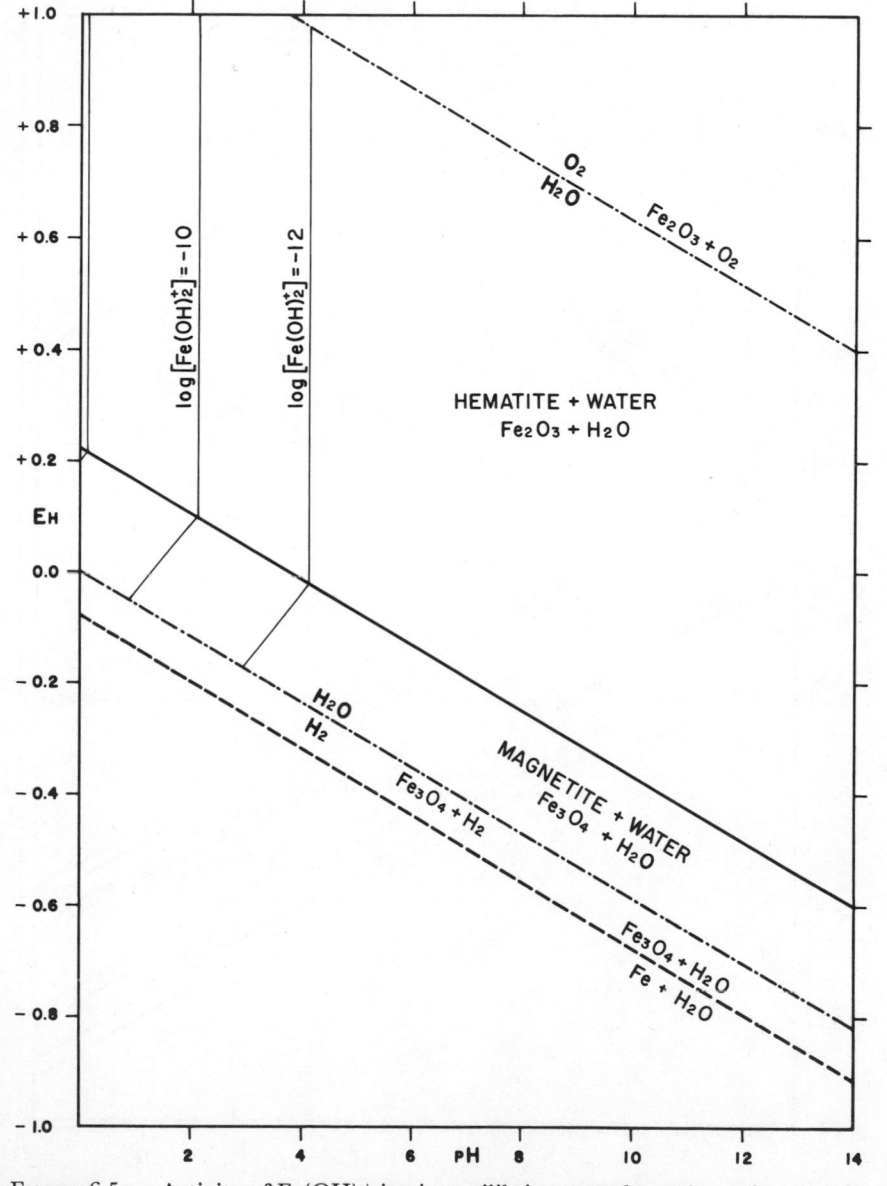

FIGURE 6.5c. Activity of Fe(OH)$_2^+$ ion in equilibrium with hematite and magnetite at 25°C and 1 atmosphere total pressure, within the stability field of water.

equilibrium, which means in turn that all ionic activities in equilibrium with one must also be in equilibrium with the other. If the Eh of the point chosen checks, then the contour can be drawn through the magnetite field, because at a fixed value of [Fe^{+++}] the *slope* of the con-

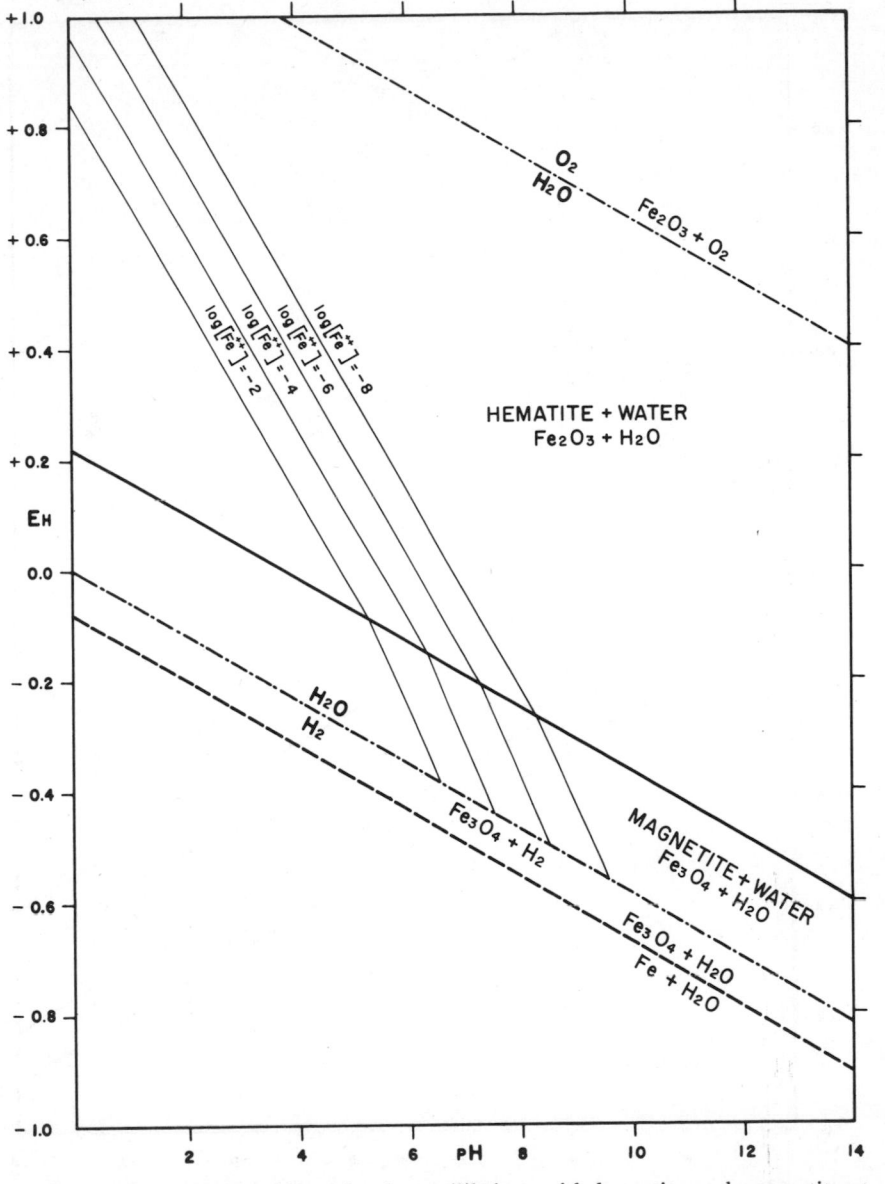

FIGURE 6.5d. Activity of Fe^{++} ion in equilibrium with hematite and magnetite at 25°C and 1 atmosphere total pressure, within the stability field of water.

tour in the magnetite field is fixed. Alternatively, Eh values within the magnetite field can be chosen arbitrarily, and the pH calculated for the given activity of Fe^{+++}.

Specifically let us calculate Eh at the hematite-magnetite boundary

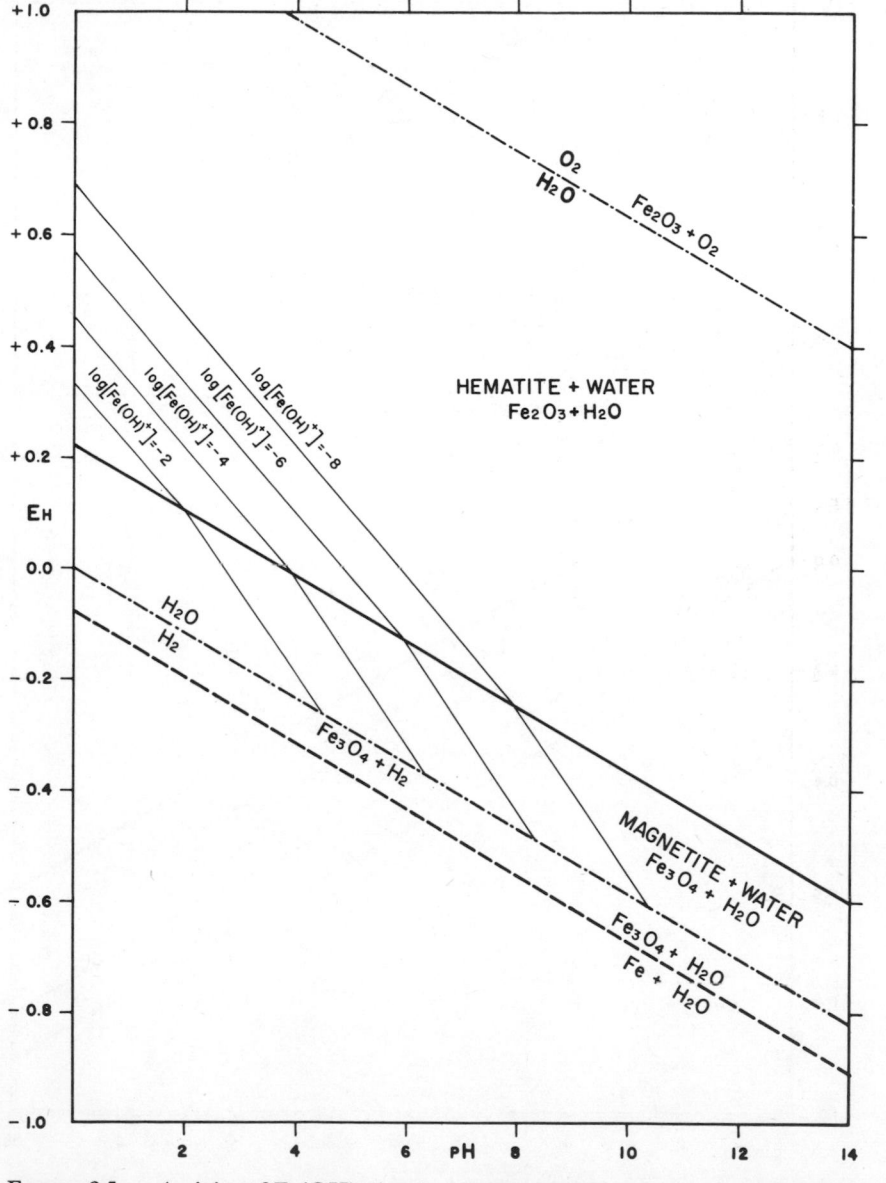

FIGURE 6.5e. Activity of $Fe(OH)^+$ ion in equilibrium with hematite and magnetite at 25°C and 1 atmosphere total pressure, within the stability field of water.

for the pair of values $\log [Fe^{+++}] = -6$; $pH = 1.76$ from Table 6.1. Substituting these values into equation (6.23):

$$Eh = 0.377 + 0.177 \times -6 + 0.472 \times 1.76 = +0.106$$

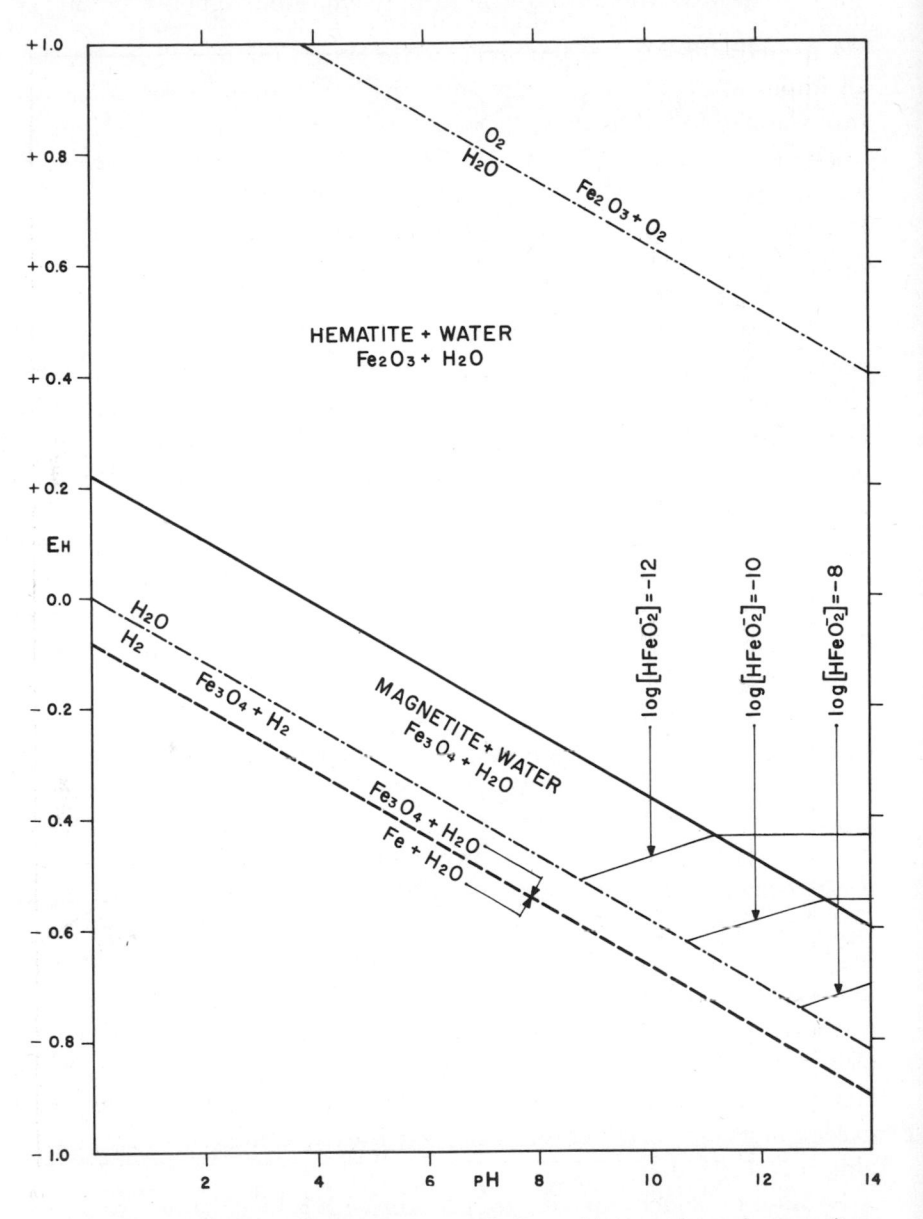

FIGURE 6.5f.   Activity of $HFeO_2^-$ ion in equilibrium with hematite and magnetite at 25°C and 1 atmosphere total pressure, within the stability field of water.

This point is circled on Figure 6.5a, and shows that the check is within the limits of plotting. The contours in the magnetite field have been drawn in this instance with a slope of 0.472 volt per pH unit. If we translate activity of ferric ion into molality of ferric ion, we see that $m_{Fe^{+++}}$ is entirely negligible above pH values of about 2, and is low at pH values of 1. In passing we note that the role of ferric ion as an important species in nature may have been overplayed, for it is a rare water that has a pH of 2 or less.

The contours are arbitrarily ended at the lower limit of stability of water, because Fe_{aq}^{+++} cannot exist at equilibrium below that point. In some later diagrams the contours will be continued into the metastable region to show the pattern of behavior expected if water persists beyond its stable limits.

Other Ionic Species. For the rest of the ionic species, the reactions necessary to express their relations to hematite and magnetite, and the corresponding Eh-pH equations, as well as those already developed for Fe^{+++} are given in Table 6.2. The mechanics of calculation are parallel to those for ferric ion. Diagrams illustrating the distribution of each ion in the fields of the two solids constitute Figure 6.5a–f.

Composite Diagram. Figure 6.6 is a composite diagram drawn according to conventions set up by Pourbaix. The limit of the stability field of a given solid is arbitrarily drawn where the sum of the activities of the ions in equilibrium with the solid exceeds some chosen value. For geologic purposes, a value of 10^{-6} is chosen, on the premise that if the sum of the activities of known dissolved species in equilibrium with a solid is less than 10^{-6} that solid will behave as an immobile constituent in its environment. This rule, developed largely from experience, seems to correlate well with the observed behavior of minerals. A contour representing $\sum$ activity ions $= 10^{-4}$ is also drawn to show the slope of the "solubility" as a function of pH and Eh. Boundaries are drawn between the fields of ions. A given field is labeled with the ion that is preponderant within it, and a boundary is placed where the ion becomes equal to an adjacent preponderant ion. Reference to Figure 6.5a–f shows that the distribution of ions is such that the fields labeled Fe_{aq}^{++} and Fe_{aq}^{+++} on Figure 6.6 in fact are overwhelmingly populated by ferrous and ferric ions, and except in local areas the hidden contribution from the other ions is almost negligible.

Because ionic activities in equilibrium with solids change so rapidly with change in Eh and pH, it is relatively rare that any region on an

TABLE 6.2. Reactions and Equations Relating Ionic Activities to Magnetite and Hematite

Reaction		Equation	
A. Fe^{+++}_{aq}			
$Fe_2O_{3c} + 6H^+_{aq} = 2Fe^{+++}_{aq} + 3H_2O_l$	(6.20)	$\log [Fe^{+++}] = -0.72 - 3pH$	(6.21)
$Fe_3O_{4c} + 8H^+_{aq} = 3Fe^{+++}_{aq} + 4H_2O_l + e$	(6.22)	$Eh = 0.337 + 0.177 \log [Fe^{+++}] + 0.472pH$	(6.23)
B. $Fe(OH)^{++}_{aq}$			
$2Fe(OH)^{++}_{aq} + H_2O_l = Fe_2O_{3c} + 4H^+_{aq}$	(6.24)	$\log [FeOH^{++}] = -3.151 - 2pH$	(6.25)
$Fe_3O_{4c} + 5H^+_{aq} = 3Fe(OH)^{++}_{aq} + H_2O_l + e$	(6.26)	$Eh = 0.780 + 0.177 \log [FeOH^{++}] + 0.295pH$	(6.27)
C. $Fe(OH)^+_{2\,aq}$			
$Fe_2O_{3c} + H_2O_l + 2H^+ = 2Fe(OH)^+_{2\,aq}$	(6.28)	$\log [Fe(OH)^+_2] = -7.84 - pH$	(6.29)
$Fe_3O_{4c} + 2H_2O_l + 2H^+ = 3Fe(OH)^+_{2\,aq} + e$	(6.30)	$Eh = 1.61 + 0.177 \log [Fe(OH)^+_2] + 0.118pH$	(6.31)
D. Fe^{++}_{aq}			
$2Fe^{++}_{aq} + 3H_2O_l = Fe_2O_{3c} + 6H^+_{aq} + 2e$	(6.32)	$Eh = 0.728 - 0.059 \log [Fe^{++}] - 0.177pH$	(6.33)
$3Fe^{++}_{aq} + 4H_2O_l = Fe_3O_{4c} + 8H^+_{aq} + 2e$	(6.34)	$Eh = 0.980 - 0.0885 \log [Fe^{++}] - 0.236pH$	(6.35)
E. $Fe(OH)^+_{aq}$			
$2Fe(OH)^+_{aq} + H_2O_l = Fe_2O_{3c} + 4H^+_{aq} + 2e$	(6.36)	$Eh = 0.217 - 0.059 \log [Fe(OH)^+] - 0.118pH$	(6.37)
$3Fe(OH)^+_{aq} + H_2O_l = Fe_3O_{4c} + 5H^+_{aq} + 2e$	(6.38)	$Eh = 0.214 - 0.0885 \log [Fe(OH)^+] - 0.148pH$	(6.39)
F. $HFeO^-_{2\,aq}$			
$2HFeO^-_{2\,aq} = Fe_2O_{3c} + H_2O_l + 2e$	(6.40)	$Eh = -1.139 - 0.059 \log [HFeO^-_2]$	(6.41)
$3HFeO^-_{2\,aq} + H^+_{aq} = Fe_3O_{4c} + 2H_2O_l + 2e$	(6.42)	$Eh = -1.819 - 0.0885 \log [HFeO^-_2] + 0.0295pH$	(6.43)

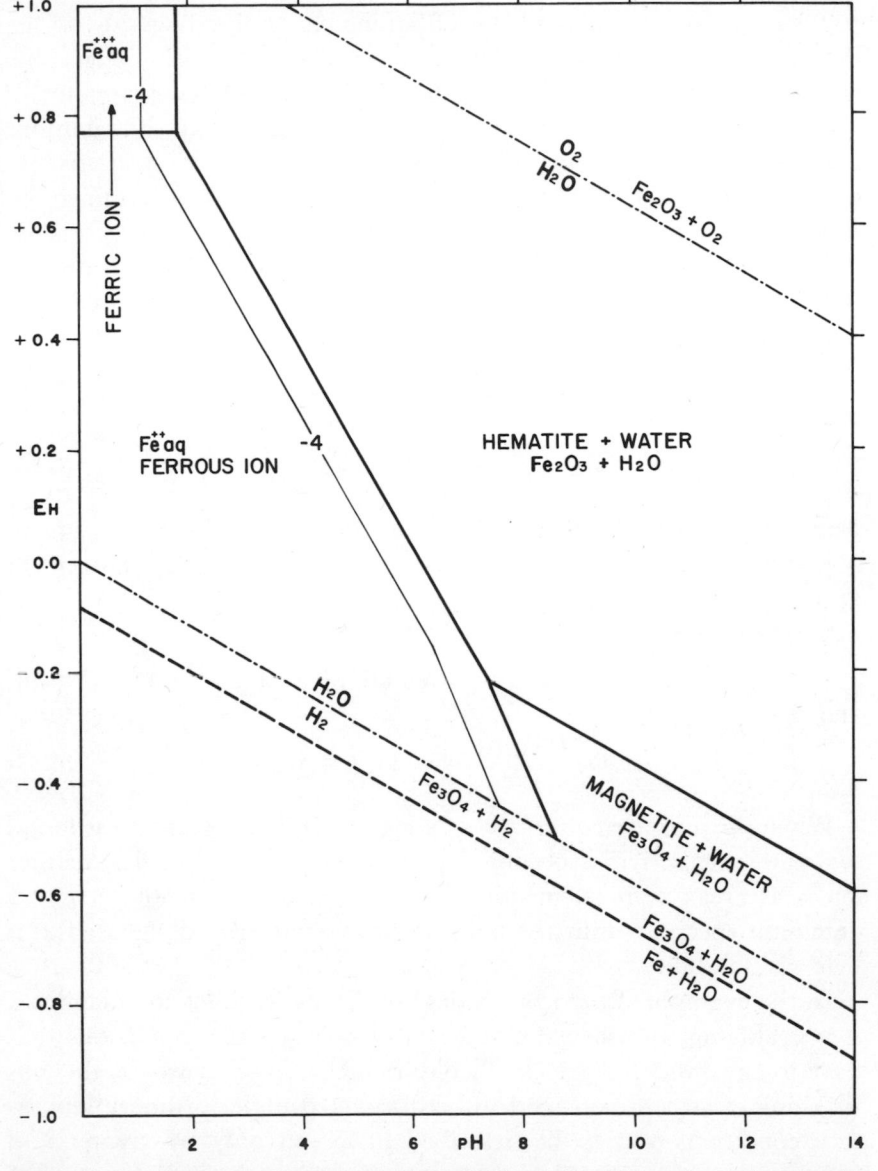

FIGURE 6.6. Composite diagram showing stability fields of hematite and magnetite in water. Fields of ions are designated where total activity of dissolved species $> 10^{-6}$. Fields of ions are labeled with dominant species. Contour of log [dissolved species] $= -4$ included to show slope of activity change. Plot at 25°C and 1 atmosphere total pressure.

Eh-pH diagram cannot be ascribed satisfactorily to a single ion that makes up 99 percent or more of the total ionic activity.

There are several methods for obtaining composite diagrams. One that appeals to geologists, because of their experience with topographic maps, is to make tracings of the Eh-pH diagrams showing contours of individual ions, and then to add the individual ion contributions graphically by overlaying the tracings. A boundary, such as that between Fe_{aq}^{++} and Fe_{aq}^{+++} on Figure 6.6, is quickly determined by connecting points of intersection of equal contours.

The composite diagram also can be assembled analytically by writing reactions between the ions, and solving for the Eh-pH conditions at which they are equal. For example, if we write:

$$Fe_{aq}^{++} = Fe_{aq}^{+++} + e \tag{6.44}$$

then

$$Eh = E° + 0.059 \log \frac{[Fe^{+++}]}{[Fe^{++}]} \tag{6.45}$$

And under the condition that $Fe_{aq}^{++} = Fe_{aq}^{+++}$, $Eh = E°$. Consequently the boundary between the ions is at $E°$ for the half-cell, or at 0.771 volt.

Similarly, for the pair $Fe_{aq}^{++} - Fe(OH)_{aq}^{+}$:

$$Fe_{aq}^{++} + H_2O_1 = Fe(OH)_{aq}^{+} + H_{aq}^{+} \tag{6.46}$$

and

$$\log \frac{[Fe(OH)^{+}]}{[Fe^{++}]} = \log k + pH \tag{6.47}$$

When the ions are equal $pH = -\log k$. In this instance it is found that the ionic activities become equal at such a high pH that neither ion is as great as 10^{-6}, in other words $Fe(OH)^{+}$ does not become a dominant species within the field we have arbitrarily designated as a field of "solubility."

In the example of the iron oxides, and in many following diagrams, it is gratifying to discover that in dilute solution the major ions that have to be considered are chiefly old friends. In other words, the ions we think of as common tend to be discovered under ordinary laboratory conditions and to be described first, and only by greater and greater refinement, or by extension of chemical work to unusual conditions, are fields entered in which they are displaced by other species.

Among the most striking aspects of the composite diagram for iron is the highly restricted field of predominance of ferric ion. Only under

strongly acid and oxidizing conditions does the activity of the ion exceed 10^{-6}. The great stability of hematite is evidenced by the size of its field, which ranges from moderately acid oxidizing conditions to strongly reducing neutral and alkaline environments. "Solubility" in this system is achieved almost exclusively through the contribution of the ferrous ion, which strikes deepest into the fields of the solids in reducing environments. Neither hematite nor magnetite shows appreciable amphoteric behavior in the pH range 0–14; the activity of $HFeO_2^-$ does not exceed 10^{-6}, so that it does not even appear on the final diagram.

EFFECT OF CO_2 ON IRON-WATER-OXYGEN RELATIONS

In natural environments, iron occurs as magnetite, hematite, and as siderite, the carbonate, as well as in the form of iron sulfides and silicates. Thus the next step is to consider the influence of CO_2 on the stability relations of magnetite and hematite. From the earlier development of partial pressure diagrams, the most obvious attack is to try to develop relations among Eh, pH, and P_{CO_2}. Inasmuch as Eh and pH can be considered as a two-variable representation of P_{O_2}, it should be possible to consider siderite in relation to magnetite and hematite by using a 3-dimensional representation with Eh, pH, and P_{CO_2} as the axes.

Stability as a Function of P_{CO_2}. Such a treatment requires writing reactions between magnetite and siderite, and between hematite and siderite. Considering hematite first:

$$2FeCO_{3\,c} + H_2O_l = Fe_2O_{3\,c} + 2CO_{2\,g} + 2H_{aq}^+ + 2e \qquad (6.48)$$

The corresponding Eh equation is:

$$Eh = E° + 0.059 \log P_{CO_2} - 0.059pH \qquad (6.49)$$

$$Eh = 0.286 + 0.059 \log P_{CO_2} - 0.059pH$$

For the reaction between siderite and magnetite:

$$3FeCO_{3\,c} + H_2O_l = Fe_3O_{4\,c} + 3CO_{2\,g} + 2H^+ + 2e \qquad (6.50)$$

and

$$Eh = 0.319 + 0.0885 \log P_{CO_2} - 0.059pH \qquad (6.51)$$

Then, as shown in Figure 6.7, it is possible to plot magnetite-hematite relations as previously developed, and to show them on the front face

of the figure. Then, plotting P_{CO_2} as a third dimension, the magnetite-hematite boundaries, which are independent of P_{CO_2}, can be extended as planes parallel to the P_{CO_2} axis. Equations (6.49) and (6.51), on the other hand, are functions of all three variables, so they plot as sloping planes in 3 dimensions, and serve to show how the fields of magnetite and hematite are encroached upon by siderite as P_{CO_2} increases. The double arrow at a P_{CO_2} of $10^{-3.5}$ atmosphere indicates the partial pressure of CO_2 in the earth's atmosphere, and it is of

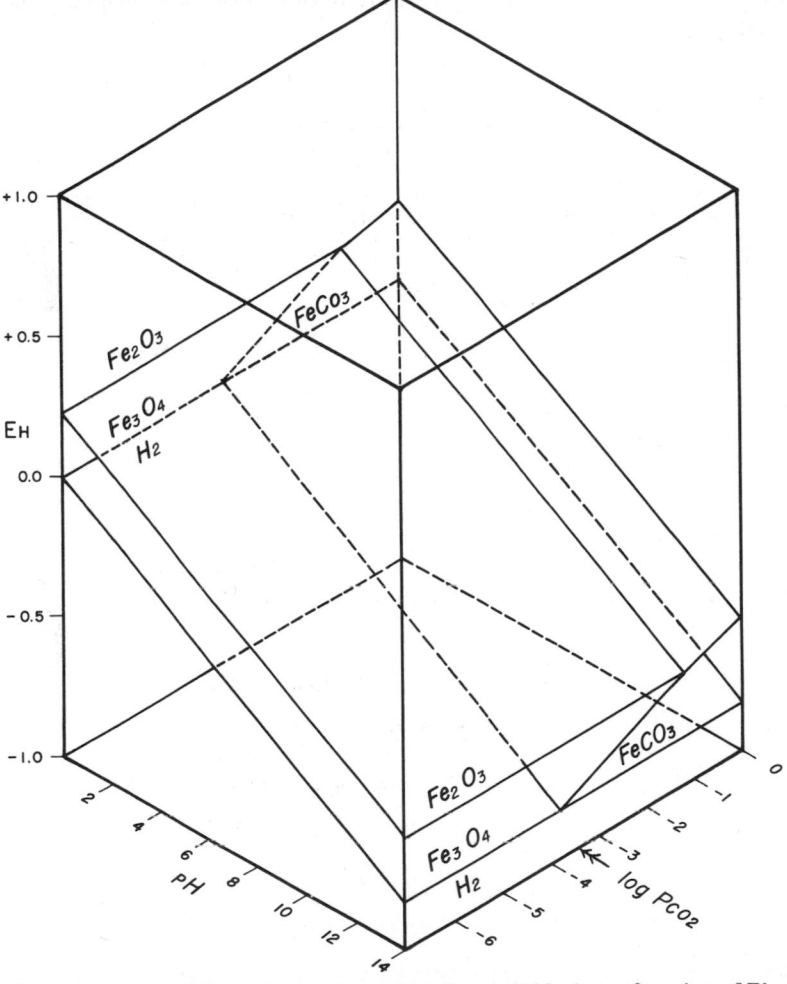

FIGURE 6.7. Stability of hematite-magnetite and siderite as function of Eh, pH, and P_{CO_2} at 25 °C and 1 atmosphere total pressure. Relations shown are terminated at lower stability limit of water. Double arrow on log P_{CO_2} axis shows partial pressure of CO_2 in present earth atmosphere.

interest that under such conditions siderite has only a small field of stability. On the other hand, magnetite is entirely displaced by siderite when P_{CO_2} reaches a value of about $10^{-1.4}$ atmosphere.

The 3-dimensional diagram is useful for showing gross relations in the system, but for many purposes iso-P_{CO_2} sections are more convenient. Such sections can be used to show the equilibrium activities of dissolved ions more easily than can the 3-dimensional diagrams.

Figure 6.8a is a section of Figure 6.7 at $P_{CO_2} = 10^{-2.0}$ atmosphere. The boundary between siderite and magnetite is plotted directly from equation (6.51), rather than attempting to transfer it graphically from Figure 6.7. In Figure 6.8b the activity of dissolved ionic species is shown for the new system including siderite. Because the field of stability of siderite relative to hematite and magnetite has already been defined by equations (6.49) and (6.51), it is necessary to alter the hematite-magnetite-ion activity diagram (Figure 6.6) only within the field of this new stable solid. At first glance it might appear necessary to calculate equilibrium between siderite and Fe^{+++}, $Fe(OH)^{++}$, $Fe(OH)_2^+$, $HFeO_2^-$, $Fe(OH)^+$ and Fe^{++}, but inasmuch as only Fe^{++} was important ($> 10^{-6}$) in the field of magnetite now occupied by siderite, and inasmuch as siderite is more stable than magnetite in the region it has displaced magnetite, the activities of all ions in equilibrium with siderite will be less than they were for magnetite. Consequently only the activity of Fe^{++} need be considered.

Only one reaction need be written:

$$FeCO_{3c} + 2H^+ = Fe^{++}_{aq} + CO_{2g} + H_2O_l \qquad (6.52)$$

The equation is:

$$\log[Fe^{++}] = 7.47 - \log P_{CO_2} - 2pH \qquad (6.53)$$

P_{CO_2} has been stipulated as fixed at $10^{-2.0}$, so that $\log[Fe^{++}]$ is a function only of pH, and must be plotted as contours parallel to the Eh axis. A check of the validity of the free energy values used, as well as of the arithmetic and plotting, is obtained if the Fe^{++} contours in the field of $FeCO_3$ join appropriately those carried forward from the magnetite-hematite diagram.

At a $P_{CO_2} = 10^{-3.5}$, that of the earth's atmosphere, the field of $FeCO_3$ is so small that it barely gets above the stability limit of water. Thus it was necessary to choose a larger value to show the behavior of the dissolved Fe^{++}.

Stability as a Function of $\Sigma\, CO_2$. Siderite is an important primary sedimentary mineral of iron ores, but the preceding discussion shows

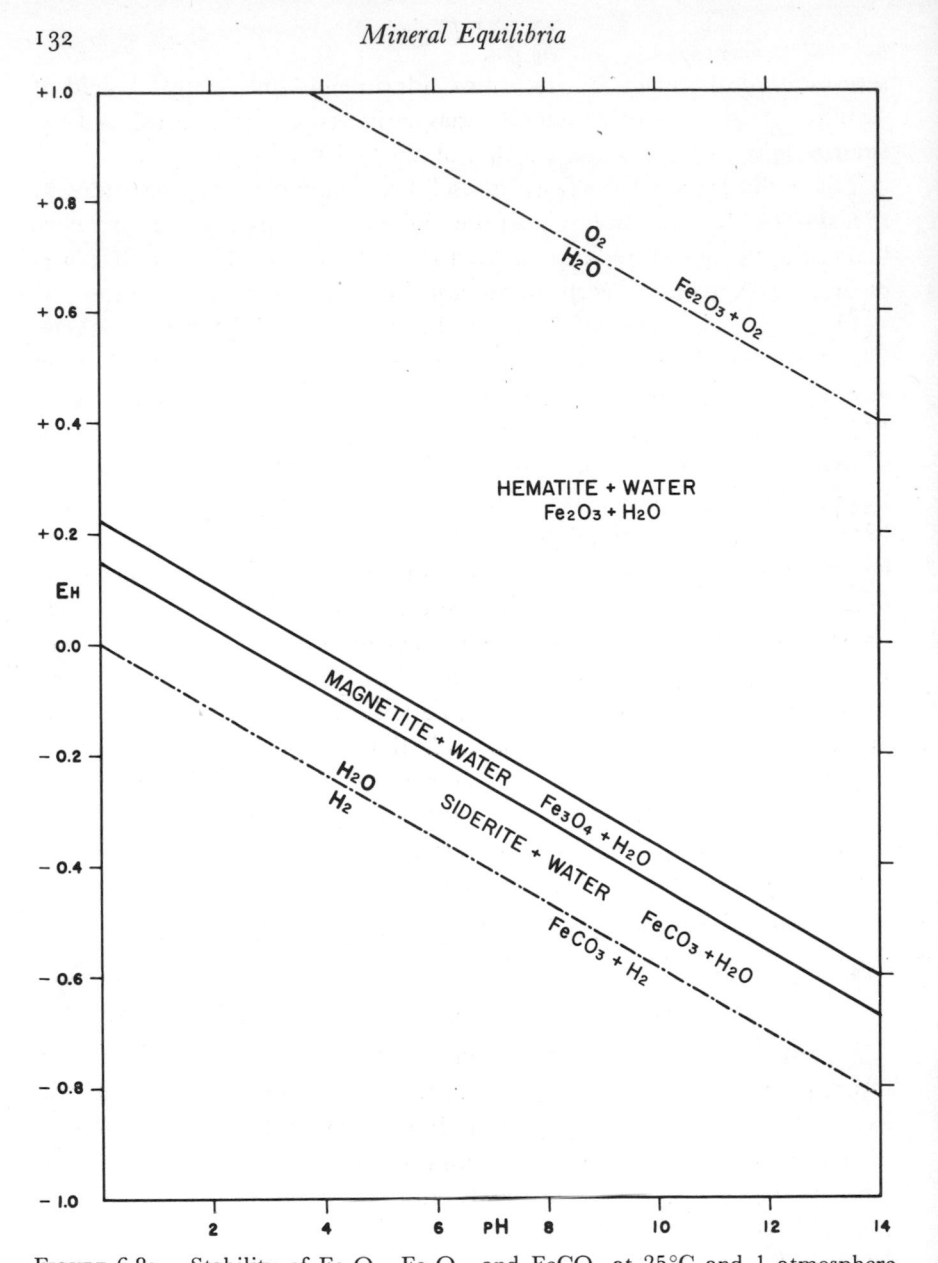

FIGURE 6.8a.   Stability of Fe_2O_3, Fe_3O_4, and $FeCO_3$ at 25°C and 1 atmosphere total pressure, with $P_{CO_2} = 10^{-2.0}$ atmosphere.   Relations shown are for stability range of water.

that it is not an equilibrium species in the presence of the atmosphere. Its occurrence is indicative of strongly reducing conditions and the presence of CO_2 in more than atmospheric amounts.   Let us now

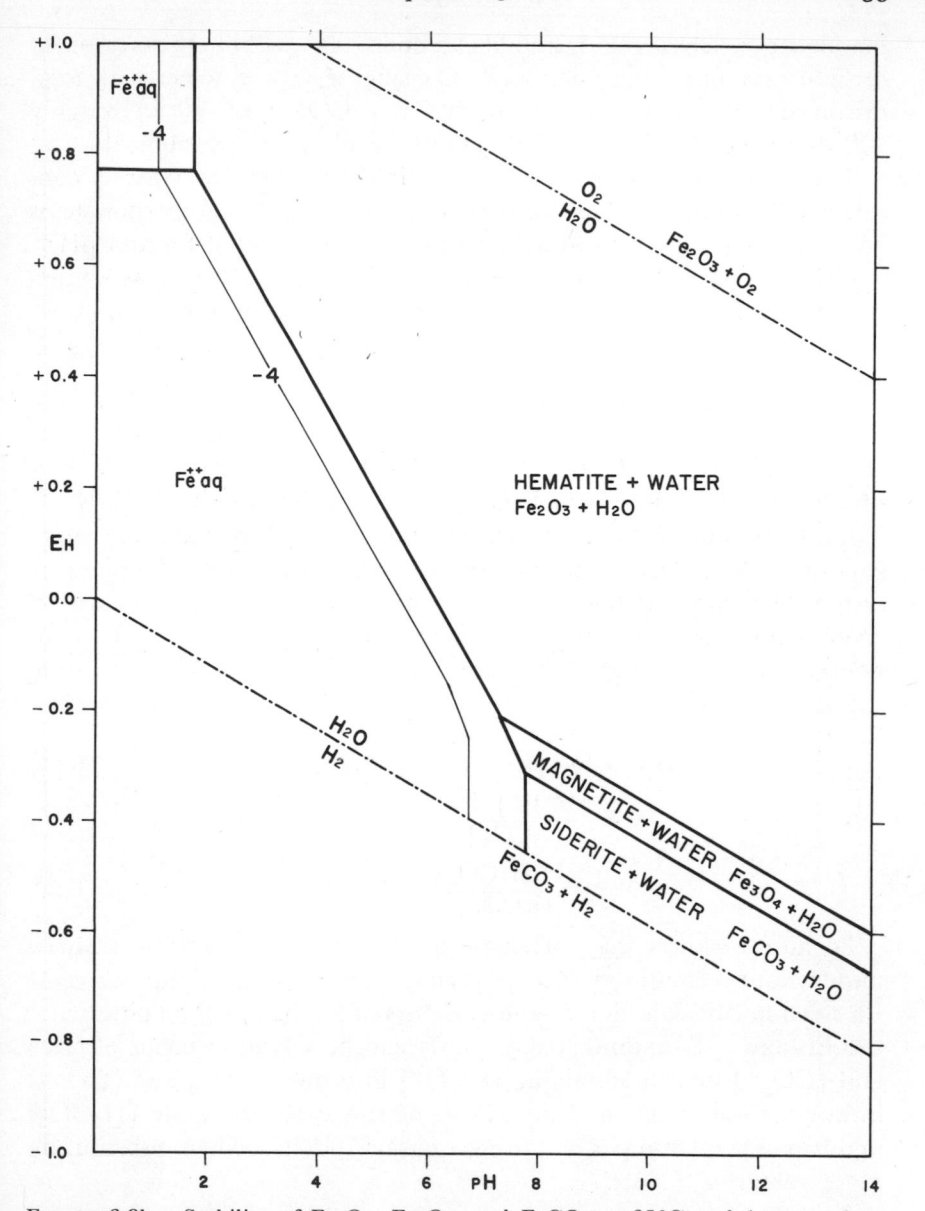

FIGURE 6.8b.   Stability of Fe_2O_3, Fe_3O_4, and $FeCO_3$ at $25°C$ and 1 atmosphere total pressure, with $P_{CO_2} = 10^{-2·0}$ atmosphere.   Contour is for Σ activity ions = 10^{-4}.   Boundary of solids is at Σ activity ions = 10^{-6}.   Relations shown only within boundaries of water stability.

consider siderite stability in terms of the total dissolved carbonate. In a given solution, free or nearly free from oxygen, how much carbonate or bicarbonate ion is necessary to stabilize siderite relative to

magnetite? Does the required amount fall within the range of ordinary ground water analyses? Consider a natural water with total dissolved carbonate (H_2CO_3 + HCO_3^- + CO_3^{--}) of 10^{-2} (roughly 600 ppm) molal. Under what conditions, if any, is siderite stable?

The problem to be solved is essentially identical to Case 3 considered in Chapter 3 on carbonate equilibria. Total carbonate is known. What happens at arbitrarily selected values of Eh and pH?

One approach is to determine the distribution of $[CO_3^{--}]$ as a function of pH, and then to draw contours of $[Fe^{++}]$ from the relation:

$$[Fe^{++}][CO_3^{--}] = k_{FeCO_3} \qquad (6.54)$$

Then, by superimposing these contours for $[Fe^{++}]$ on the diagram for $[Fe^{++}]$ in equilibrium with Fe_2O_3 and Fe_3O_4 (Figure 6.5d), the field of stability of $FeCO_3$ is delineated as that area in which $[Fe^{++}]$ is smaller in equilibrium with $FeCO_3$ than with the other two solids.

Both methods will be illustrated; the first has perhaps the more general utility, because it can be used, no matter how complex the system becomes. If the activity of a given ion in equilibrium with a given solid is less than that in equilibrium with any other solid considered, the region of the minimum is a stability field of the given solid.

For a total carbonate of 10^{-2}, we can write, without serious error (Chapter 3):

$$[H_2CO_3] + [HCO_3^-] + [CO_3^{--}] = 10^{-2} \qquad (6.55)$$

$$\frac{[H^+][CO_3^{--}]}{[HCO_3^-]} = 10^{-10.3} \qquad (6.56)$$

$$\frac{[H^+][HCO_3^-]}{[H_2CO_3]} = 10^{-6.4} \qquad (6.57)$$

Because we know that carbonate species are not reduced or oxidized under natural conditions, except perhaps under special circumstances,[1] Eh need not be considered, and contours of $[CO_3^{--}]$ will lie parallel to the Eh axis. Equations (6.55)–(6.57) can be solved in terms of $[H^+]$ and $[CO_3^{--}]$ first by obtaining $[HCO_3^-]$ in terms of $[H^+]$ and $[CO_3^{--}]$ from equation (6.56), and then by using this value to obtain $[H_2CO_3]$ in terms of $[H^+]$ and $[CO_3^{--}]$ from equation (6.57). Then, substituting these values in (6.55):

$$\frac{[H^+]^2[CO_3^{--}]}{10^{-16.7}} + \frac{[H^+][CO_3^{--}]}{10^{-10.3}} + [CO_3^{--}] = 10^{-2}$$

Simplifying:

$$[H^+]^2 + 10^{-6.4}[H^+] + 10^{-16.7} = \frac{10^{-18.7}}{[CO_3^{--}]} \qquad (6.58)$$

---

[1] The various carbonate species are in fact thermodynamically unstable with respect to carbon near the lower oxidation potential limit of water, a fact that may have considerable geologic significance, but is ignored in the present treatment.

From this equation, substitution of various arbitrary values of $[CO_3^{--}]$ allows calculation of the corresponding pH.   The result is Figure 6.9.

Then, substituting the numerical value of k into equation (6.54), and rearranging:

$$\log [Fe^{++}] = -10.67 - \log [CO_3^{--}] \tag{6.59}$$

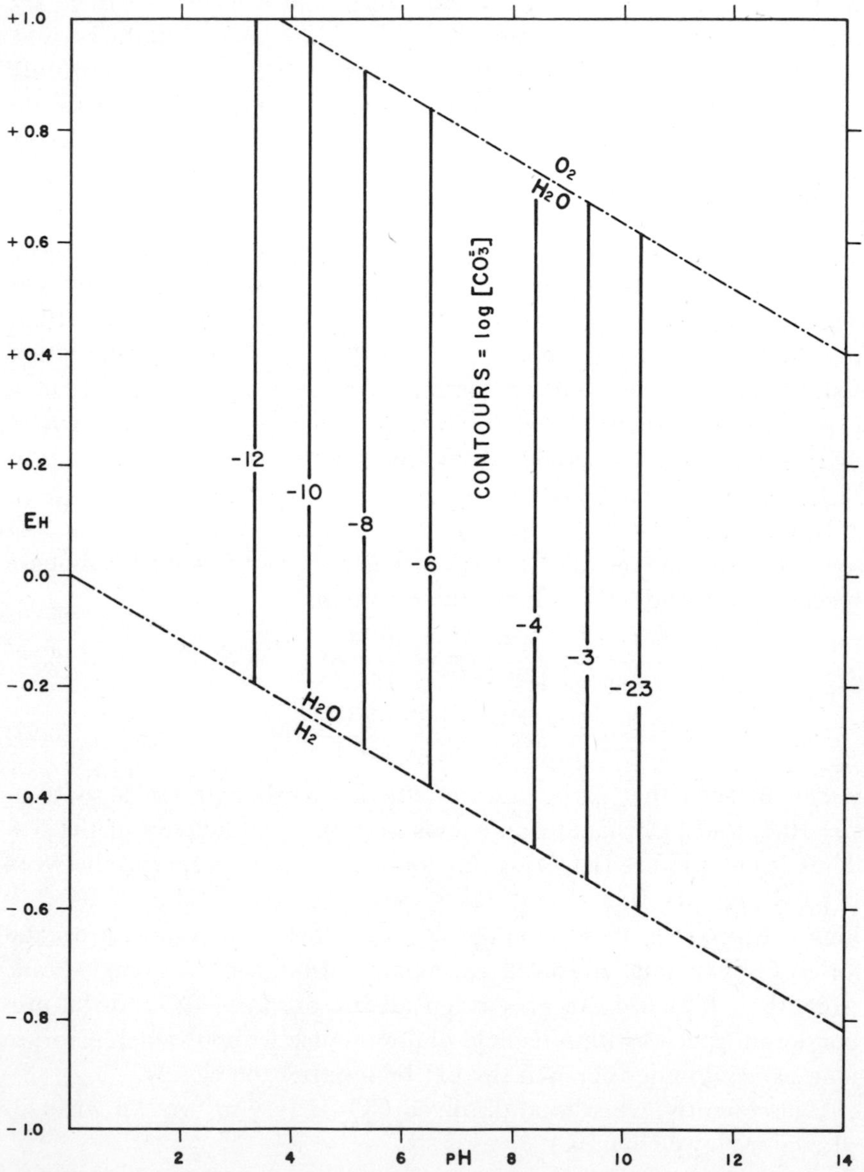

FIGURE 6.9.   Contours of $\log [CO_3^{--}]$ shown on an Eh-pH plot for the condition that $[H_2CO_3] + [HCO_3^-] + [CO_3^{--}] = 10^{-2}$ at 25°C and 1 atmosphere total pressure.

Thus for every contour of $\log [CO_3^{--}]$ a corresponding contour of $\log [Fe^{++}]$ can be obtained. In Figure 6.10 these contours for $[Fe^{++}]$ in equilibrium with $FeCO_3$ are superimposed on the contours of $[Fe^{++}]$ in equilibrium with Fe_2O_3 and Fe_3O_4 (Figure 6.5d), and the boundary between $FeCO_3$ and the oxides is indicated. Figure 6.11 shows a composite diagram for the oxides and siderite, obtained by overlaying Figure 6.10 on Figure 6.6. Note the similarities and differences of Figure 6.8b, which is at constant P_{CO_2}, and Figure 6.11, with fixed total dissolved carbonate. When total dissolved carbonate is fixed, $[CO_3^{--}]$ rises to a maximum at a pH of about 10.5, and remains constant, whereas at a constant P_{CO_2}, $[CO_3^{--}]$ rises continuously with increasing pH. This is reflected in a restricted field of siderite at high pH at constant total carbonate, for the oxides become continuously more stable as pH is increased (they are precipitated by OH^-), whereas the stability of siderite remains constant above a pH of about 10.5. In other words fluctuations of pH, without a change in oxidation conditions, can cause an alternation of siderite and magnetite in a sediment in a system closed to CO_2, but in the open system, where P_{CO_2} is constant, the change from siderite to magnetite cannot take place without a change in P_{O_2}.

In the second method of obtaining the siderite stability field, the first step is to delineate the pH-Eh areas in which a given dissolved carbonate species is preponderant. From the equations

$$\frac{[CO_3^{--}]}{[HCO_3^-]} = \frac{10^{-10.3}}{[H^+]} \qquad (6.56)$$

$$\frac{[HCO_3^-]}{[H_2CO_3]} = \frac{10^{-6.4}}{[H^+]} \qquad (6.57)$$

it can be seen that carbonate ion equals bicarbonate ion activity at pH 10.3, and bicarbonate ion equals carbonic acid activity at pH 6.4. Thus below pH 6.4 H_2CO_3 is the dominant dissolved species, between pH 6.4 and pH 10.3 HCO_3^- takes over, and above pH 10.3 CO_3^{--} is king. Moreover, these boundaries, being based on ratios, are valid for any given total dissolved carbonate. In the dilute range (ionic strength ≤ 0.2), we can also assign all the dissolved CO_2 to the preponderant species within its field of dominance without much error, so long as we do not approach the pH boundaries too closely.

Consequently, when total dissolved CO_2 is 10^{-2} m, we can write for pH values lower than 6.4:

$$3FeCO_{3c} + 4H_2O_1 = Fe_3O_{4c} + 3H_2CO_{3\,aq} + 2H_{aq}^+ + 2e \qquad (6.60)$$

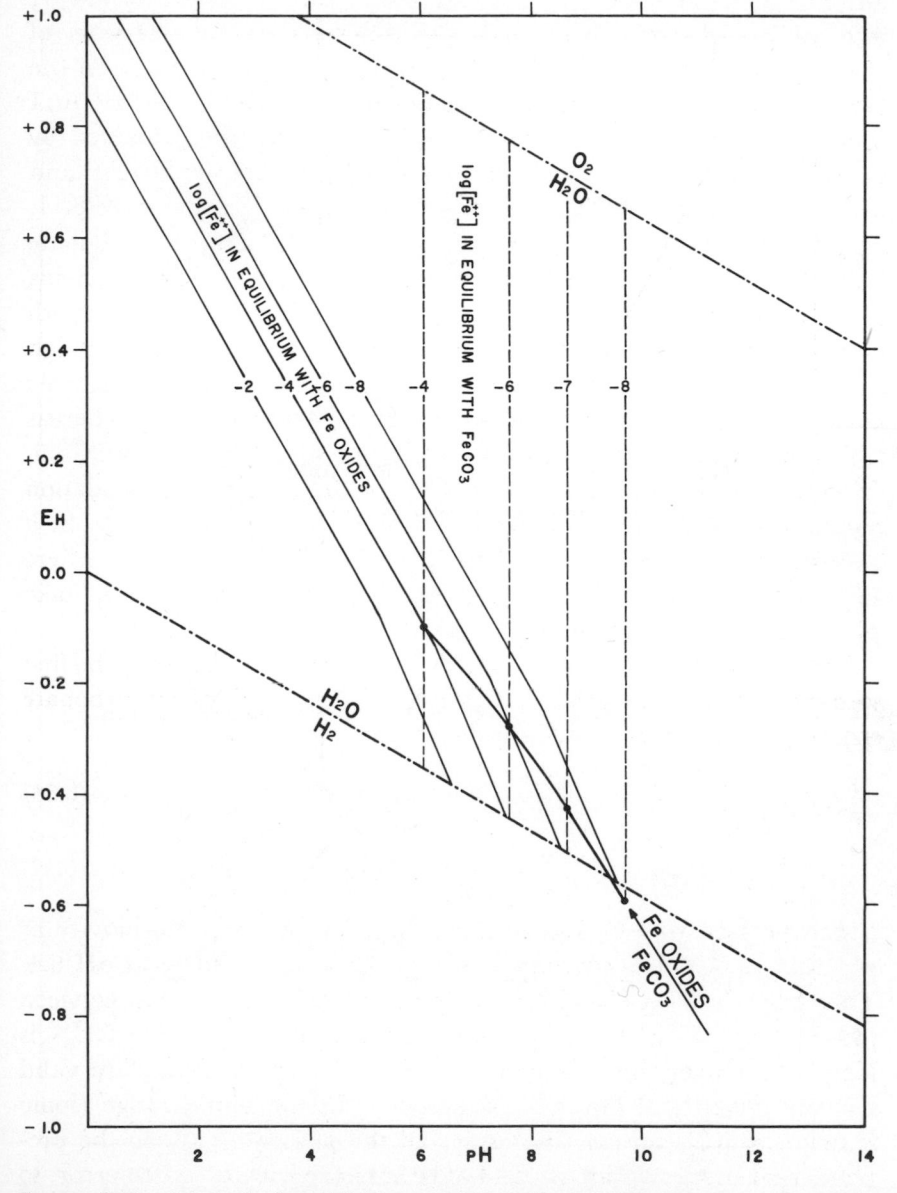

FIGURE 6.10. Method of establishing stability field of $FeCO_3$ relative to Fe oxides by delineating area in which $[Fe^{++}]$ is a minimum in equilibrium with $FeCO_3$. Solution contains $10^{-2}\,m\ H_2CO_3 + HCO_3^- + CO_3^{--}$. Dashed lines are $\log[Fe^{++}]$ in equilibrium with $FeCO_3$; solid lines in equilibrium with Fe oxides. Black dots are points of equal $[Fe^{++}]$. System at 25°C and 1 atmosphere total pressure.

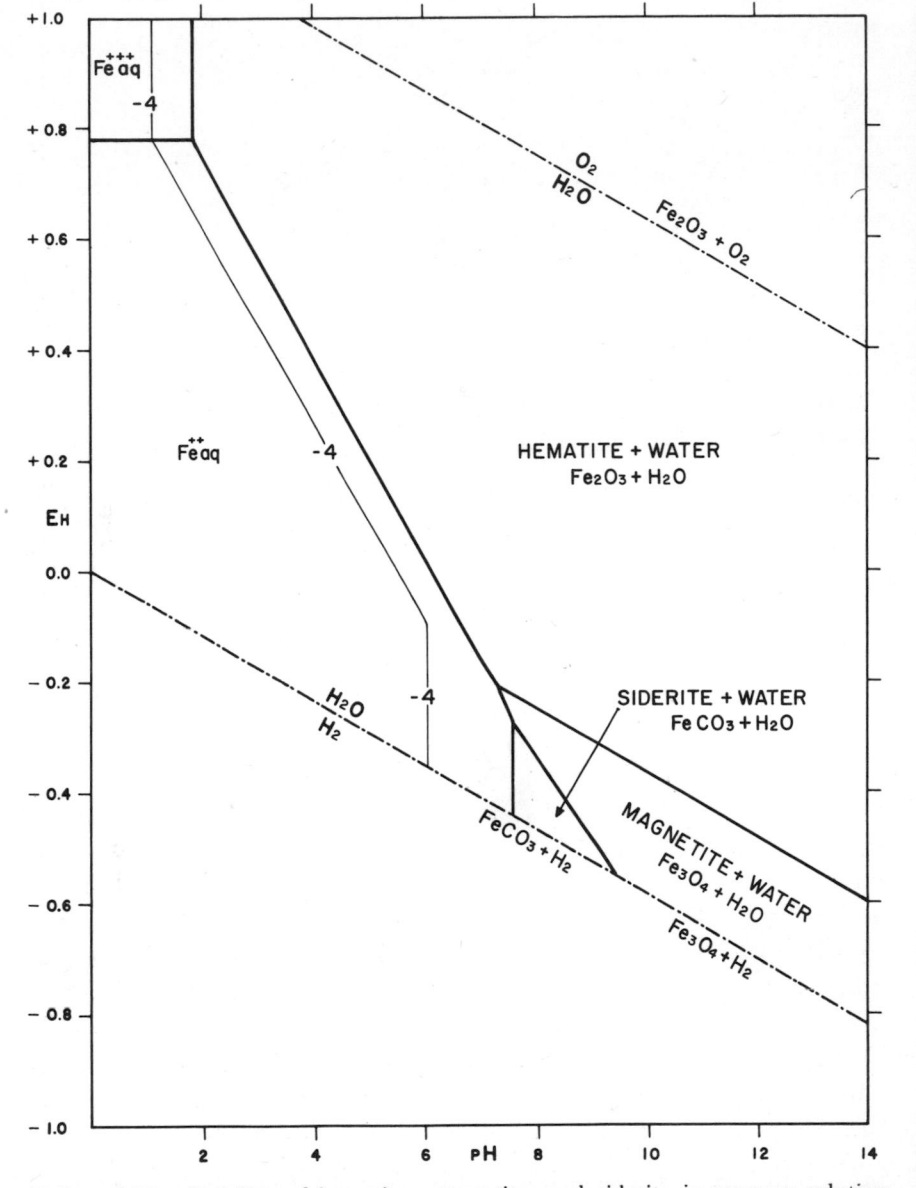

FIGURE 6.11. Stability of hematite, magnetite, and siderite in aqueous solution containing total dissolved carbonate species of 10^{-2} m, at 25°C and 1 atmosphere total pressure. Contour is for log [dissolved iron] = −4. Boundary between solids and ions at log [dissolved iron] = −6.

and we can express the result entirely in terms of Eh and pH, because the activity of $H_2CO_{3\,aq}$ is fixed at 10^{-2}.

In the field of HCO_3^-, the corresponding reaction is:

$$3FeCO_{3\,c} + 4H_2O_l = Fe_3O_{4\,c} + 3HCO_{3\,aq}^- + 5H_{aq}^+ + 2e \qquad (6.61)$$

In the CO_3^{--} field, the reaction is:

$$3FeCO_{3\,c} + 4H_2O_l = Fe_3O_{4\,c} + 3CO_{3\,aq}^{--} + 8H^+ + 2e \qquad (6.62)$$

The Eh-pH equations are:

$$Eh = 0.445 - 0.059pH + 0.0885 \log [H_2CO_3] \qquad (6.63)$$

$$Eh = 1.010 - 0.148pH + 0.0885 \log [HCO_3^-] \qquad (6.64)$$

$$Eh = 1.920 - 0.236pH + 0.0885 \log [CO_3^{--}] \qquad (6.65)$$

Also, the relations between $FeCO_3$ and Fe_2O_3 must be considered:

$$2FeCO_{3\,c} + 3H_2O_l = Fe_2O_{3\,c} + 2H_2CO_{3\,aq} + 2H_{aq}^+ + 2e \qquad (6.66)$$

$$2FeCO_{3\,c} + 3H_3O_l = Fe_2O_{3\,c} + 2HCO_{3\,aq}^- + 4H_{aq}^+ + 2e \qquad (6.67)$$

$$2FeCO_{3\,c} + 3H_2O_l = Fe_2O_{3\,c} + 2CO_{3\,aq}^{--} + 6H_{aq}^+ + 2e \qquad (6.68)$$

And the Eh-pH equations are:

$$Eh = 0.370 - 0.059pH + 0.059 \log [H_2CO_3] \qquad (6.69)$$

$$Eh = 0.747 - 0.118pH + 0.059 \log [HCO_3^-] \qquad (6.70)$$

$$Eh = 1.359 - 0.177pH + 0.059 \log [CO_3^{--}] \qquad (6.71)$$

All six Eh-pH equations, (6.63)—(6.65) and (6.69)—(6.71), are plotted in Figure 6.12 and labeled, as well as the boundaries between the carbonate species (6.56) and (6.57). Note that the reactions are plotted only in the field of the carbonate ion concerned, i.e., the reaction from $FeCO_3$ to Fe_2O_3 is shown only in the range of pH from 0 to 6.4, in which H_2CO_3 constitutes essentially all the dissolved carbonate. The stable and metastable reactions are determined by working from the bottom of the diagram upwards; in the field of H_2CO_3, Fe_3O_4 cannot go to Fe_2O_3, because $FeCO_3$ is not yet oxidized to Fe_3O_4; and $FeCO_3$ oxidizes to Fe_2O_3 before it oxidizes to Fe_3O_4. Thus in this region the stable reaction is from $FeCO_3$ directly to Fe_2O_3.

As shown, the lines change slope abruptly at pH 6.4 and 10.3, in fact they must bend, inasmuch as the carbonate species do not persist as 10^{-2} all the way to the pH boundaries. In Figure 6.13 the stable boundaries are traced from Figure 6.12 to show the relations of $FeCO_3$, Fe_2O_3, and Fe_3O_4 at a total dissolved carbonate of 10^{-2}.

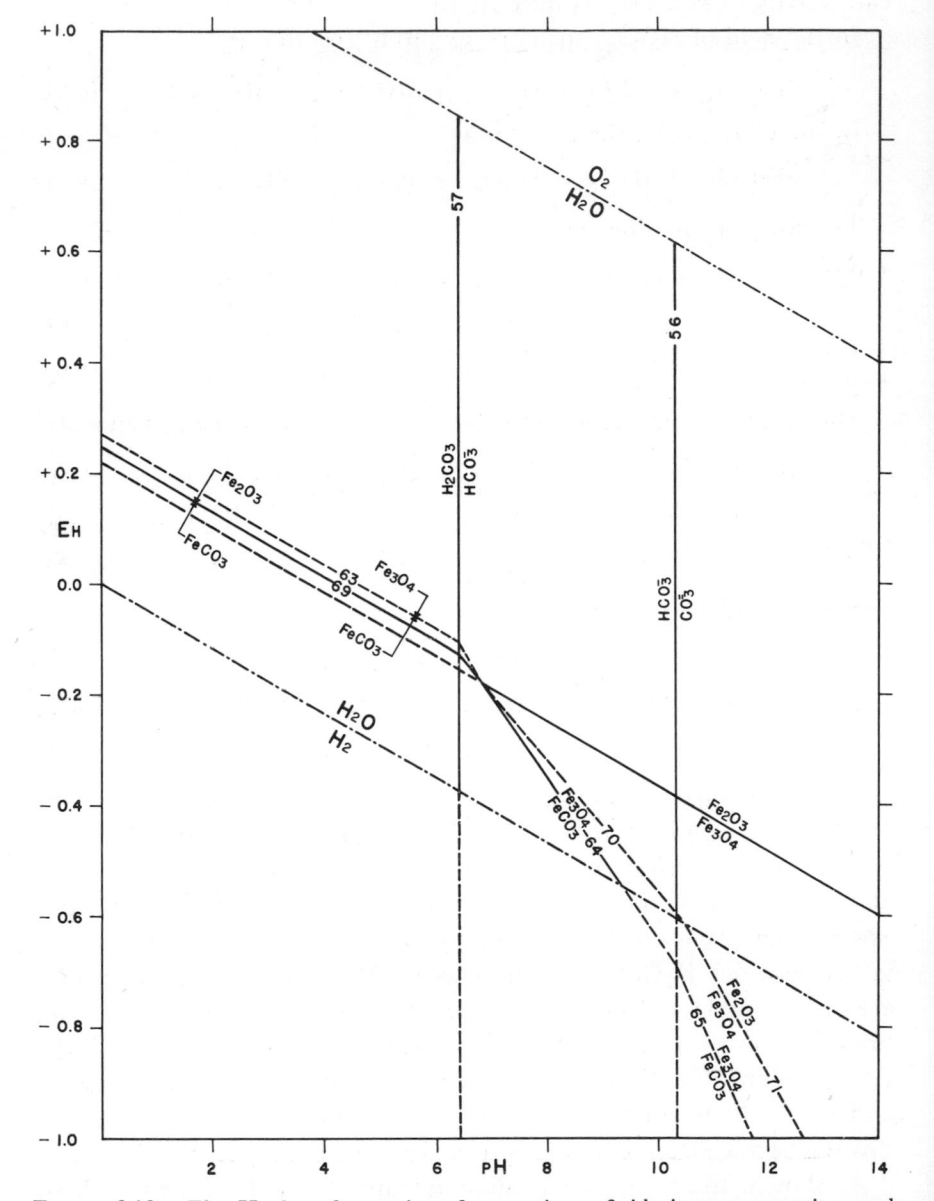

FIGURE 6.12.   Eh-pH plot of equations for reactions of siderite to magnetite, and siderite to hematite at a total dissolved carbonate of 10^{-2}.   Solid lines are stable boundaries, short dashed lines metastable boundaries.   Numbers refer to equations in text.   Conditions are 25°C and 1 atmosphere total pressure.

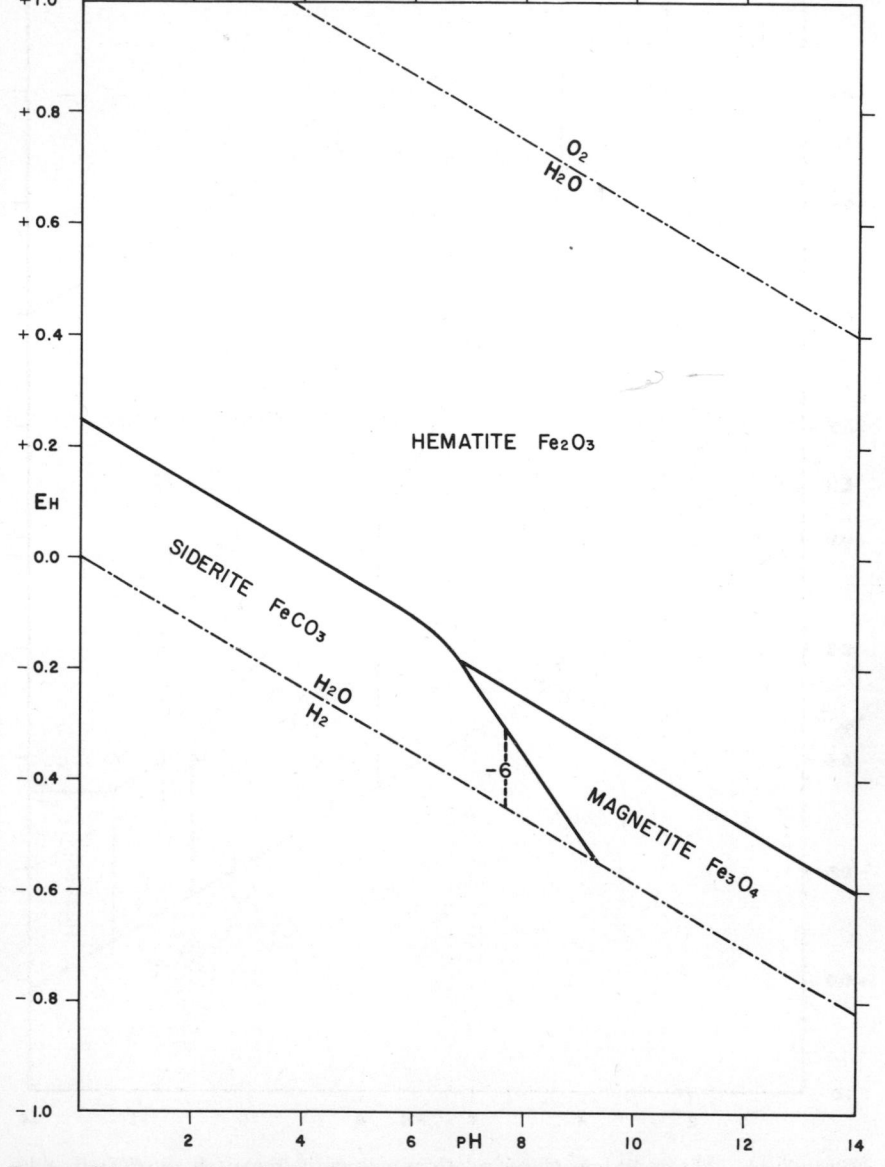

FIGURE 6.13. Stability fields of hematite, magnetite, and siderite in water at 25°C, 1 atmosphere total pressure, and total dissolved carbonate of 10^{-2}. Dotted line is for log $[Fe^{++}] = -6$.

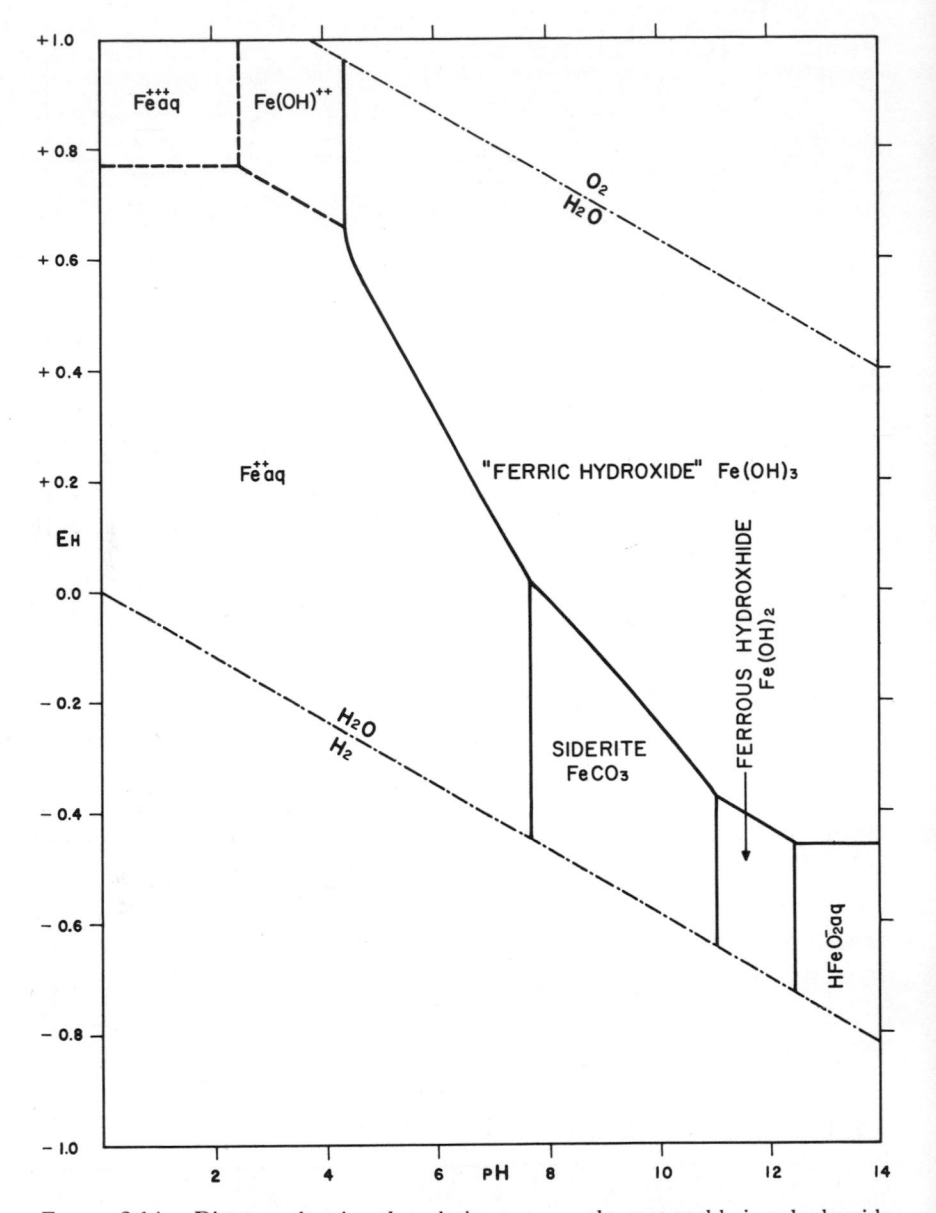

FIGURE 6.14. Diagram showing the relations among the metastable iron hydroxides and siderite at 25°C and 1 atmosphere total pressure. Boundary between solids and ions at total activity of dissolved species = 10^{-6}. Total dissolved carbonate species = 10^{-2}. Dashed lines are boundaries between fields dominated by the labeled ion.

Once the fields of the solids are delineated in this fashion, the contour for $[Fe^{++}] = 10^{-6}$ can be found from the relation:

$$FeCO_{3c} + H^+_{aq} = Fe^{++}_{aq} + HCO^-_{3aq} \qquad (6.72)$$

In the field of dominance of HCO_3^- (pH 6.4–10.3), $[HCO_3^-] = 10^{-2}$, and the equilibrium relations can be expressed:

$$\frac{[Fe^{++}][HCO_3^-]}{[H^+]} = k$$

or

$$\log [Fe^{++}] - 2 + pH = \log k \qquad (6.73)$$

If k is obtained from standard free energy values, the equation becomes:

$$\log [Fe^{++}] = -0.33 - pH + 2 \qquad (6.74)$$

Substituting -6 for $\log [Fe^{++}]$, and solving for pH, we obtain a value of 7.67, which agrees well with that obtained graphically (Figure 6.11). This contour of $[Fe^{++}]$ is shown as a dotted line on Figure 6.13. The field of $FeCO_3$ delineated by this contour and the boundaries between $FeCO_3$ and Fe_3O_4, and H_2-H_2O is identical to that obtained by the method of contouring used before (Figure 6.10).

If the total dissolved carbonate is increased, the field of siderite expands; if it is decreased, it contracts. If total dissolved carbonate drops below about 10^{-3}, the field of siderite disappears, if defined as the area in which the activity of dissolved iron-containing species is less than 10^{-6}.

On the other hand, at the same total dissolved carbonate considered here (10^{-2}), the field of siderite relative to the freshly precipitated iron hydroxides is much larger, as shown in Figure 6.14. This figure can be considered the "experimental" representation, inasmuch as precipitation of iron in the laboratory follows the relations shown here fairly well. Because of the lesser stability of the iron hydroxides, note the appearance of fields of $Fe(OH)^{++}$ and $HFeO_2^-$.

EFFECT OF SULFUR ON IRON-WATER-OXYGEN RELATIONS

Adding CO_2 to the iron-water-oxygen system permitted assessment of the stability of siderite relative to the oxides; addition of sulfur should give information on pyrite and pyrrhotite. As in the development of CO_2 relations, the most obvious type of diagram to construct

is a 3-variable plot of Eh, pH, and P_{S_2}. Again we can start with the relations of magnetite and hematite in water and write reactions from these species to pyrrhotite and pyrite with addition of sulfur:

$$3FeS_c + 4H_2O_l = Fe_3O_{4c} + 3/2S_{2g} + 8H_{aq}^+ + 8e \qquad (6.75)$$

$$2FeS_c + 3H_2O_l = Fe_2O_{3c} + S_{2g} + 6H_{aq}^+ + 6e \qquad (6.76)$$

$$3FeS_{2c} + 4H_2O_l = Fe_3O_{4c} + 3S_{2g} + 8H_{aq}^+ + 8e \qquad (6.77)$$

$$2FeS_{2c} + 3H_2O_l = Fe_2O_{3c} + 2S_{2g} + 6H_{aq}^+ + 6e \qquad (6.78)$$

The corresponding Eh-pH-P_{S_2} equations are:

$$Eh = 0.444 + 0.011 \log P_{S_2} - 0.059pH \qquad (6.79)$$

$$Eh = 0.419 + 0.0098 \log P_{S_2} - 0.059pH \qquad (6.80)$$

$$Eh = 0.811 + 0.0221 \log P_{S_2} - 0.059pH \qquad (6.81)$$

$$Eh = 0.746 + 0.0197 \log P_{S_2} - 0.059pH \qquad (6.82)$$

We must also consider the boundary between pyrrhotite and pyrite:

$$2FeS_c + S_{2g} = 2FeS_{2c} \qquad (6.83)$$

This boundary is at a fixed P_{S_2} and is independent of Eh and pH. The value of P_{S_2} is 10^{-33} atmosphere.

The easiest method of plotting is to make first an Eh-log P_{S_2} section at pH $= 0$, plotting the lines for the various equilibria. Then, after eliminating metastable relations, the planes can be drawn to obtain the 3-dimensional diagram. Construction is easy after elimination of metastable boundaries, inasmuch as all the lines have the same slope, except for reaction (6.83). The results are shown in Figure 6.15. The similarity to the diagram for Eh-pH-log P_{CO_2} (Figure 6.7) is striking.

Stability as a Function of $\sum S$. As shown in the diagrams concerning CO_2, it is frequently useful to construct constant P_{S_2} sections of Eh-pH diagrams. The procedure is identical to that already discussed for CO_2-bearing systems, so that none is illustrated here. On the other hand, new complexities arise in systems with a fixed amount of dissolved sulfur. There are but 3 important dissolved carbonate species, H_2CO_3, HCO_3^-, and CO_3^{--}, and they are not Eh-sensitive. More than 40 ionic and molecular species containing sulfur have been isolated and studied, and their relative stabilities are functions of both Eh and pH. Fortunately, it has been shown by Valensi (G. Valensi, Contribution au diagramme potential-pH du soufre. *Compt rend 2ème Réunion, Comité Intern. Thermo. Kinetics Electrochem.*, Milan, 1950, 51–68) that

only those familiar in nature are thermodynamically stable in appreciable quantity at room temperature. Valensi's diagrams of major species shows only sulfate ion, bisulfate ion, native sulfur, hydrogen sulfide, bisulfide ion, and sulfide ion. As for the carbonates, it is

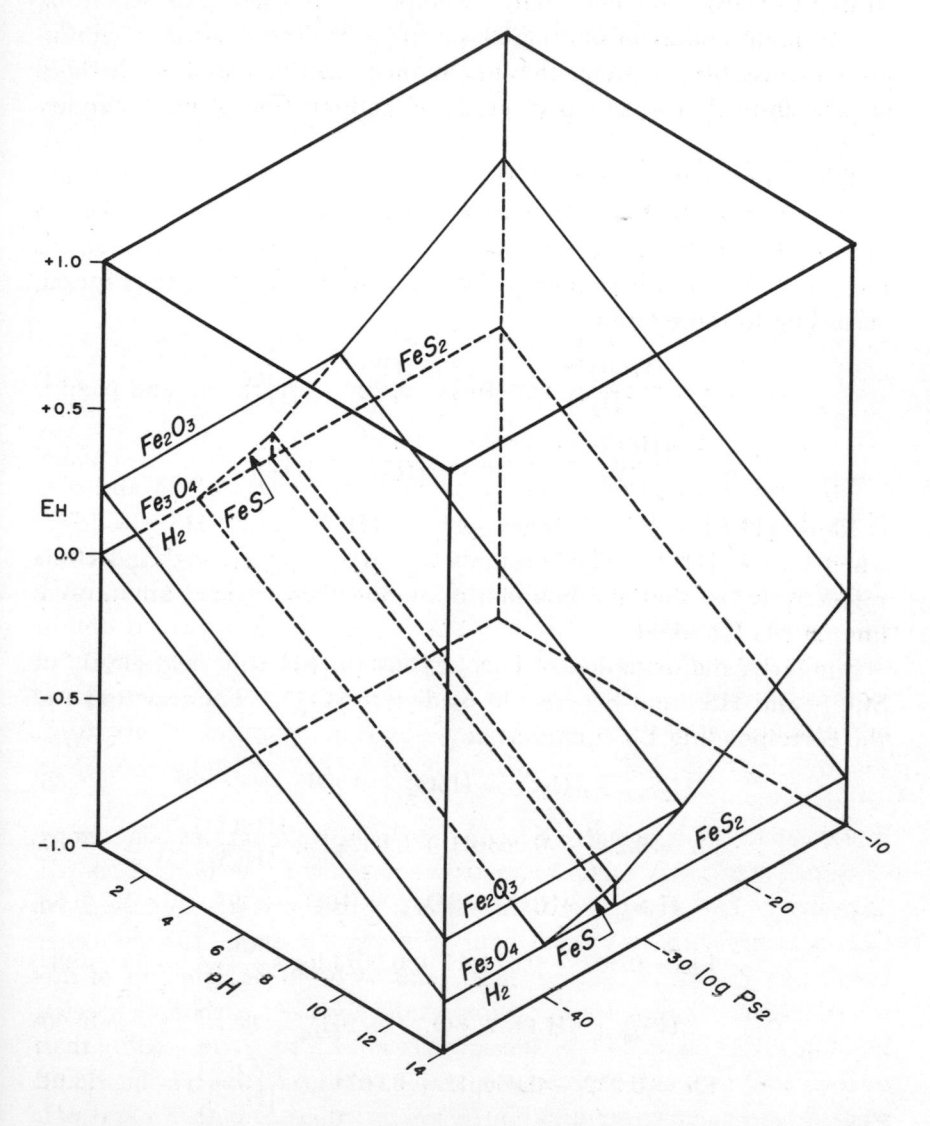

FIGURE 6.15. Stability relations of Fe_2O_3, Fe_3O_4, FeS, and FeS_2 as functions of Eh, pH, and log P_{S_2} at 25°C and 1 atmosphere total pressure in the presence of water. Note the small field of stability of FeS, and the small values of P_{S_2} for the association pyrite, pyrrhotite, and magnetite.

possible to write reactions involving dissolved species by limiting the
reaction to the field in which the sulfur species involved makes up by
far the greater part of the dissolved sulfur.

The construction of the sulfur species distribution diagram is fairly
straightforward. Rather than attempt a "formal" presentation,
which might consist of plotting all possible equilibria and then eliminating metastable reactions, the development will be based on the kind
of procedure that in practice speeds up construction of most stability
diagrams.

The completed diagram is shown in Figure 6.16. The following
discussion is best followed by continuous reference to it. First, we can
be sure that the stable sulfur species under acid reducing conditions is
H_2S, and that it will change to HS^- and to S^{--} as the pH is raised,
according to the relations:

$$\frac{[H^+][HS^-]}{[H_2S]} = k_{H_2S}; \quad \frac{[HS^-]}{[H_2S]} = \frac{k_{H_2S}}{[H^+]} \tag{6.84}$$

$$\frac{[H^+][S^{--}]}{[HS^-]} = k_{HS^-}; \quad \frac{[S^{--}]}{[HS^-]} = \frac{k_{HS^-}}{[H^+]} \tag{6.85}$$

Thus $[H_2S] = [HS^-]$ when $k_{H_2S} = [H^+]$, and $[HS^-] = [S^{--}]$
when $k_{HS^-} = [H^+]$. The constants k_{H_2S} and k_{HS^-} are 10^{-7} and 10^{-14}
respectively, so that the boundaries among these species are vertical
lines at pH 7 and 14.

Similarly, the oxidation of H_2S at constant pH will yield HSO_4^- or
SO_4^{--}, and HS^- and S^{--} should oxidize to SO_4^{--}. The reactions and
the corresponding Eh equations are:

$$H_2S_{aq} + 4H_2O_l = HSO_{4\,aq}^- + 9H_{aq}^+ + 8e \tag{6.86}$$

$$Eh = 0.290 - 0.066pH + 0.0074 \log \frac{[HSO_4^-]}{[H_2S]} \tag{6.87}$$

$$H_2S_{aq} + 4H_2O_l = SO_{4\,aq}^{--} + 10H^+ + 8e \tag{6.88}$$

$$Eh = 0.303 - 0.074pH + 0.0074 \log \frac{[SO_4^{--}]}{[H_2S]} \tag{6.89}$$

$$HS_{aq}^- + 4H_2O_l = SO_{4\,aq}^{--} + 9H_{aq}^+ + 8e \tag{6.90}$$

$$Eh = 0.252 - 0.066pH + 0.0074 \log \frac{[SO_4^{--}]}{[HS^-]} \tag{6.91}$$

$$S_{aq}^{--} + 4H_2O_l = SO_{4\,aq}^{--} + 8H^+ + 8e \tag{6.92}$$

$$Eh = 0.148 - 0.059pH + 0.0074 \log \frac{[SO_4^{--}]}{[S^{--}]} \tag{6.93}$$

When the sulfur species are equal, i.e., if $[S^{--}] = [SO_4^{--}]$, the term containing sulfur species in the Eh equation becomes zero, so that lines can be drawn solely as functions of Eh and pH which are boundaries between the dominant species.

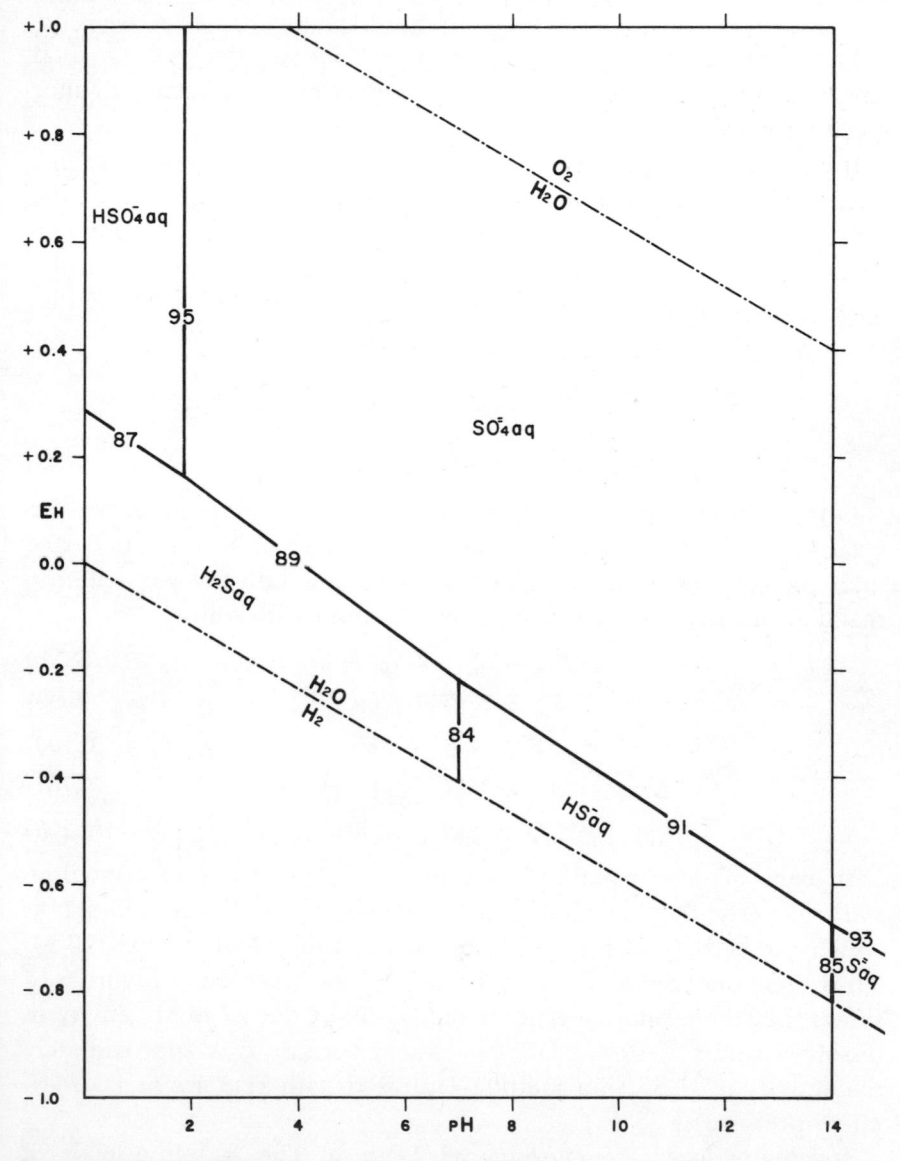

FIGURE 6.16. Equilibrium distribution of sulfur species in water at 25°C and 1 atmosphere total pressure. Numbers refer to equations in text used to plot boundaries between ions.

Finally, the boundary between HSO_4^- and SO_4^{--} is obtained from the reaction:

$$HSO_{4\,aq}^- = H_{aq}^+ + SO_{4\,aq}^{--} \qquad (6.94)$$

$$\frac{[SO_4^{--}]}{[HSO_4^-]} = \frac{k_{HSO_4^-}}{[H^+]} = \frac{10^{-1.9}}{[H^+]} \qquad (6.95)$$

The relations shown in Figure 6.16 are independent of the total dissolved sulfur considered; they show only where the ratios of sulfur species are unity.

If we consider a given value for the total activity of dissolved sulfur, such as 10^{-1}, then it can be considered that within any given field the activity of the species shown is very nearly 10^{-1}, and this relation can be used to calculate the abundance of other sulfur species within the field.　For example, within the H_2S field the activity of sulfide ion is:

$$H_2S_{aq} = S_{aq}^{--} + 2H_{aq}^+ \qquad (6.96)$$

$$\frac{[S^{--}][H^+]^2}{[H_2S]} = k$$

$$\log [S^{--}] = -22 + 2pH \qquad (6.97)$$

Once a given total sulfur ($\sum S$) is chosen, it becomes of interest to see if the amount chosen can stay in solution in equilibrium with native sulfur, which is a possible solid phase.　To ascertain this we write the reactions for the various species in equilibrium with sulfur:

$$H_2S_{aq} = S_c^0 + 2H_{aq}^+ + 2e \qquad (6.98)$$

$$HS_{aq}^- = S_c^0 + H_{aq}^+ + 2e \qquad (6.99)$$

$$S_{aq}^{--} = S_c^0 + 2e \qquad (6.100)$$

$$S_c^0 + 4H_2O_1 = HSO_{4\,aq}^- + 7H^+ + 6e \qquad (6.101)$$

$$S_c^0 + 4H_2O_1 = SO_{4\,aq}^{--} + 8H^+ + 6e \qquad (6.102)$$

In each of these equations, inasmuch as the activity of crystalline sulfur is unity, there is but one line representing the Eh-pH relation at which the activity of the dissolved species is the chosen value (10^{-1}). Thus these lines define the stability field of native sulfur.　Figure 6.17 shows the stable sulfur species at the specific value of total activity of dissolved sulfur = 10^{-1}.　(10^{-1} is chosen because it is approximately the activity of H_2S_{aq} in a solution saturated with H_2S gas at 1 atmosphere pressure at $25°C$.)

Stability Relations of Pyrrhotite and Pyrite.　The stability fields of pyrrhotite and pyrite relative to magnetite and hematite in solutions with given total dissolved sulfur can now be determined.　The methods

are entirely similar to those used for the relation of siderite to magnetite and hematite. [Fe⁺⁺] in equilibrium with each sulfide can be determined and the field of stability of each sulfide in relation to the oxides

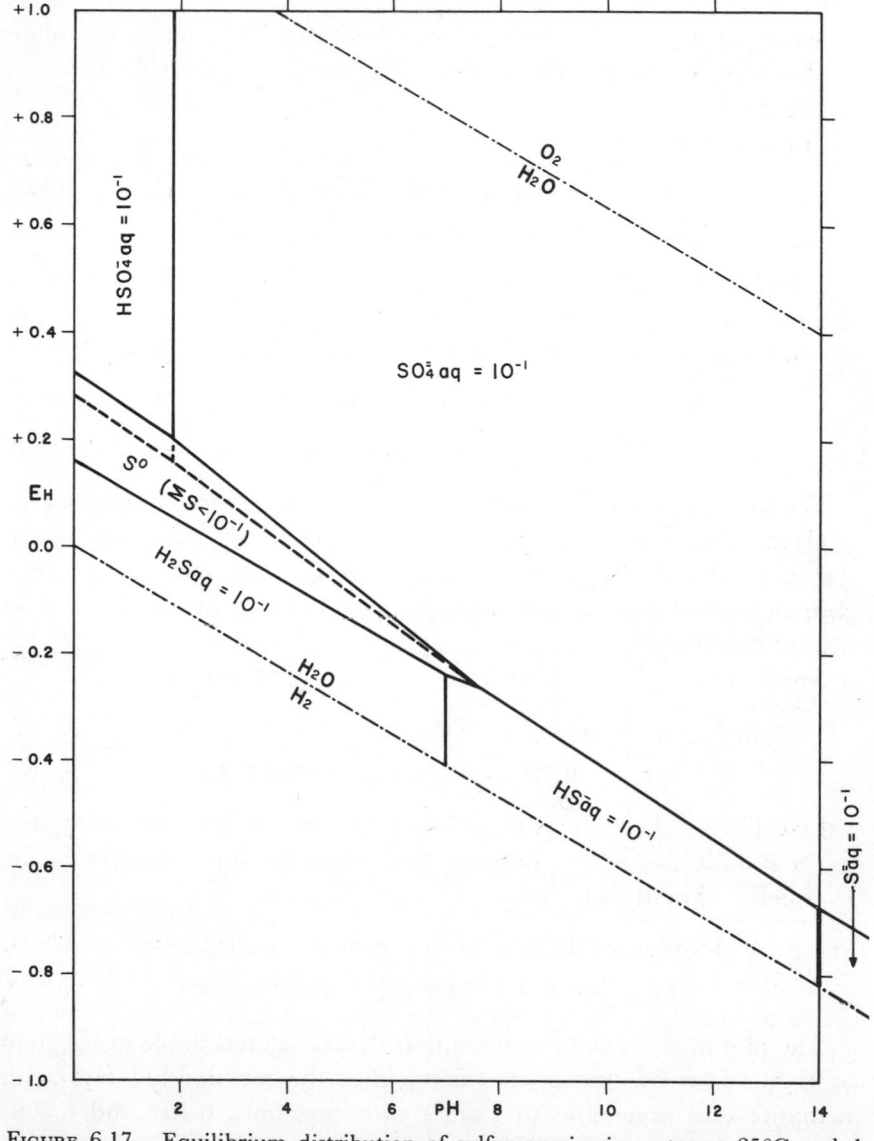

FIGURE 6.17. Equilibrium distribution of sulfur species in water at 25°C and 1 atmosphere total pressure for activity dissolved sulfur $= 10^{-1}$. Under these conditions native sulfur is a stable phase. Dashed line indicates equal values of dissolved species within sulfur field.

found graphically by superimposing upon the $[Fe^{++}]$ in equilibrium with the oxides. Alternatively the reactions between the sulfides, and between the sulfides and oxides can be written for each domain of a given dissolved sulfur species. This second method will be illustrated here.

Assuming a total dissolved sulfur activity of 10^{-1}, let us calculate the boundaries between the solids. The development can be followed on Figure 6.18.

In the H_2S field:

$$FeS_c + H_2S_{aq} = FeS_{2c} + 2H_{aq}^+ + 2e \qquad (6.103)$$

$$Eh = -0.133 - 0.059pH - 0.0295 \log 10^{-1} \qquad (6.104)$$

The plot of the boundary shows that pyrrhotite oxidizes to pyrite in the presence of H_2S before the water boundary is reached. Thus pyrrhotite is not stable in water in the presence of 10^{-1} H_2S. Next:

$$3FeS_c + 4H_2O_l = Fe_3O_{4c} + 3H_2S_{aq} + 2H_{aq}^+ + 2e \qquad (6.105)$$

$$Eh = 0.754 - 0.059pH + 0.088 \log 10^{-1} \qquad (6.106)$$

The line indicated by equation (6.106) does not even plot in the H_2S field, in other words, pyrrhotite is stable relative to magnetite within the entire H_2S field. To put it another way, $[H_2S]$ would have to be extremely low before a field of magnetite could appear within the H_2S field of dominance.

Now consider the reaction from magnetite to pyrite:

$$Fe_3O_{4c} + 6H_2S_{aq} = 3FeS_{2c} + 4H_2O_l + 4H_{aq}^+ + 4e \qquad (6.107)$$

$$Eh = -0.577 - 0.059pH - 0.088 \log 10^{-1} \qquad (6.108)$$

Like the pyrrhotite-pyrite boundary (6.104), it plots far below the water stability boundary, showing that magnetite does not exist in the H_2S field. Finally we write:

$$Fe_2O_{3c} + 4H_2S_{aq} = 2FeS_{2c} + 3H_2O_l + 2H_{aq}^+ + 2e \qquad (6.109)$$

$$Eh = -0.831 - 0.059pH - 0.118 \log 10^{-1} \qquad (6.110)$$

The plot of this reaction shows that it, too, is metastable in the field of H_2S. It is of interest in passing that the reactions of H_2S with hematite and magnetite to yield pyrite (reactions 6.107 and 6.109) are oxidation reactions—the reduction of iron is more than over-balanced by the oxidation of the sulfide ion of the H_2S to the disulfide ion in pyrite.

In summary, for the field where $[H_2S] = 10^{-1}$, pyrite is the stable species.   Inasmuch as the reactions in the HS^- field are similar, except for a slight change in slope, only the pyrrhotite-pyrite reaction need be

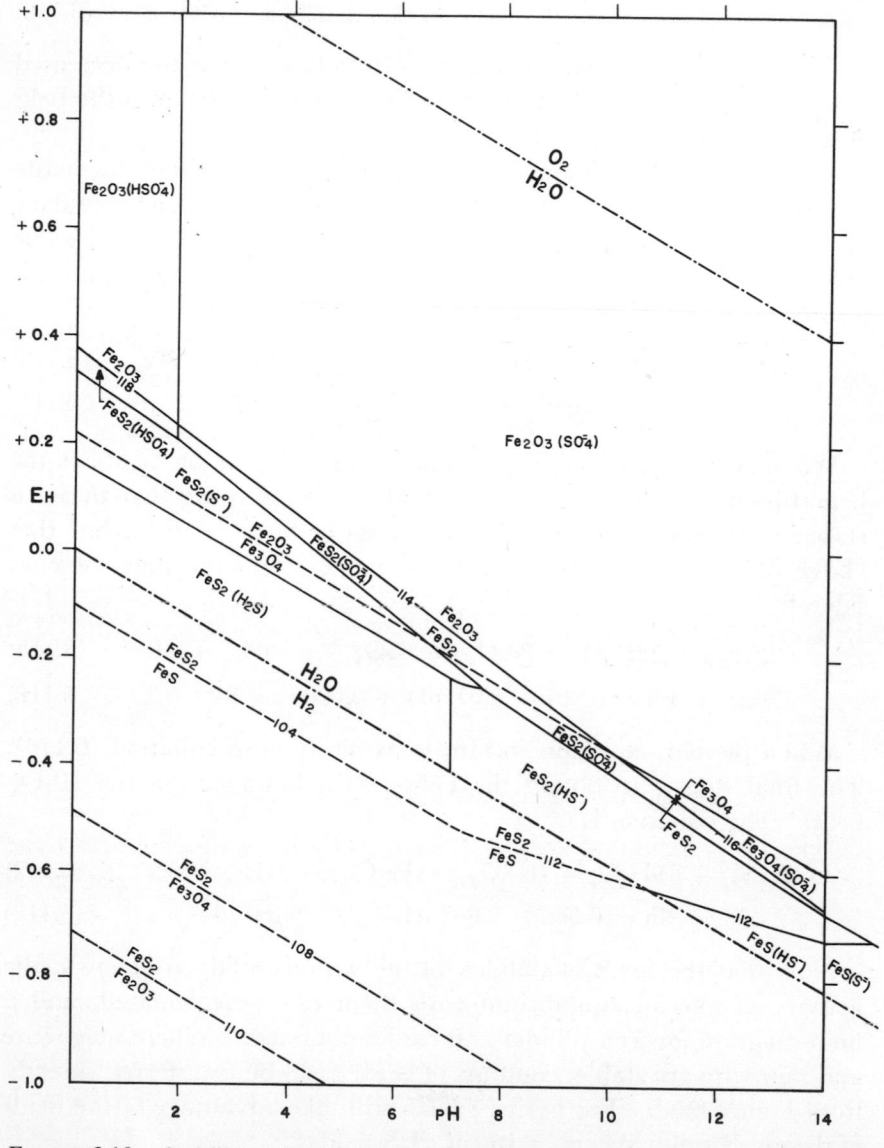

FIGURE 6.18.   Stability relations of iron sulfides and oxides in water at 25°C and 1 atmosphere total pressure, and total dissolved sulfur $= 10^{-1}$.   Heavy solid lines are stable boundaries of oxides and sulfides or boundaries of dissolved sulfur species; dashed lines are metastable boundaries.   Numbers refer to equations in text.

considered, for it is the only one for which the change in slope might intersect the lower water stability boundary. Accordingly:

$$FeS_c + HS^-_{aq} = FeS_{2c} + H^+_{aq} + 2e \qquad (6.111)$$

$$Eh = -0.340' - 0.0295pH - 0.0295 \log 10^{-1} \qquad (6.112)$$

The reaction, as shown on Figure 6.18 indicates that the decreased slope is sufficient to pull the pyrrhotite-pyrite boundary into the field of water stability at high pH ($\simeq 10.6$).

At this stage of development we can guess that the field of magnetite is going to be obliterated by that of pyrite, and try to find the boundary between pyrite and hematite in the SO_4^{--} field. If it is found to be above the magnetite-hematite boundary, then this assumption is justified. So we write:

$$2FeS_{2c} + 19H_2O_l = Fe_2O_{3c} + 4SO^{--}_{4\,aq} + 38H^+_{aq} + 30e \qquad (6.113)$$

$$Eh = 0.380 - 0.075pH + 0.0079 \log 10^{-1} \qquad (6.114)$$

When equation (6.114) is plotted, it is found to lie on or above the hematite-magnetite boundary up to pH $= 10$, showing that pyrite is stable relative to magnetite in that range if $SO_4^{--} = 10^{-1}$, but that above pH $= 10$ the reaction from pyrite to magnetite must be considered:

$$3FeS_{2c} + 28H_2O_l = Fe_3O_{4c} + 6SO^{--}_{4\,aq} + 56H^+_{aq} + 44e \qquad (6.115)$$

$$Eh = 0.384 - 0.075pH + 0.0080 \log 10^{-1} \qquad (6.116)$$

When plotted, equation (6.116) joins nicely onto equation (6.114). The final step is to obtain the FeS_2-Fe_2O_3 boundary in the HSO_4^- field. The equation is:

$$2FeS_{2c} + 19H_2O_l = 4HSO^-_{4\,aq} + Fe_2O_{3c} + 34H^+_{aq} + 30e \qquad (6.117)$$

$$Eh = 0.366 - 0.067pH + 0.0079 \log 10^{-1} \qquad (6.118)$$

Now that the fields of stability of the various solids are known, the activity of ions in equilibrium with them can be calculated, and a final diagram for iron sulfides and oxides obtained. Where magnetite and hematite are stable, contours of $[Fe^{++}]$ can be transferred directly from Figure 6.5d. For pyrite we can still take advantage of the fields of dissolved sulfur species. In the H_2S field:

$$2H_2S_{aq} + Fe^{++}_{aq} = FeS_{2c} + 4H^+_{aq} + 2e \qquad (6.119)$$

$$Eh = 0.057 - 0.118pH - 0.059 \log 10^{-1} - 0.0295 \log [Fe^{++}] \qquad (6.120)$$

In the HSO_4^- field:

$$FeS_{2c} + 8H_2O_1 = 2HSO_{4aq}^- + Fe_{aq}^{++} + 14H_{aq}^+ + 14e \quad (6.121)$$

$$Eh = 0.339 - 0.059pH + 0.0084 \log 10^{-1} + 0.0042 \log [Fe^{++}] \quad (6.122)$$

In the SO_4^{--} field:

$$FeS_{2c} + 8H_2O_1 = 2SO_{4aq}^{--} + Fe_{aq}^{++} + 16H_{aq}^+ + 14e \quad (6.123)$$

$$Eh = 0.354 - 0.067pH + 0.0084 \log 10^{-1} + 0.0042 \log [Fe^{++}] \quad (6.124)$$

In the HS^- field:

$$2HS_{aq}^- + Fe_{aq}^{++} = FeS_{2c} + 2H_{aq}^+ + 2e \quad (6.125)$$

$$Eh = -0.470 - 0.059pH - 0.059 \log 10^{-1} - 0.029 \log [Fe^{++}] \quad (6.126)$$

In the native sulfur field:

$$FeS_{2c} = Fe_{aq}^{++} + 2S_c^\circ + 2e \quad (6.127)$$

$$Eh = 0.340 + 0.0295 \log [Fe^{++}] \quad (6.128)$$

Because the only variables in the equations are Eh, pH, and log $[Fe^{++}]$, it is possible to substitute arbitrary values of $[Fe^{++}]$ and obtain contours for their values within the field of pyrite. If all relations have been calculated correctly, the contours in the pyrite field should join those in the oxide fields without a break. Figure 6.19 shows the "solubility" diagram thus obtained. Contours for the small field of pyrrhotite can be obtained from the single reaction:

$$FeS_c + H_{aq}^+ = Fe_{aq}^{++} + HS_{aq}^- \quad (6.129)$$

$$\log [Fe^{++}] = -4.4 - pH - \log 10^{-1} \quad (6.130)$$

The diagram has some interesting and perhaps unsuspected relations. First, it shows that if an activity of dissolved iron of 10^{-6} is used as a criterion of stability pyrite cannot oxidize to yield sulfur at pH values higher than about 3. Above that pH sulfur is not a stable phase at the potential at which pyrite oxidizes. Marcasite, on the other hand, which is less stable than pyrite, would be expected to yield sulfur at higher pH values. This pH relation probably explains why marcasite yields sulfur on oxidation by ferric salts, whereas pyrite does not, except when the ferric salt is highly concentrated. Also, the bulge acidward of the pyrite stability field at intermediate Eh values shows why inorganic nonoxidizing acids have no effect on pyrite, whereas oxidizing acids do. Also, there is a field of "solubility" under acid-reducing conditions, showing that pyrite can be decomposed by

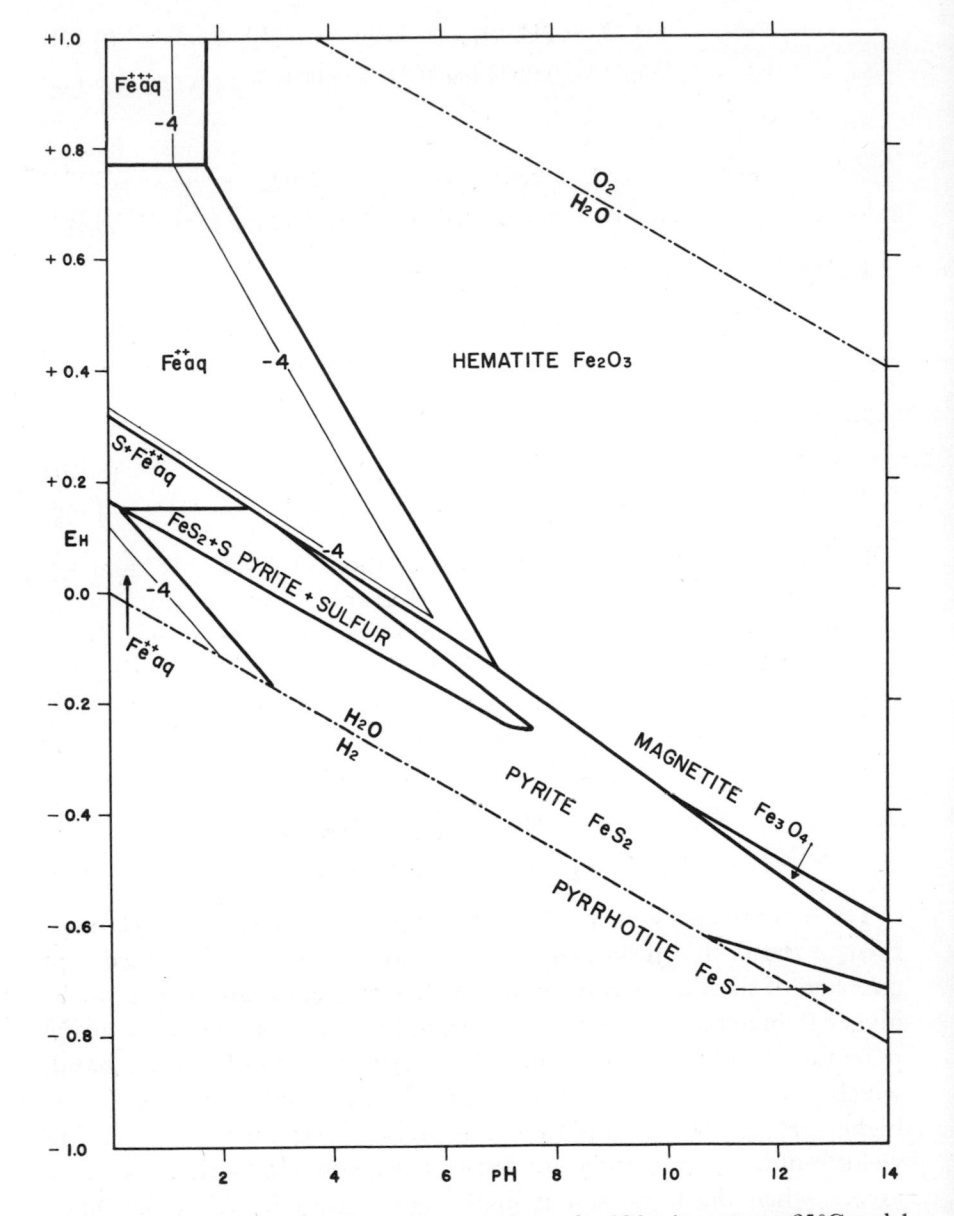

FIGURE 6.19. Stability relations of iron oxides and sulfides in water at 25°C and 1 atmosphere total pressure at an activity of dissolved sulfur of 10^{-1}. Boundaries between ions and solids are at an activity of 10^{-6} of dissolved iron species. The numeral -4 is the log of the iron activity used to show the rate of change of "solubility."

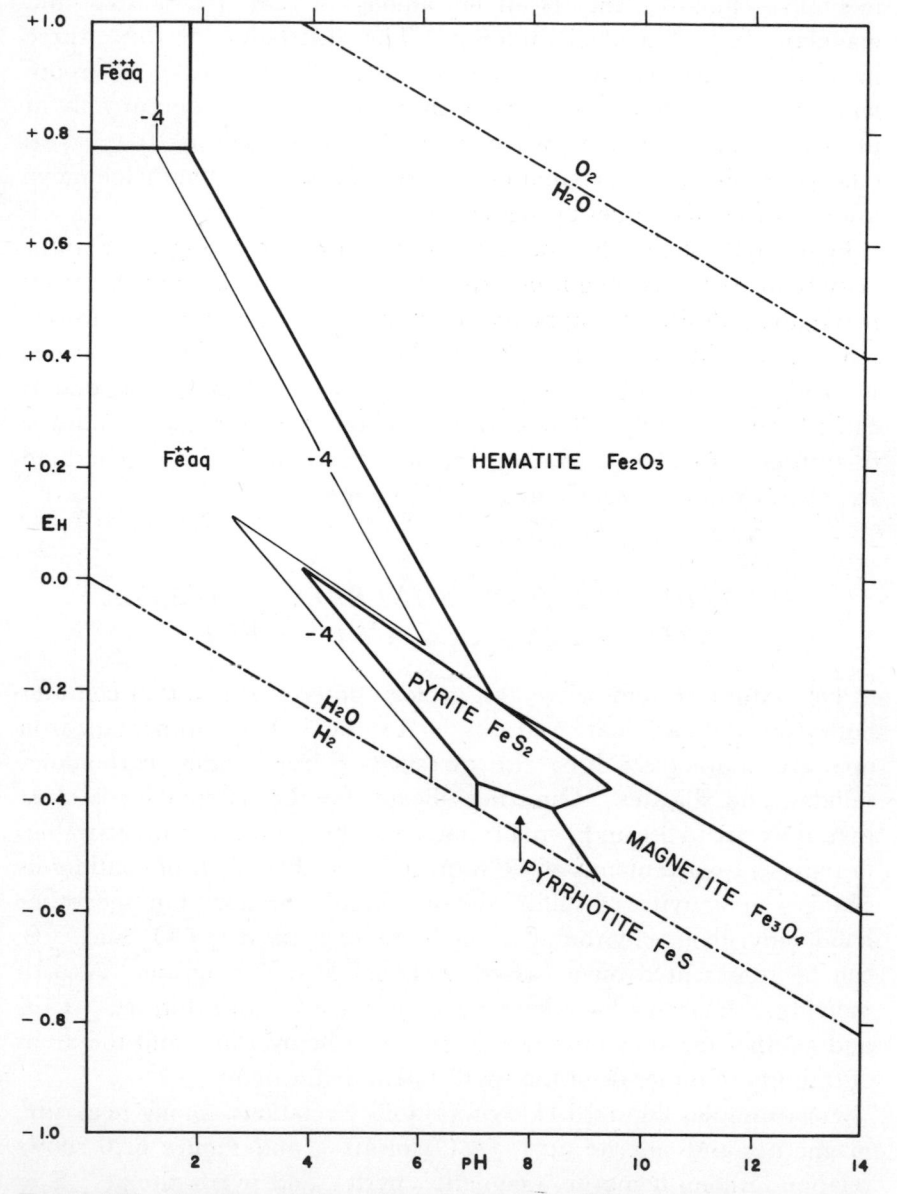

FIGURE 6.20. Stability relations of iron oxides and sulfides in water at 25°C and 1 atmosphere total pressure, when $\Sigma S = 10^{-6}$. Note shrinkage of sulfide boundaries and appearance of FeS as a stable phase at intermediate pH under strongly reducing conditions, as well as marked increase in the area of "acid solubility" over a wide range of Eh.

reducing agents in acid solutions. This conclusion is verifiable experimentally. Finally, the relations among pyrite, pyrrhotite, and magnetite are of geologic interest. The association of these three minerals is characteristic of high-temperature deposits. At room temperature, as shown here, the 3-phase association can occur only at pH values higher than 14 when total sulfur is as high as 10^{-1}. This relation implies that the conditions of stability of the assemblage move toward lower pH values at higher temperatures.

Figure 6.20 shows the changes resulting from lowering total sulfur activity to 10^{-6}. As might be expected, the fields of the sulfides shrink markedly. Pyrrhotite appears as a stable phase under strongly reducing conditions at pH $\simeq$ 8, and the area of "solubility" increases markedly on the acid side. From this figure and the preceding one, it can be seen that the first appearance of stable sulfides, where minute quantities of divalent sulfur appear in the system (perhaps generated by organisms), is at nearly neutral pH values.

RELATIONS OF IRON MINERALS IN WATER CONTAINING CO_2 AND SULFUR

The natural system of greatest geologic interest is one that contains both dissolved carbonate and dissolved sulfur. The sedimentary iron ores are characterized by the presence of iron oxides, carbonates, sulfides, and silicates. Omitting silicates for the moment, it is clear that, if we are to use an Eh-pH framework, there are too many variables to represent conveniently if we want to assess the effects of continuous changes in activity of sulfur and carbonate species. On the other hand, any given environment, in terms of a fixed $\sum CO_2$ and $\sum S$, can be represented on a two-dimensional Eh-pH diagram. Also, if individual diagrams have been prepared, one for an arbitrary $\sum CO_2$ and another for an arbitrary $\sum S$, they can be overlain, and the areas of stability of minerals of the total system delineated.

For example, Figure 6.11 shows stability relations among hematite, magnetite, and siderite at a $\sum CO_2$ of 10^{-2}, and Figure 6.20 shows relations among hematite, magnetite, pyrite, and pyrrhotite at $\sum S = 10^{-6}$. If the sulfide diagram is overlain on the carbonate diagram, it is immediately apparent that the activity of dissolved iron in equilibrium with the compounds on the $\sum S$ diagram is everywhere less than on the $\sum CO_2$ diagram. In other words, when $\sum S$ is 10^{-6} and $\sum CO_2$

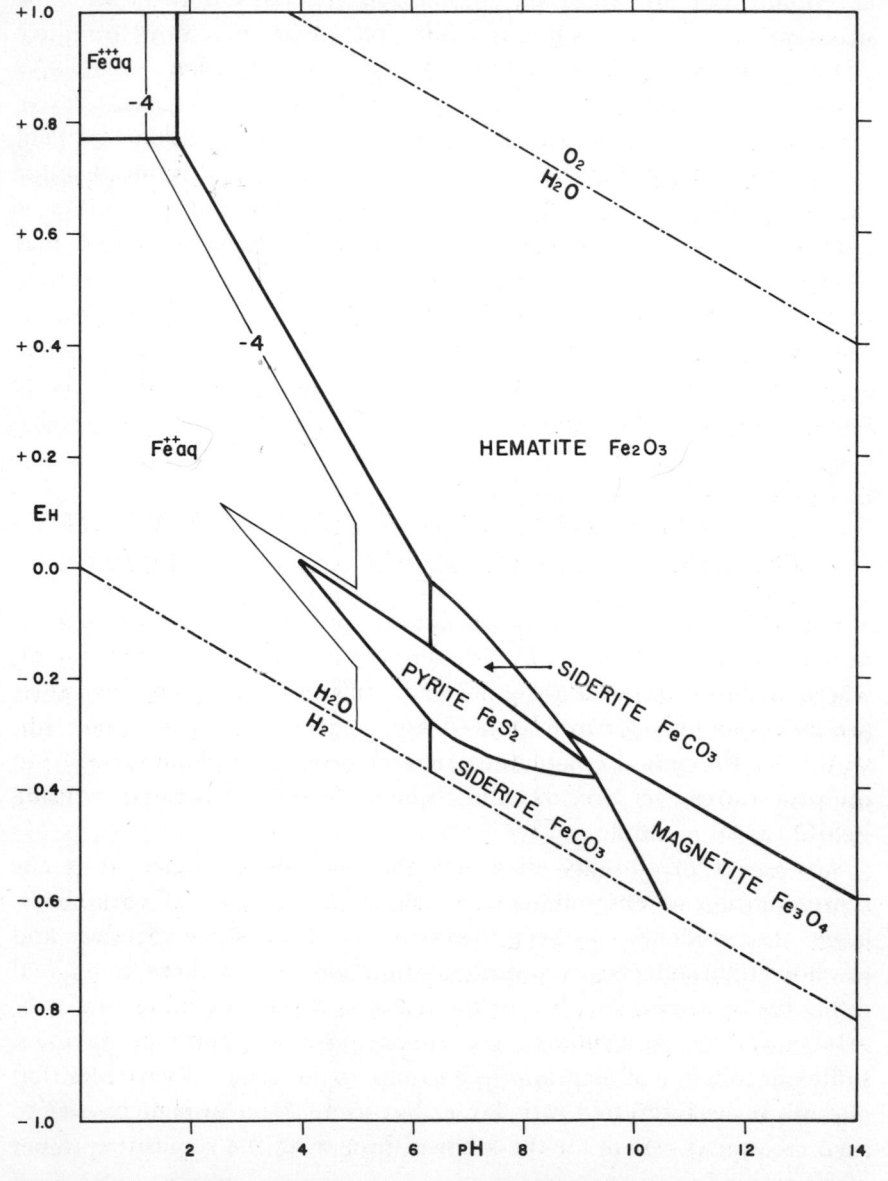

FIGURE 6.21. Stability relations of iron oxides, sulfides, and carbonate in water at 25°C and 1 atmosphere total pressure. Total dissolved sulfur = 10^{-6}. Total dissolved carbonate = 10^{0}. Note elimination of FeS field by $FeCO_3$ under strongly reducing conditions, and remarkable stability of pyrite in presence of small amount dissolved sulfur.

is 10^{-2}, only oxides and sulfides are stable, and siderite does not appear at equilibrium. It must be emphasized that this is the *equilibrium* situation—it is well known that sulfate ion is extremely slow to reduce at low temperature in the absence of organic intervention.

Figure 6.21 shows the relations when $\sum CO_2 = 10°$, and $\sum S = 10^{-6}$, and serves to illustrate that if siderite is to have an important field of stability, dissolved carbonate must be very high and reduced sulfur extremely low. Under these conditions the field of pyrrhotite is eliminated, but a considerable field of pyrite remains. Note that siderite, under these conditions, may be a criterion of very strongly reducing conditions, or of moderately reducing conditions, and its presence in many iron ores apparently indicates the essential absence of appreciable bivalent sulfur and the presence of relatively large amounts of dissolved carbonate.

THE INFLUENCE OF OTHER CONSTITUENTS IN THE IRON SYSTEM: SILICA AS AN EXAMPLE

Unfortunately thermochemical data at present are not sufficient to permit handling of the total sedimentary iron mineral environment, which includes important quantities of silicates. Free energy values are available only for iron metasilicate, $FeSiO_3$, which is a poor substitute for the actual compounds, iron chlorites and chamosites. Yet the procedures necessary to handle silicates can be illustrated by using $FeSiO_3$ as an example.

An aspect of stability diagrams that has been neglected is the representation of environments in which the number of variables is large—the tendency has been to restrict to two or three variables and to show their effects as continuous functions. But there is no real difficulty in working with 5 or 6 variables, if one is willing to choose arbitrary values of each for a given diagram. The chore of making a sufficient number of diagrams to encompass the range of variables that one might be interested in is large, but there is no present barrier to such treatment except for the labor of preparing the requisite number of diagrams.

To return to the problem of iron silicates, we can see the relation of iron silicate to the iron oxides, if it can be assumed that solid silica is present in the environment. Because there is abundant evidence that opaline silica has been a primary associate of all the other iron minerals,

one is justified in assuming that amorphous silica (silica glass) is an invariable associate of the other iron minerals of sedimentary iron ores. Then, if we recognize the limitations of substituting ferrous metasilicate for the real silicates found in sedimentary iron ores, we can write:

$$3FeSiO_{3c} + H_2O_l = Fe_3O_{4c} + 3SiO_{2\,glass} + 2H^+_{aq} + 2e \qquad (6.131)$$

$$Eh = 0.272 - 0.059pH \qquad (6.132)$$

Equation (6.132) is plotted on Figure 6.22, and the boundary between $FeSiO_3$ and Fe_3O_4 is found to be above that for Fe_3O_4-Fe_2O_3. In other words, in the presence of silica glass, or a system saturated with respect to amorphous silica, magnetite is unstable relative to iron metasilicate. The next step is to obtain the boundary between $FeSiO_3$ and Fe_2O_3:

$$2FeSiO_{3c} + H_2O_l = Fe_2O_{3c} + 2SiO_{2\,glass} + 2H^+_{aq} + 2e \qquad (6.133)$$

$$Eh = 0.258 - 0.059pH \qquad (6.134)$$

This equation also plots above the Fe_3O_4-Fe_2O_3 line, showing that in the presence of silica glass the phases expected are iron silicate and hematite. We can then write, for the field occupied by $FeSiO_3$:

$$FeSiO_{3c} + 2H^+_{aq} = Fe^{++}_{aq} + SiO_{2\,glass} + H_2O_l \qquad (6.135)$$

$$\log [Fe^{++}] = 8.03 - 2pH \qquad (6.136)$$

Substituting values of 10^{-6} and 10^{-4} for $[Fe^{++}]$, we obtain a "solubility" diagram for the iron silicate-iron oxide system. Therefore, if we consider only iron oxides and iron silicate in the presence of amorphous silica, magnetite disappears as a solid phase. Undoubtedly the actual iron silicates found as primary sedimentary minerals in iron ores are somewhat more stable than pure $FeSiO_3$, but the relations using $FeSiO_3$ show that if bottom waters are saturated with amorphous silica, and if there is enough silica to satisfy all the iron present, iron silicate will form in preference to magnetite. On the other hand, the general conditions of stability of ferrous metasilicate are remarkably similar to those of magnetite.

All kinds of fascinating games can be played by determining stability relations for various values of total carbonate, total sulfur, and total dissolved silica, and the conditions can be endlessly varied. Figure 6.23 is a summary diagram for a particular set of conditions, namely $\sum CO_2 = 10°$; $\sum S = 10^{-6}$, $\sum SiO_2$ equals that in equilibrium with silica glass (amorphous silica). This diagram was obtained by superimposing Figures 6.22 and 6.23.

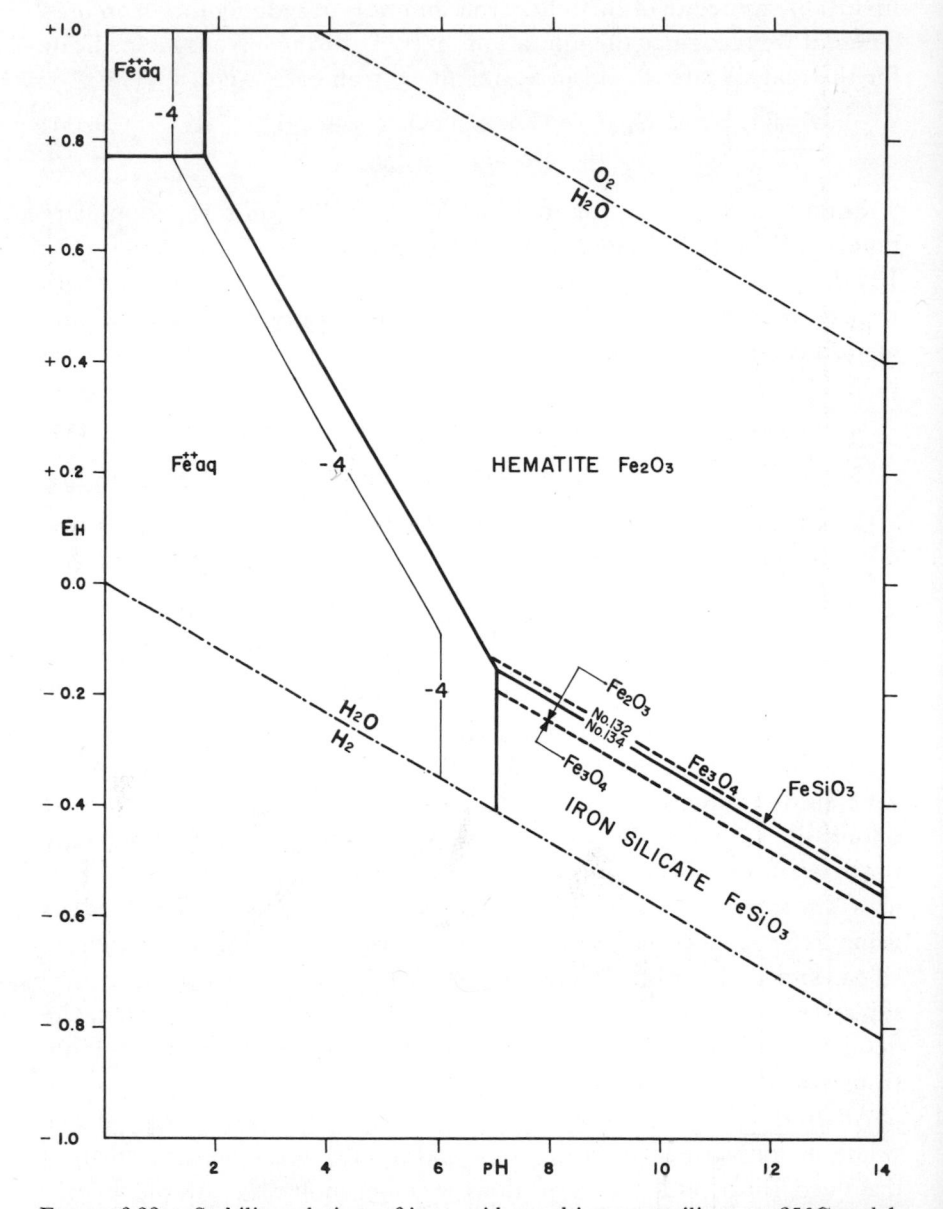

FIGURE 6.22. Stability relations of iron oxides and iron metasilicate at 25°C and 1 atmosphere total pressure in the presence of water. Solid silica glass assumed present. Numbers on lines refer to equations in text. −4 on thin solid lines is log total dissolved iron in equilibrium with solids.

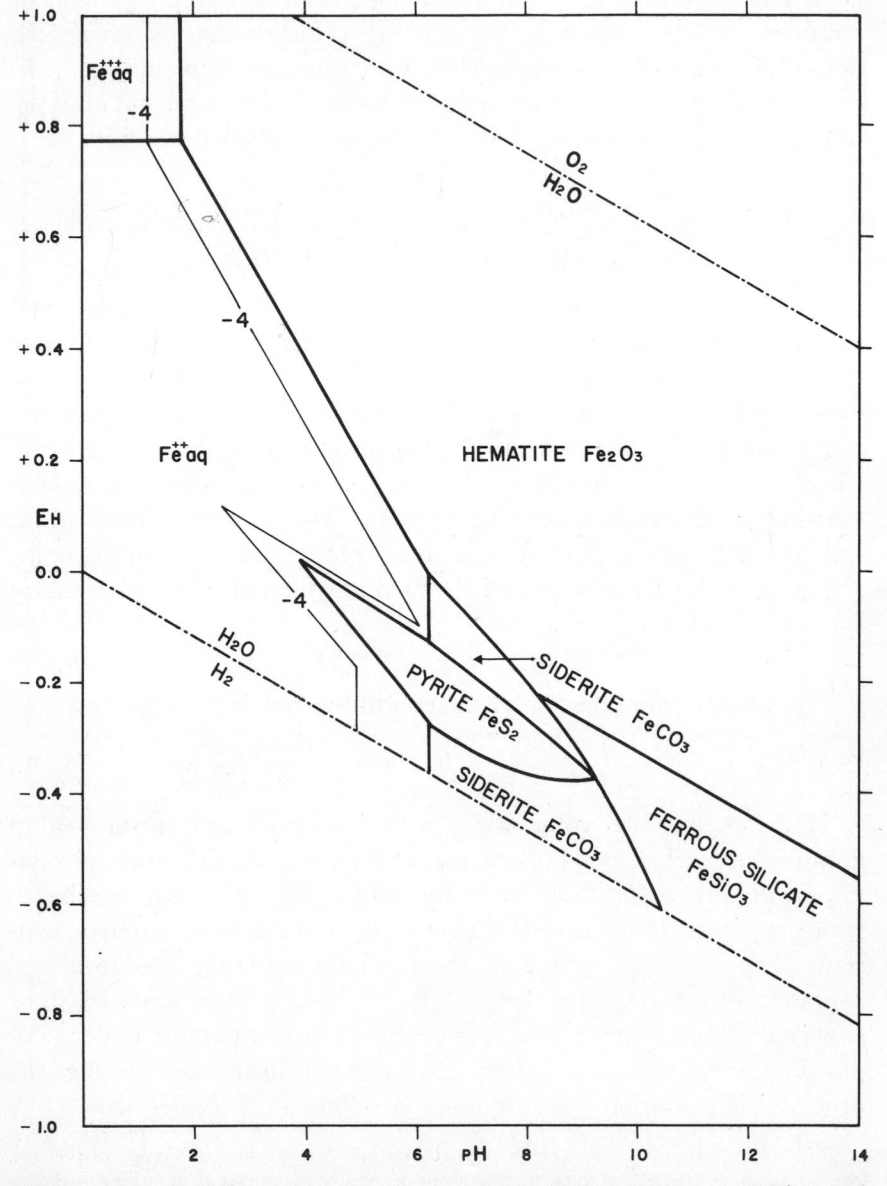

FIGURE 6.23. Stability relations among iron oxides, carbonates, sulfides and silicates at 25°C, and 1 atmosphere total pressure in the presence of water. Other conditions: Total $CO_2 = 10^\circ$; total sulfur $= 10^{-6}$; amorphous silica is present. This diagram is intended to suggest the innumerable components that can be considered in pH-Eh representation, if arbitrary values are selected for each constituent.

In terms of the primary sedimentary iron ores, it is obvious that a siderite facies can be obtained by having a high dissolved CO_2 and by removing sulfide sulfur from the system; a silicate facies by removing sulfur and high CO_2 content, while preserving enough silica to yield chert; a magnetite facies by reducing sulfur, CO_2, and maintaining silica at a value undersaturated with respect to amorphous silica.[2]

THE TRANSITION FROM PARTIAL PRESSURE DIAGRAMS TO Eh-pH DIAGRAMS

In Chapter 5 stability diagrams of various oxides, sulfides, and carbonates were shown as functions of P_{O_2}, P_{CO_2}, and P_{S_2}. One of the most interesting geologically is that relating copper and iron oxides and sulfides (Figure 6.16). R. Natarajan (unpublished manuscript, Harvard University, 1958) has transposed such diagrams into Eh-pH diagrams. As shown before, P_{O_2} values can be shown as contours on an Eh-pH diagram (Figure 6.1). Also, at a given total sulfur, contours of P_{S_2} also can be drawn on Eh-pH diagrams. For example, if $\sum S = 10^{-1}$, we can write, for the field in which H_2S is the dominant species (Figure 6.17):

$$2H_2S_{aq} = S_{2g} + 4H^+_{aq} + 4e \qquad (6.137)$$

The Eh-pH equation, under the condition that $H_2S = 10^{-1}$, is:

$$Eh = E^\circ + \frac{0.059}{4} \log P_{S_2} - 0.059pH - \frac{0.059}{2} \log 10^{-1} \qquad (6.138)$$

Thus for a selected value of P_{S_2}, a line can be drawn in the field of dominance of H_2S to represent this selected value. Because all relations on Figure 5.16 are shown in terms of P_{S_2} and P_{O_2}, it is possible to transpose them to an Eh-pH diagram, if total dissolved sulfur is constant. Figures 6.24 and 6.25 show relations among the iron and copper sulfides at $\sum S = 10^{-1}$ and $\sum S = 10^{-4}$ and serve to show expected stability fields of a large number of compounds under conditions corresponding to those encountered in nature during the processes of oxidation and secondary enrichment of copper ores.

---

[2] The word "chert" is used here on the assumption that the siliceous layers of the iron formations, now cryptocrystalline quartz, were originally polymerized amorphous silica—opaline silica.

FIGURE 6.24 (*opposite page*). The system Cu–Fe–S–O–H (in part) at 25°C and 1 atmosphere total pressure. Total dissolved sulfur = 10^{-1} m. (Courtesy R. Natarajan and R. Garrels.)

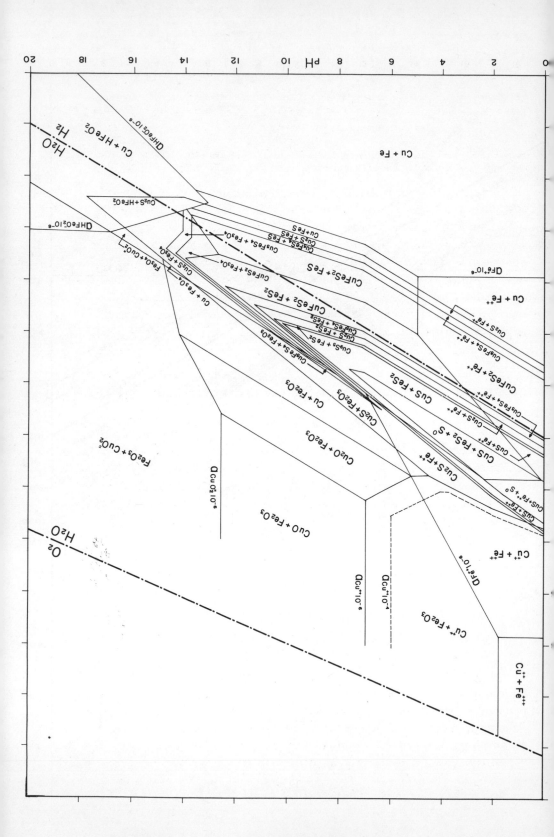

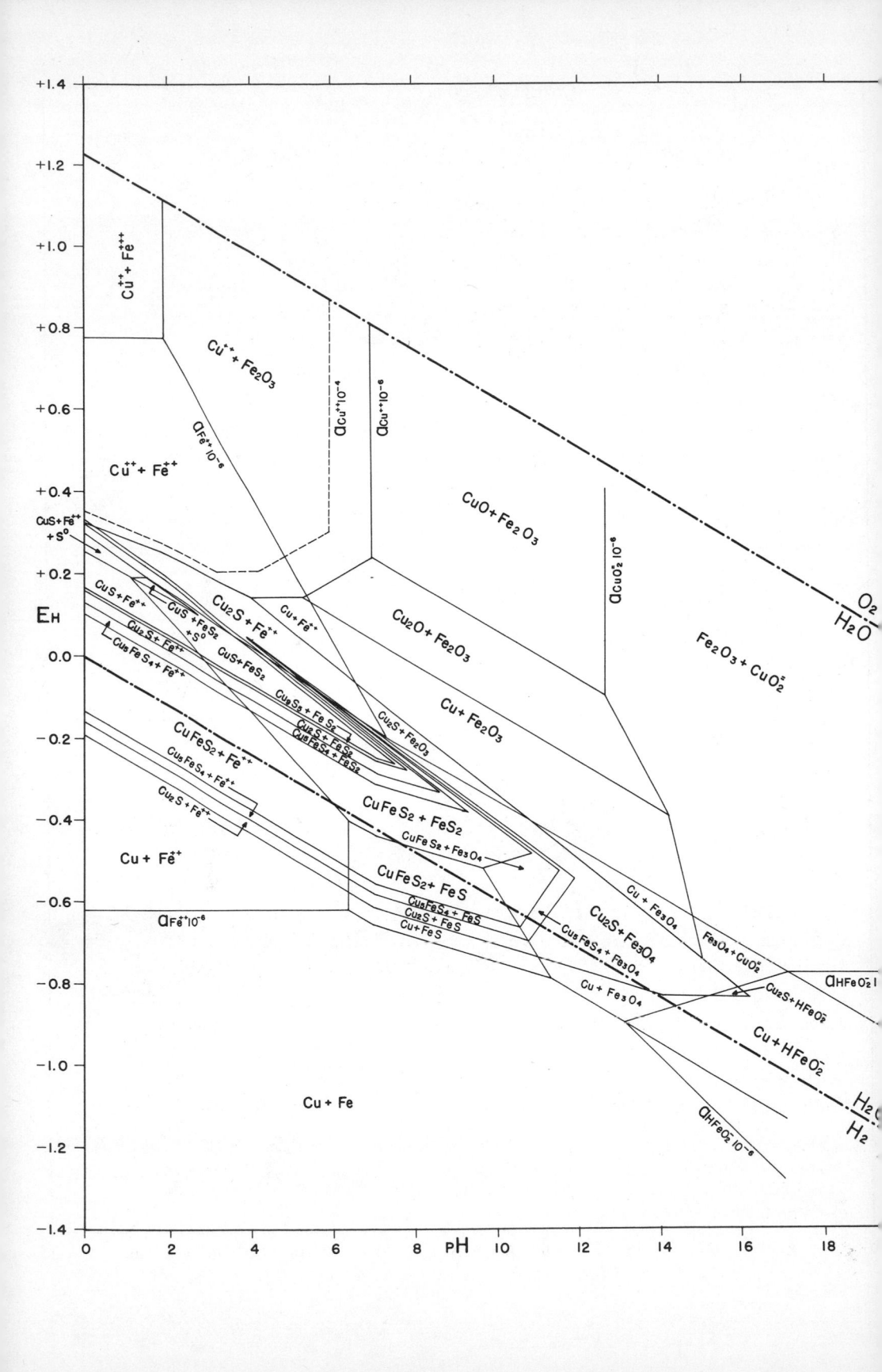

SUMMARY OF IRON MINERAL RELATIONS

The foregoing detailed development of relations among the iron minerals has been documented in the hope that the procedures illustrated are sufficient to permit anyone who follows them in detail to handle similar relations for any other element. Although the application to geologic relations has not been emphasized in this chapter, because of the risk of destroying the thread of the development of the mechanical aspects of stability portrayal, the diagrams of interplay among iron oxides, carbonates, sulfides, and silicates fit natural occurrences so beautifully that words may be superfluous. In addition, it is shown that the kinds of diagrams that could be made for iron compounds alone are limitless, and that anyone interested in specific conditions can examine them in the kinds of frameworks suggested.

Eh-pH DIAGRAMS FOR OTHER ELEMENTS

In the following pages Eh-pH diagrams for various elements are presented, with no more than a caption to show the conditions of calculation. In the following chapter some geologic applications that have been made of some of these diagrams are given, but for most of them the significance lies in the experience of the reader. It is obviously impossible, without tremendous increase in the length of this text, to develop such diagrams. Yet it is hoped that the details of the development of the iron diagrams is sufficient to show that the diagrams are valid only under the conditions for which they have been calculated. There is a tendency, for example, to represent relations among iron carbonates, oxides, and sulfides, without regard to the values of $\sum S$ and $\sum CO_2$ used for calculation. Such disregard is sufficient to invalidate the use of the diagram.

The diagrams showing relations for metals in oxygenated water have been individually calculated by the persons credited, but it should be reemphasized that a detailed development of each one, with many additional diagrams covering various conditions, can be found in the publications of "Cebelcor" given at the end of this chapter.

FIGURE 6.25 (*opposite page*). The system Cu–Fe–S–O–H (in part) at 25°C and 1 atmosphere total pressure. Total dissolved sulfur = 10^{-4} m. (Courtesy R. Natarajan and R. Garrels.)

These publications are the core from which all the diagrams shown here have been developed.

Figures 6.24 and 6.25. The diagrams show the best information currently available on the copper-iron-water-sulfur mineral relations at 25°C and 1 atmosphere total pressure, in the presence of dissolved sulfur at fixed activity. The diagrams have been prepared as an aid in the understanding of relations in the zones of oxidation and secondary enrichment of ore deposits. The relations appear complex at first glance, but a pattern begins to emerge after a little study. The various iron, copper-iron, and iron sulfides are separated from the iron and copper oxides by a fairly definite Eh-pH band running from an Eh of about 0.3 at pH 0 downward to the right with a slope of about 60 millivolts/pH unit. Only chalcocite (Cu_2S) projects appreciably above this boundary, which is in accord with the occurrence of chalcocite blankets as a result of secondary enrichment of copper ores. Note that oxidation under acid conditions should produce, at equilibrium, either appreciable Cu^{++} and Fe^{++} in solution, or, with slightly lower acidity, Cu^{++} and solid Fe_2O_3 (or $Fe_2O_3 \cdot H_2O$). The reason for the separation of iron and copper on oxidation is thus represented. Native copper easily can be a secondary product, if the descending copper solutions are neutralized. Cuprite and tenorite, on the other hand, show a requirement of fairly high pH before their precipitation will remove copper from solution quantitatively. Many other such relations are implicit in the interrelations shown. The diagrams were prepared by R. Natarajan and R. Garrels, under sponsorship of the Committee on Experimental Geology, Harvard University, 1957.

Figure 6.26a–e. This set of figures shows equilibria among lead compounds in water at 25°C and 1 atmosphere total pressure in the presence of CO_2 or sulfur. Various combinations are shown.

In Figure 6.26a, the presence of a small partial pressure of CO_2 removes the fields of stability of the various lead oxides, except for a small field of PbO_2, suggesting that as a mineral (plattncrite) PbO_2 is a fine indicator of alkaline oxidizing conditions.

Figure 6.26b shows the difference resulting from considering a fixed total CO_2; $Pb_3(OH)_2(CO_3)_2$ appears as a stable compound. Contours of ionic activity exceeding 10^{-4} are shown to illustrate the conditions of occurrence of Pb_3O_4 and PbO in this system. $Pb_3(OH)_2(CO_3)_2$ (hydrocerussite) should be a good indicator of alkaline conditions. Note the field of stability of native lead in these carbonated waters.

Figure 6.26c illustrates the influence of adding sulfur to the Pb-

oxygenated water system. Even if dissolved sulfur is 10^{-5}, as shown here, galena has a large stability field, and anglesite also has a large area of occurrence. Note than in this system the fields of ions, as

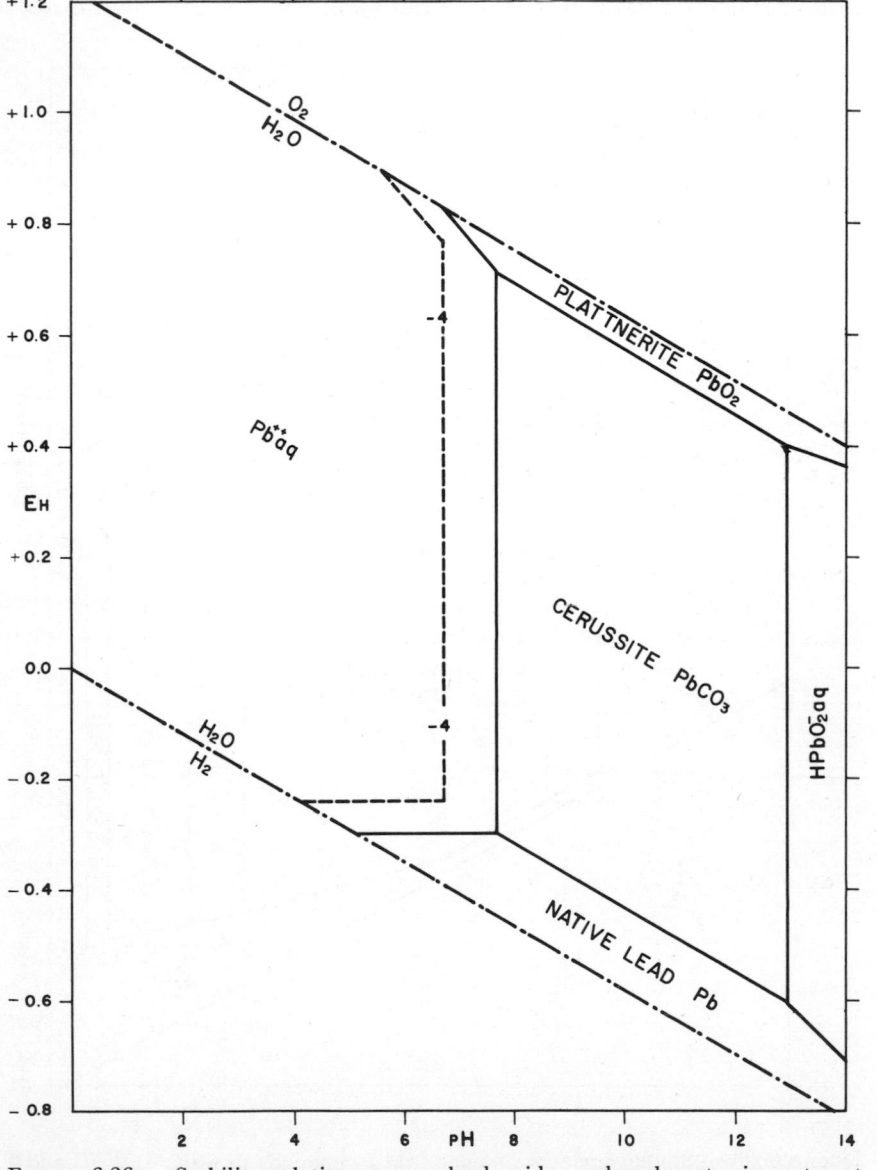

FIGURE 6.26a. Stability relations among lead oxides and carbonates in water at 25°C and 1 atmosphere total pressure. $P_{CO_2} = 10^{-4}$. Boundaries of solids at total ion activity $= 10^{-6}$, contour is at activity $= 10^{-4}$. (Courtesy W. McIntyre.)

opposed to solids, have been drawn at an activity of 10^{-2}. If 10^{-6} had been used, both $PbSO_4$ and PbO would have just disappeared, inasmuch as the contours for 10^{-6} Pb^{++} and 10^{-6} $HPbO_2^-$ coincide at pH 9.3. Also, with as little as 10^{-5} total dissolved sulfur, galena has almost squeezed native lead out of the picture.

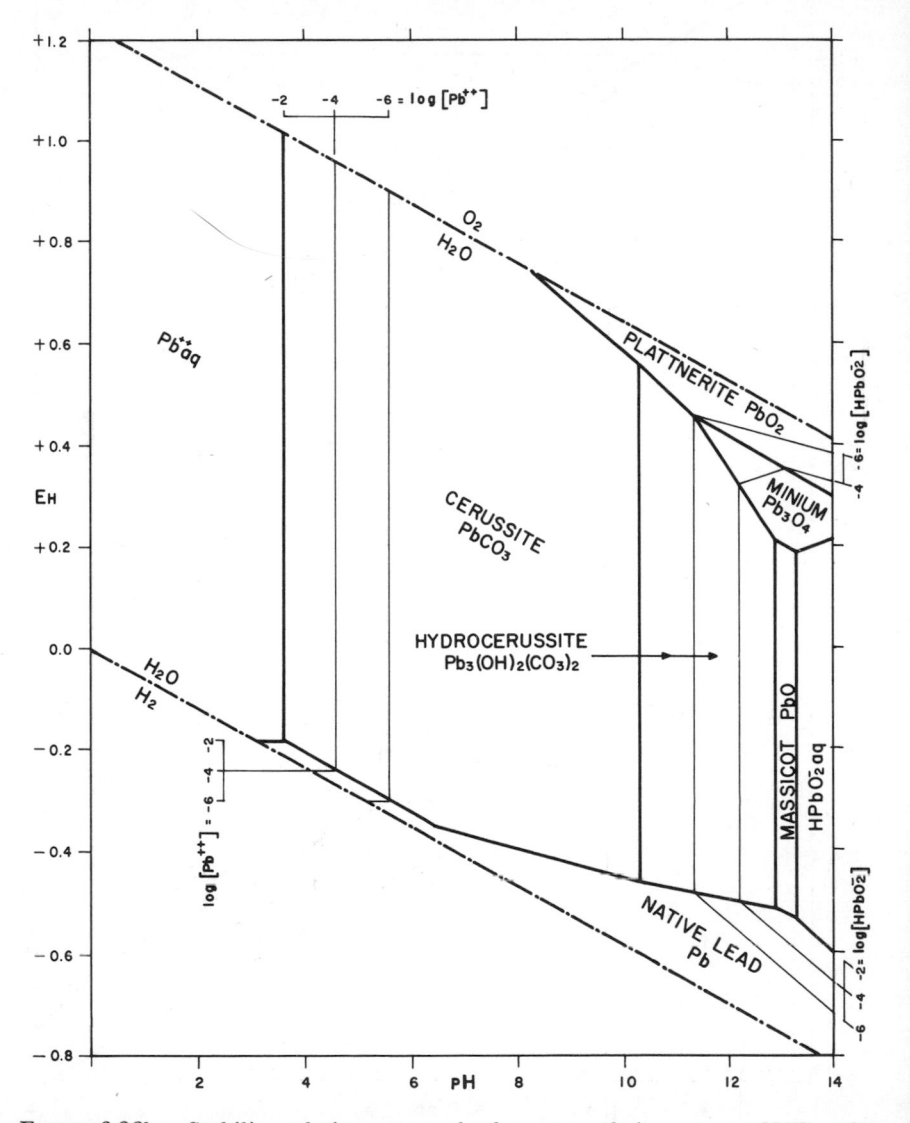

FIGURE 6.26b. Stability relations among lead compounds in water at 25°C and 1 atmosphere total pressure. Total dissolved carbonate species = $10^{-1.5}$. (Courtesy W. McIntyre.)

Figure 6.26d combines the effects of CO_2 and sulfur, and illustrates a system resembling conditions of surface oxidation. Total sulfur is high (10^{-1}), and P_{CO_2} is approximately that of the atmosphere (10^{-4}). Under such conditions, the stability diagram indicates that lead is insoluble; the activity of the ions exceeds 10^{-6} only under very alkaline

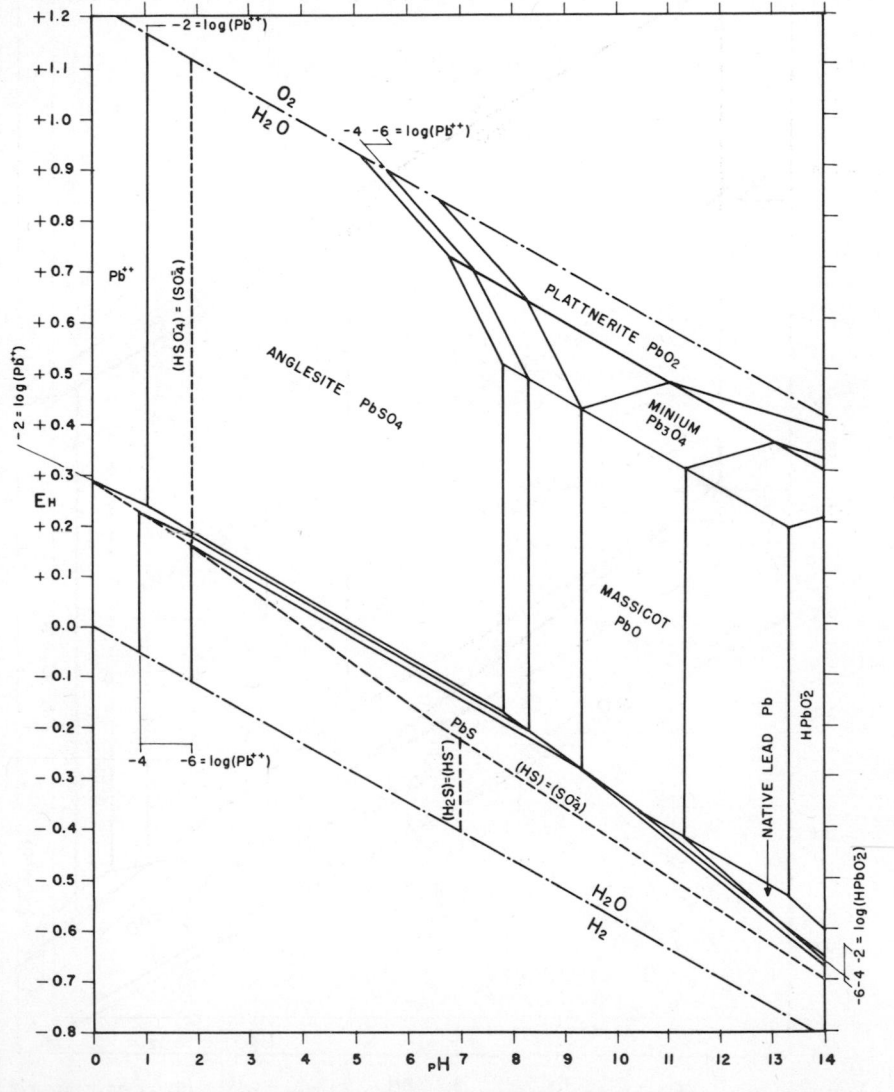

FIGURE 6.26c. Stability relations among lead compounds in water at 25°C and 1 atmosphere total pressure. Total dissolved sulfur species = 10^{-5}. (Courtesy W. McIntyre.)

or very acid conditions. Also, the diagram simplifies to the chief minerals actually observed: galena, cerussite, and anglesite, with a small field of plattnerite under unusual conditions.

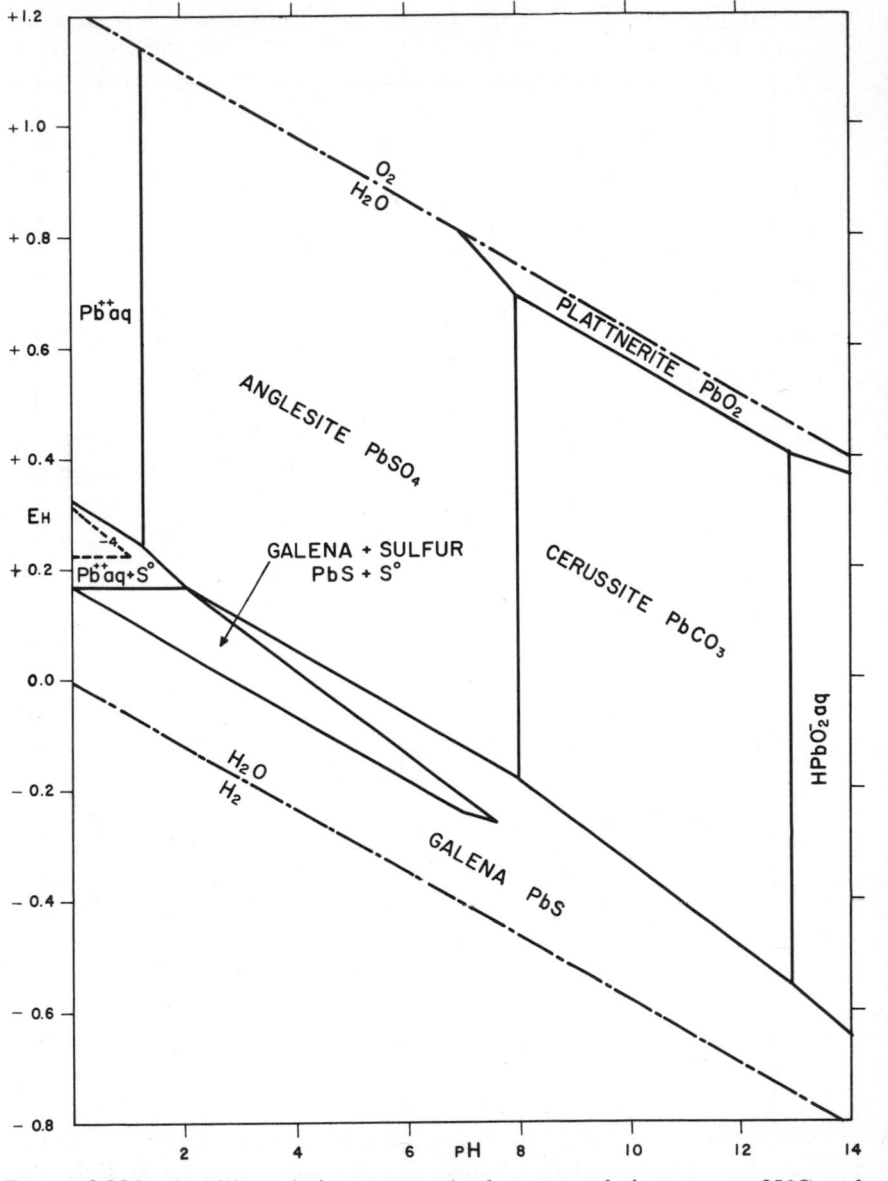

FIGURE 6.26d. Stability relations among lead compounds in water at 25°C and 1 atmosphere total pressure. Total dissolved sulfur $= 10^{-1}$, $P_{CO_2} = 10^{-4}$. Boundaries of solids at total ionic activity of 10^{-6}. Dashed line is contour at activity of dissolved lead species of 10^{-4}. (Courtesy W. McIntyre.)

Figure 6.26e is a variant on the theme of Figure 6.26d, showing conditions that might be met in an oxidizing galena deposit isolated from the atmosphere, but with fairly high total dissolved carbonate, as well as high dissolved sulfur. Hydrocerussite appears again, owing to the fact that the system has fixed total CO_2, and at high pH values the hydroxycarbonate can compete with the normal carbonate. When P_{CO_2} is constant, total carbonate rises with pH, and $PbCO_3$

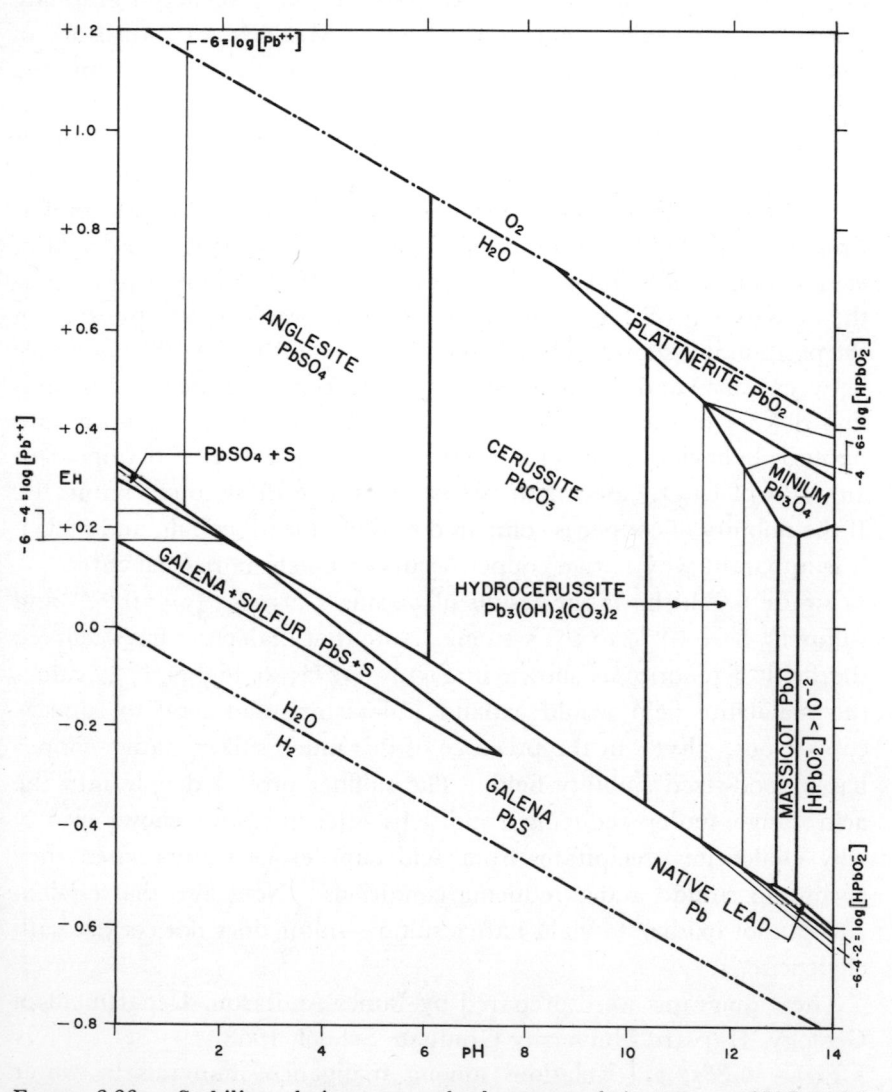

FIGURE 6.26e. Stability relations among lead compounds in water at 25°C and 1 atmosphere total pressure. Total dissolved sulfur species $= 10^{-1.5}$, total dissolved carbonate species $= 10^{-1}$. (Courtesy W. McIntyre.)

persists as the stable phase.   Both d and e of Figure 6.26 show another noteworthy relation: galena cannot oxidize to yield sulfur at pH values above about 2, but if the acidity exceeds this value, the field of native sulfur rises above that of PbS, and a small area of $PbSO_4 + S^0$ results.

In summary, the behavior of lead minerals is described usefully by the diagrams, and several of the minerals can be used as environmental indicators.   The diagrams were prepared by W. McIntyre, graduate student of the department of Geology at Massachusetts Institute of Technology, in 1957, and have been only slightly altered from the originals.

Figure 6.27a, b.   Relations among copper minerals at 25°C and 1 atmosphere total pressure in the presence of water.

Figure 6.27a shows the copper-oxygen-water relations, and emphasizes the large field of stability of native copper, as well as the field of acid solubility of copper as the cupric ion.   If 10^{-8} had been used as the activity cut-off for the fields of ions, Cu^+ would have appeared in the position it is shown in brackets.   The peculiar kink in the boundary between Cu_2O and the field of Cu^{++} results from a significant contribution of Cu^+ to the total ionic activity.   At this temperature the amphoteric behavior of copper is not important; the existence of important amounts of CuO_2^{--} occurs at pH values above those found naturally. If the nobility of copper is compared to that of lead, cobalt, and nickel, it is apparent why native copper occurs so much more frequently.

Figure 6.27b shows the results of adding CO_2 ($P_{CO_2} = 10^{-3.5}$) and sulfur ($\sum S = 10^{-1}$) to the system.   Note that malachite has occupied the field of tenorite as shown in Figure 6.27a; at higher P_{CO_2} values the malachite field would expand still farther and tend to squeeze cuprite out.   Even in the presence of this much sulfur, native copper has a good-sized stability field.   The sulfides project deeply into the acid range under reducing conditions—this diagram shows clearly why chalcocite precipitates from acid cupriferous waters when they encounter sulfide under reducing conditions.   Note also that chalcocite cannot oxidize to yield native sulfur—sulfur does not coexist with chalcocite.

These diagrams were prepared by James Anderson, Department of Geology, Harvard University Graduate School, 1958.

Figure 6.28a, b.   Relations among manganese minerals in water

containing CO_2 and sulfur at 25°C and 1 atmosphere total pressure.

Figure 6.28a shows stability relations among the oxides and the carbonate when total dissolved $CO_2 = 10^{-1.4}$; approximately a

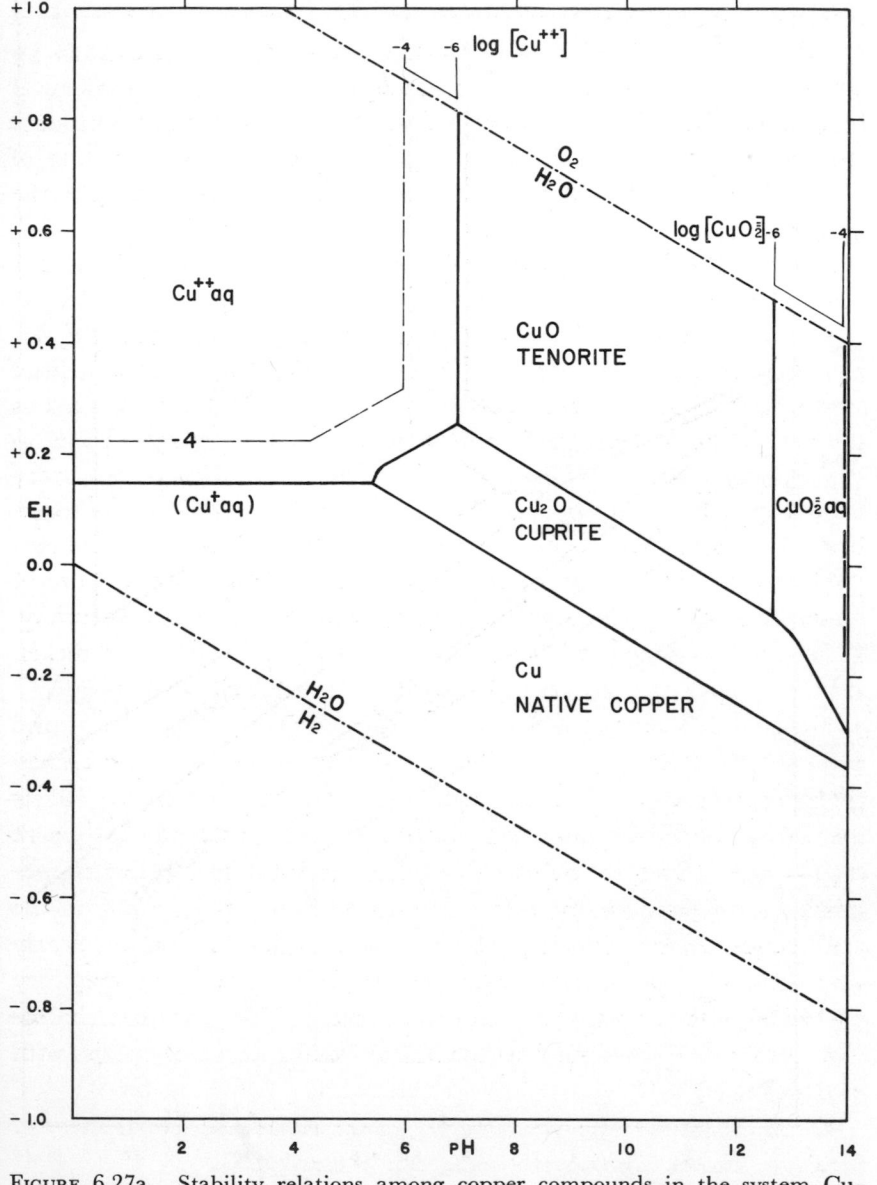

FIGURE 6.27a. Stability relations among copper compounds in the system Cu–H_2O–O_2 at 25°C and 1 atmosphere total pressure. (Courtesy J. Anderson.)

system saturated with CO_2 under 1 atmosphere pressure, then closed to CO_2. The large field of the carbonate (rhodochrosite) under these conditions is in marked contrast to the much smaller field of siderite

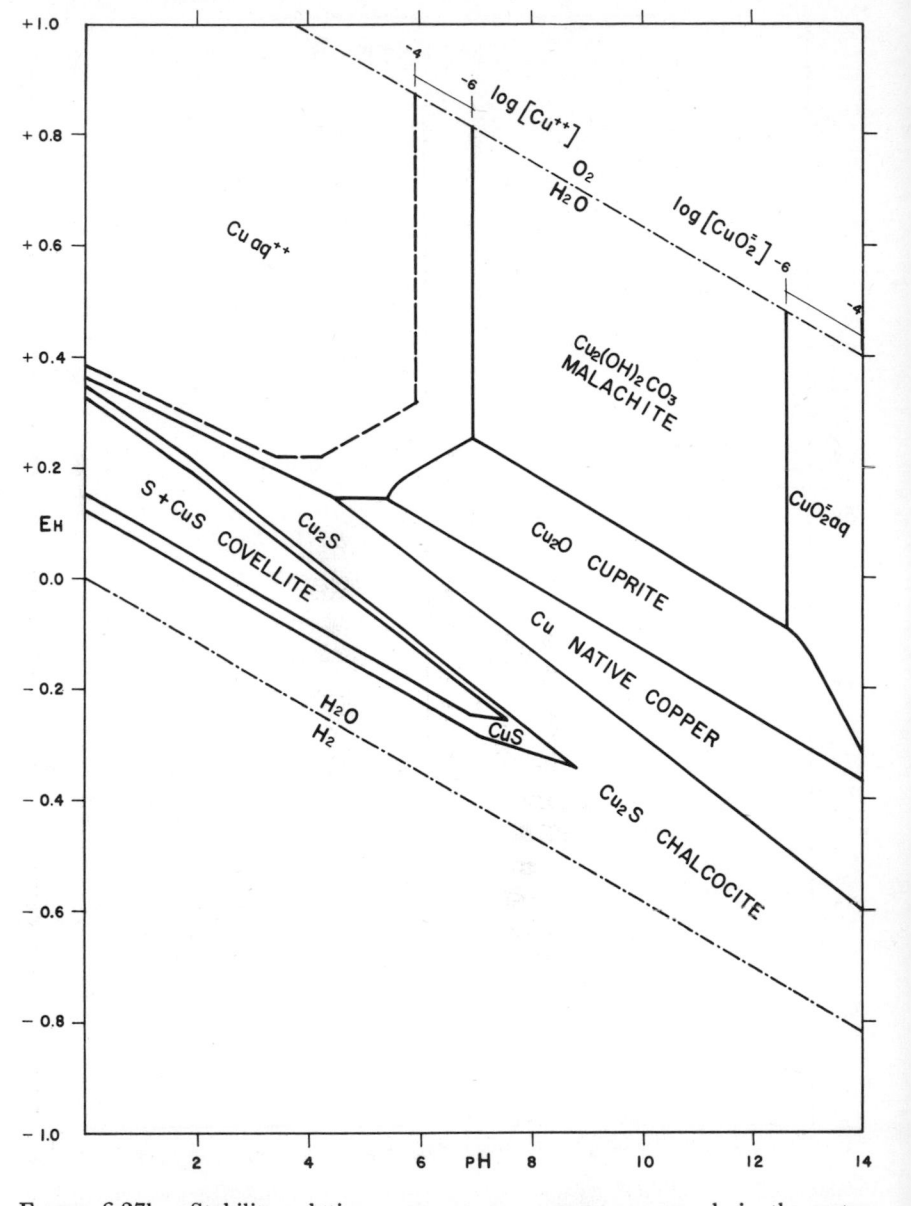

FIGURE 6.27b. Stability relations among some copper compounds in the system $Cu-H_2O-O_2-S-CO_2$ at 25°C and 1 atmosphere total pressure. $P_{CO_2} = 10^{-3.5}$, total dissolved sulfur species $= 10^{-1}$. (Courtesy J. Anderson.)

under the same conditions.   In the absence of CO_2 the higher valence oxides and the manganous hydroxide show increasing stability with increasing oxidation state.   No wonder the hydroxide pyrochroite is

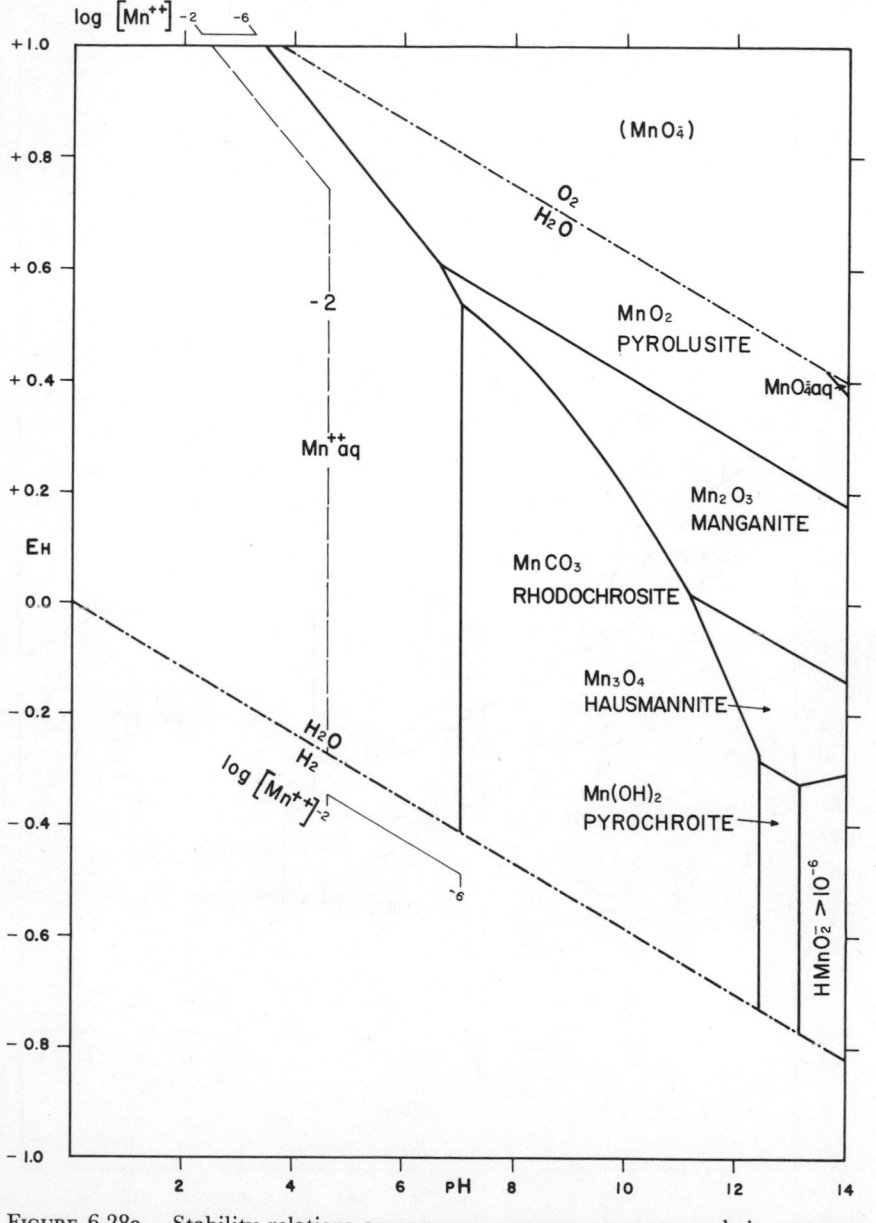

FIGURE 6.28a.   Stability relations among some manganese compounds in water at 25°C and 1 atmosphere total pressure.   Total dissolved carbonate species = $10^{-1.4}$. (Courtesy E. Gaucher.)

an extremely rare mineral; it requires alkaline reducing conditions and the practical absence of CO_2. As for iron, the amphoteric behavior of manganese is of no consequence under natural conditions. Both

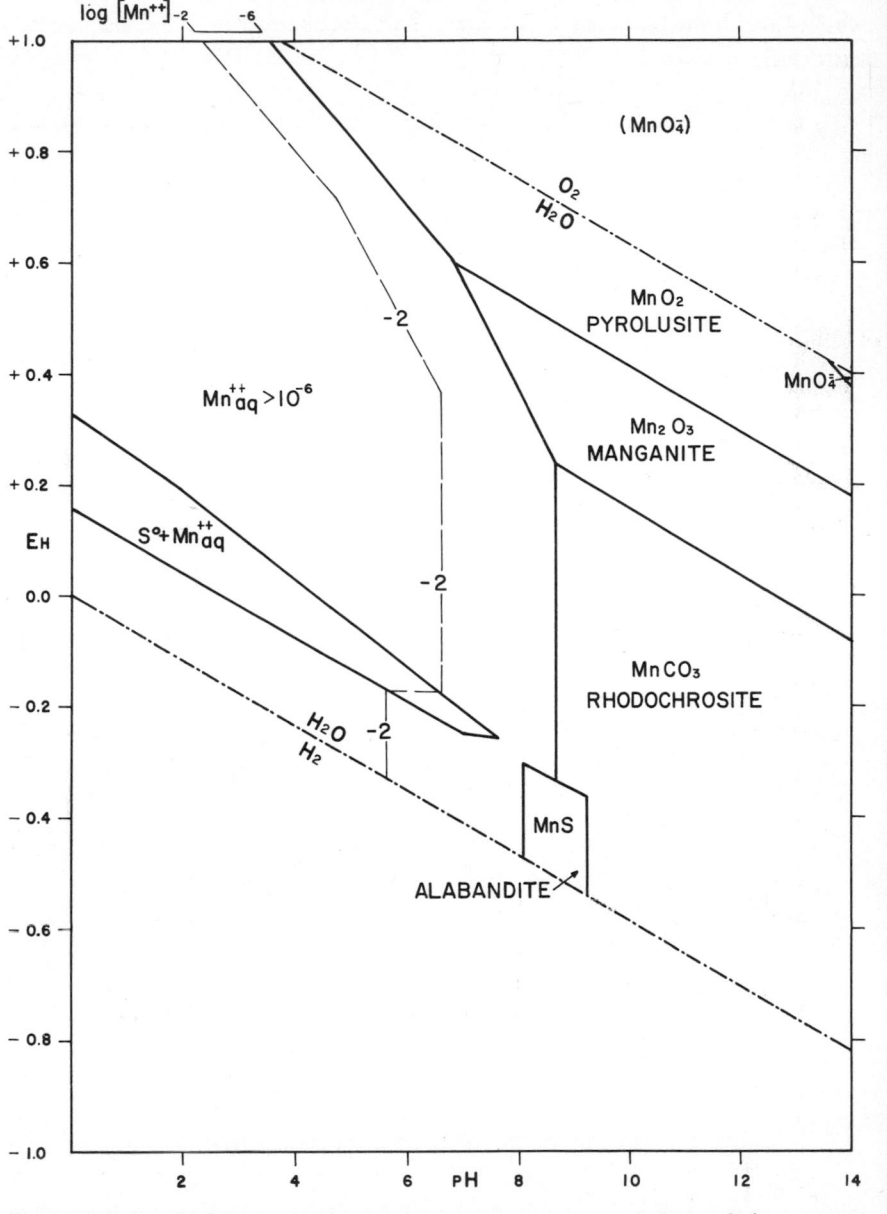

FIGURE 6.28b. Stability relations among some manganese compounds in water at 25°C and 1 atmosphere total pressure. Total dissolved sulfur species = 10^{-1}, $P_{CO_2} = 10^{-4}$. (Courtesy E. Gaucher.)

MnO_4^{--} and MnO_4^- ions are unstable with respect to water; MnO_4^{--} appears only in a small area under alkaline oxidizing conditions. This relation recalls to mind that potassium permanganate solution, over a period of months, gradually decomposes to give MnO_2. On the other hand, it also illustrates that metastability may be of considerable duration.

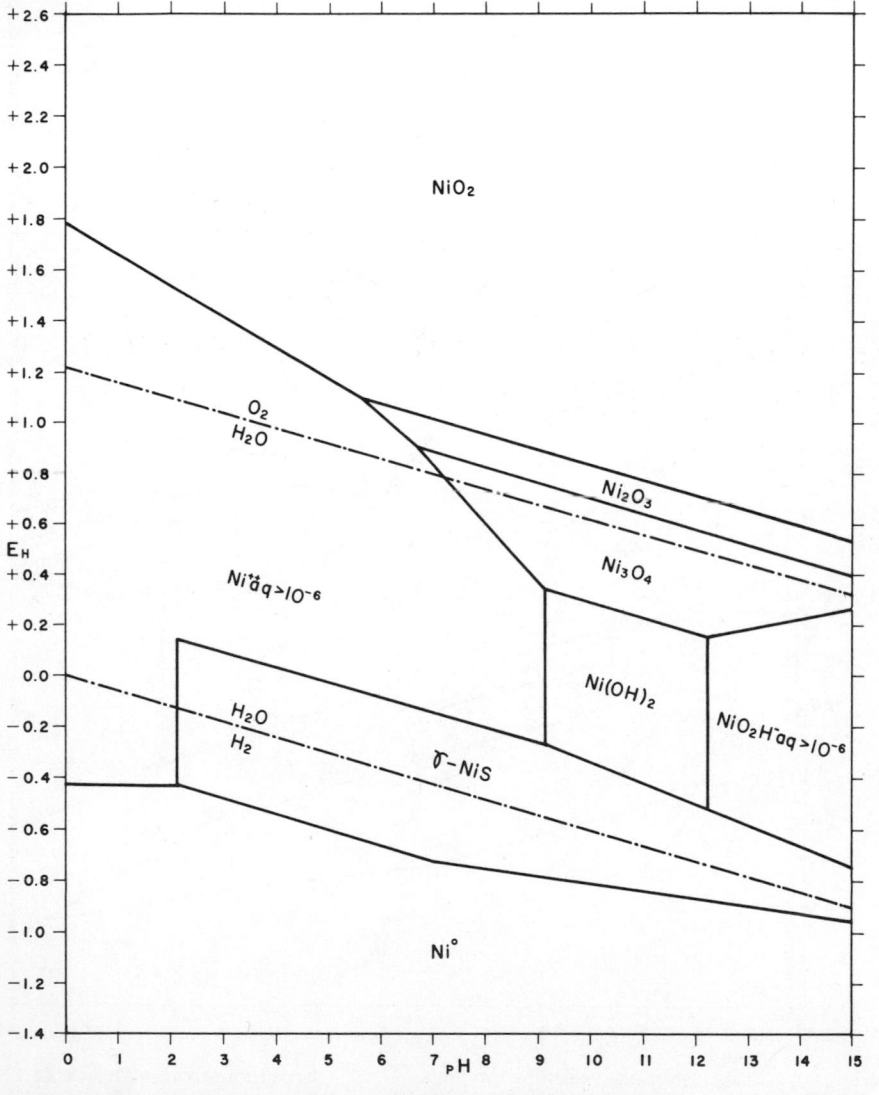

FIGURE 6.29a. Stability relations among some nickel compounds in water at 25°C and 1 atmosphere total pressure. Total dissolved sulfur species = 10^{-5}. (Courtesy J. Anthony.)

Figure 6.28b shows two major new relations. In this instance the system is open to CO_2 ($P_{CO_2} = 10^{-4}$ atmosphere), and as usual the carbonate had wiped out the field of the divalent oxide or hydroxide owing to the increase in CO_3^{--} as well as OH^- with increasing pH. Also, note the small field of alabandite (MnS) even in the presence of 10^{-1} total dissolved sulfur. As most marine environments become

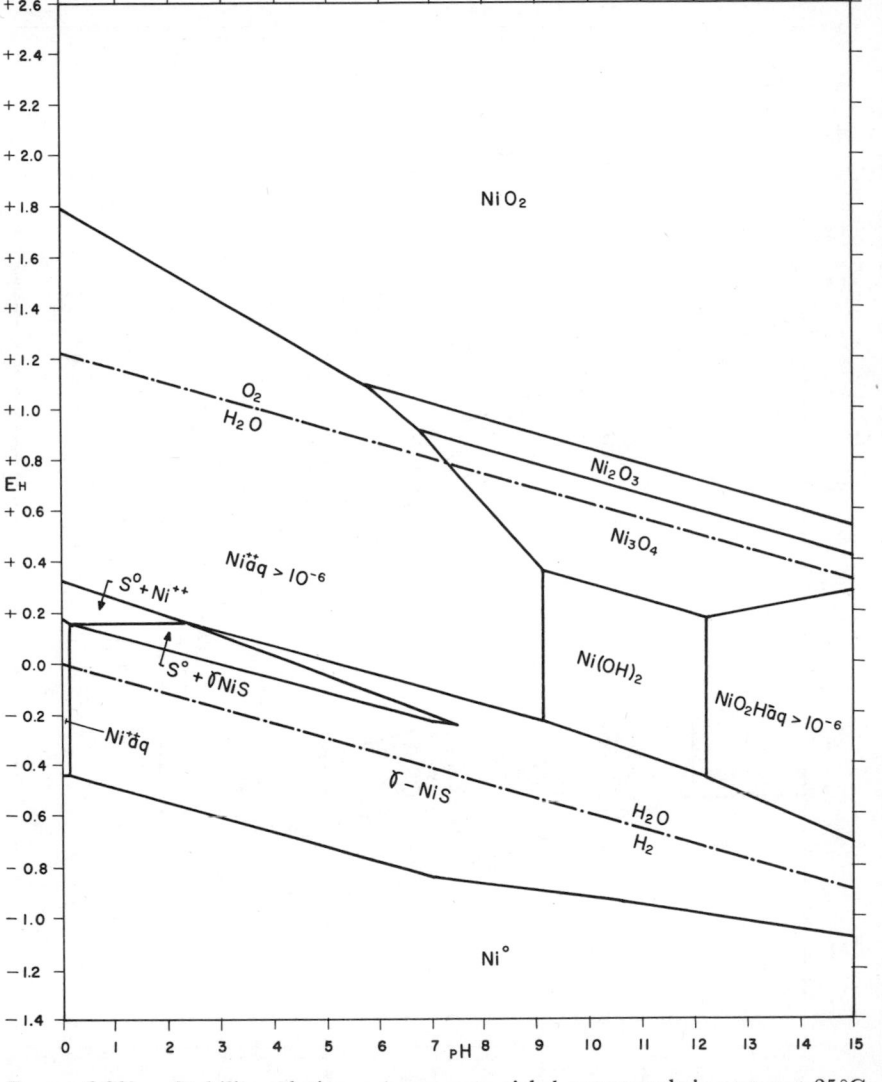

FIGURE 6.29b. Stability relations among some nickel compounds in water at 25°C and 1 atmosphere total pressure. Total dissolved sulfur species = 10^{-1}. (Courtesy J. Anthony.)

reducing and develop divalent sulfur, the pH drops to 6.5–7.0. Under such conditions manganese would tend to dissolve, or perhaps the carbonate would precipitate, but some unusual OH^--producing reaction would be required to produce alabandite. This conclusion is in accord with the sparse occurrence of alabandite in nature.

These diagrams were prepared by Edwin Gaucher, Department of Geology, Harvard University Graduate School, 1957.

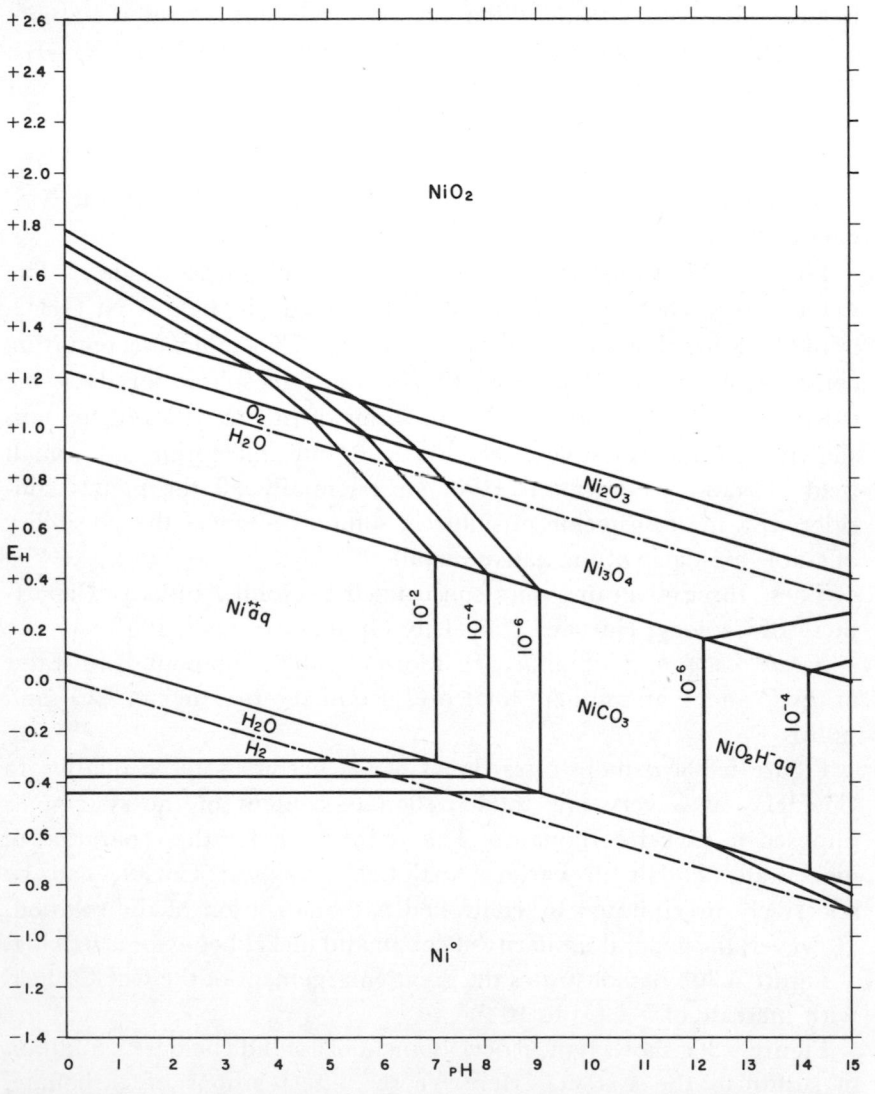

FIGURE 6.29c. Stability relations among some nickel compounds in water at 25°C and 1 atmosphere total pressure. $P_{CO_2} = 10^{-0.8}$. (Courtesy J. Anthony.)

Figure 6.29a, b, c. Relations in systems involving nickel and water at 25°C and 1 atmosphere pressure with sulfur or CO_2 added.

Figure 6.29a shows that with total dissolved sulfur activity of 10^{-5} nickel sulfide is stable over a large pH range under reducing conditions. Nickel oxides and hydroxides, on the other hand, are relatively soluble, as indicated by the large fields of Ni^{++} under acid conditions and NiO_2H^- under alkaline conditions. The general similarity to iron behavior is clear, with the difference of a respectable field of stability of $Ni(OH)_2$, as opposed to the entire lack of such a field for $Fe(OH)_2$. Unfortunately data are not available for NiS_2, the pyrite analog, but it would, if stable, sandwich in between NiS and $Ni(OH)_2$.

Figure 6.29b shows the effect of increasing total sulfur, with the appearance of a field of native sulfur and an enlargement of the NiS-occupied area.

Figure 6.29c shows the effect of CO_2 on the nickel oxides. The value of P_{CO_2} chosen is just sufficient to wipe out the field of $Ni(OH)_2$, demonstrating that nickel carbonate is a good CO_2 indicator, requiring considerably greater P_{CO_2} than that of the atmosphere for its stable existence. Contours are labeled in terms of the activities of the ions shown. Note that native nickel, like lead, but unlike iron, has a small field of stability in water. Also, for essentially all the metals considered, a mere suspicion of sulfur in solution removes the possibility of stable existence of the native metal.

These three diagrams were constructed by John Anthony, Department of Geology, Harvard University Graduate School, 1957.

Figure 6.30a, b, c. Stability relations of cobalt compounds in water at 25°C and 1 atmosphere total pressure in the presence of CO_2 and sulfur.

Figure 6.30a demonstrates that $CoCO_3$ becomes stable relative to $Co(OH)_2$ at a very low total carbonate content of the system, as opposed to nickel carbonate. This is the basis for the separation of nickel and cobalt in various analytical schemes; $CoCO_3$ can be selectively precipitated by controlled carbonatization of the solution. However, the general similarity of cobalt and nickel behavior is striking.

Figure 6.30b demonstrates the great enlargement of the $CoCO_3$ field with increase of $\sum CO_2$ to $10^{-1.5}$.

Figure 6.30c shows typical development of a sulfide field with addition of sulfur to the system. Here we see interrelations of carbonate, hydroxides, and the sulfide in carbonated sulfur bearing waters. If

the various sulfides shown in these diagrams are compared, it will be found that the oxidation potential at which they go to appreciable concentrations of metal ions and sulfate is nearly the same.   This

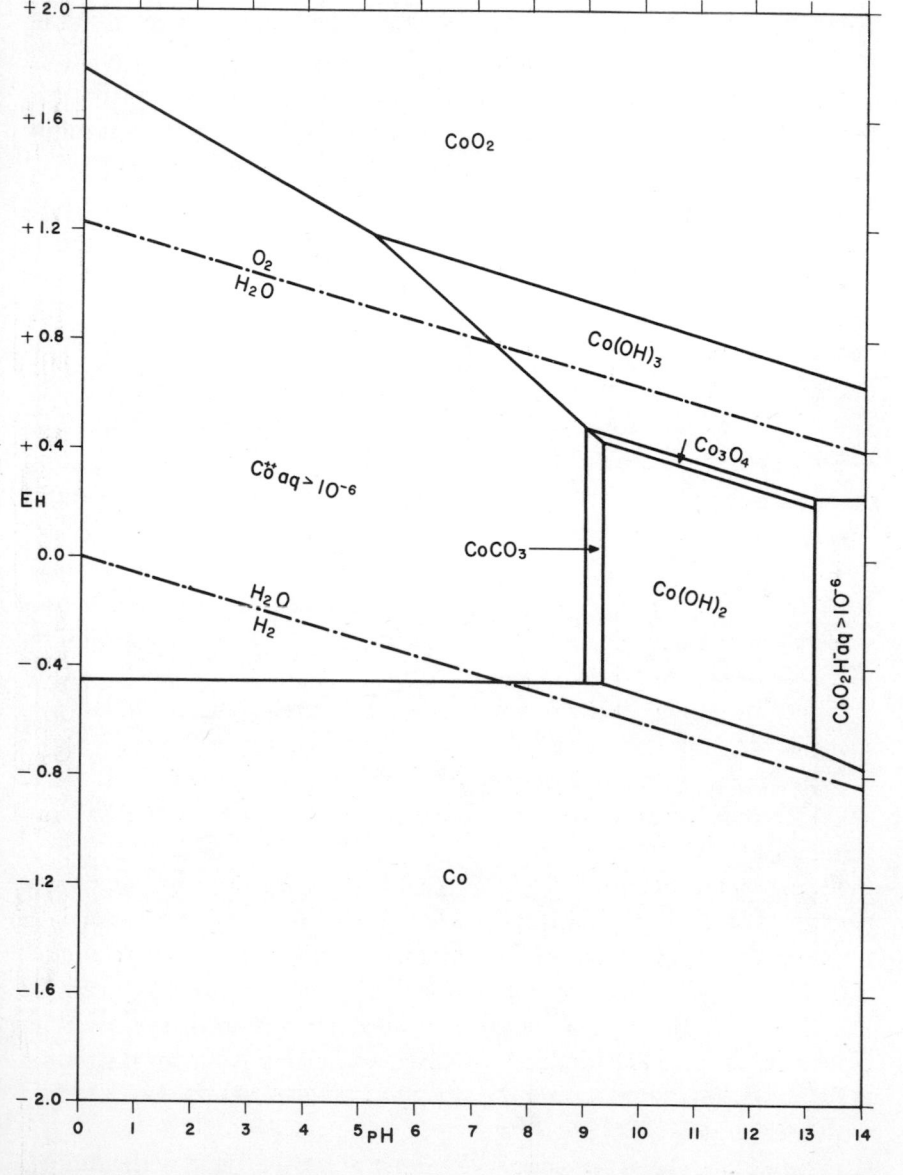

FIGURE 6.30a.   Stability relations among some cobalt compounds in water at 25°C and 1 atmosphere total pressure.   Total dissolved carbonate species $= 10^{-4 \cdot 9}$. (Courtesy I. Barnes.)

occurs because of the remarkably sharp division on an Eh basis between divalent and sexivalent sulfur. The change is so marked that
differences in the stability of the sulfides are largely obscured.

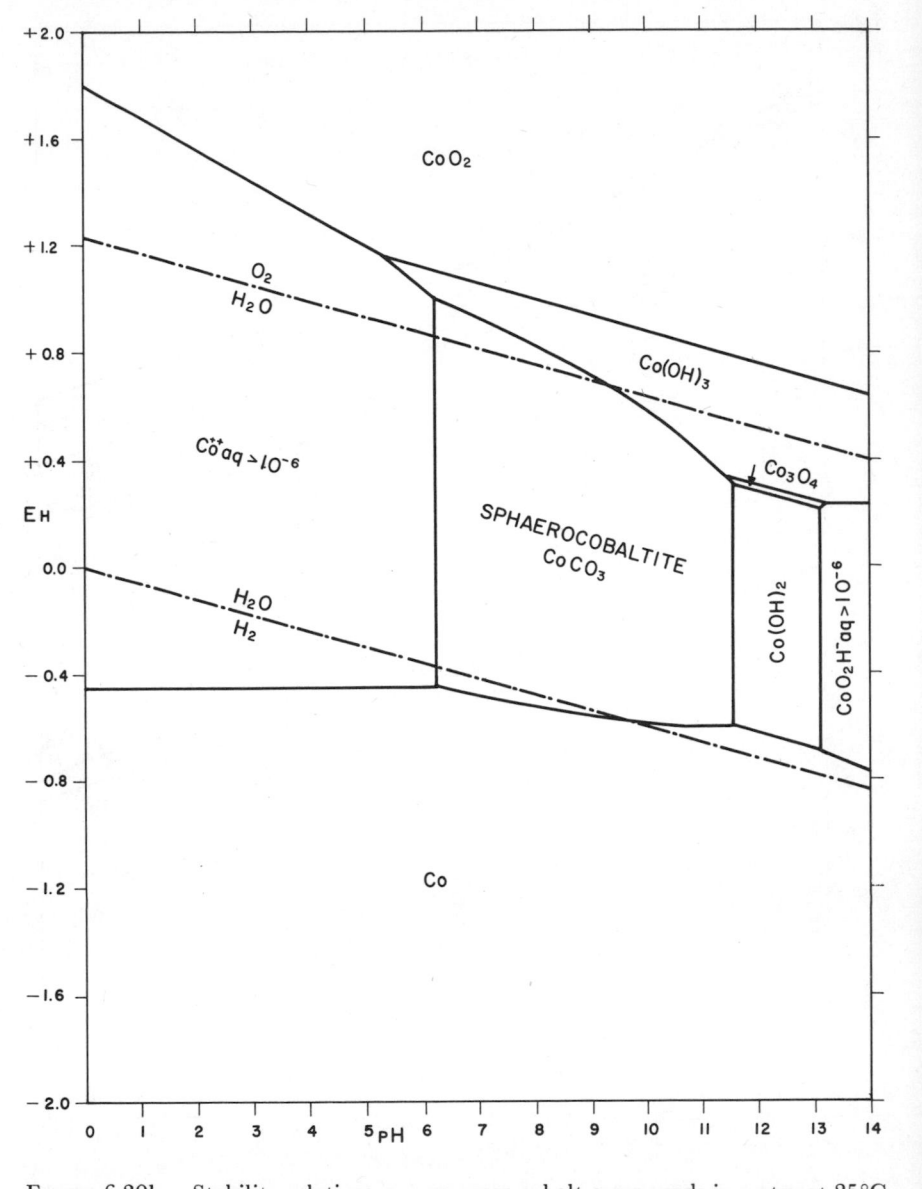

FIGURE 6.30b. Stability relations among some cobalt compounds in water at 25°C
and 1 atmosphere total pressure. Total dissolved carbonate species $= 10^{-1.4}$.
(Courtesy I. Barnes.)

These cobalt diagrams were prepared by Ivan Barnes, Department of Geology, Harvard University Graduate School, 1957.

Figure 6.31a, b.   Relations among the tungsten oxides and sulfides.

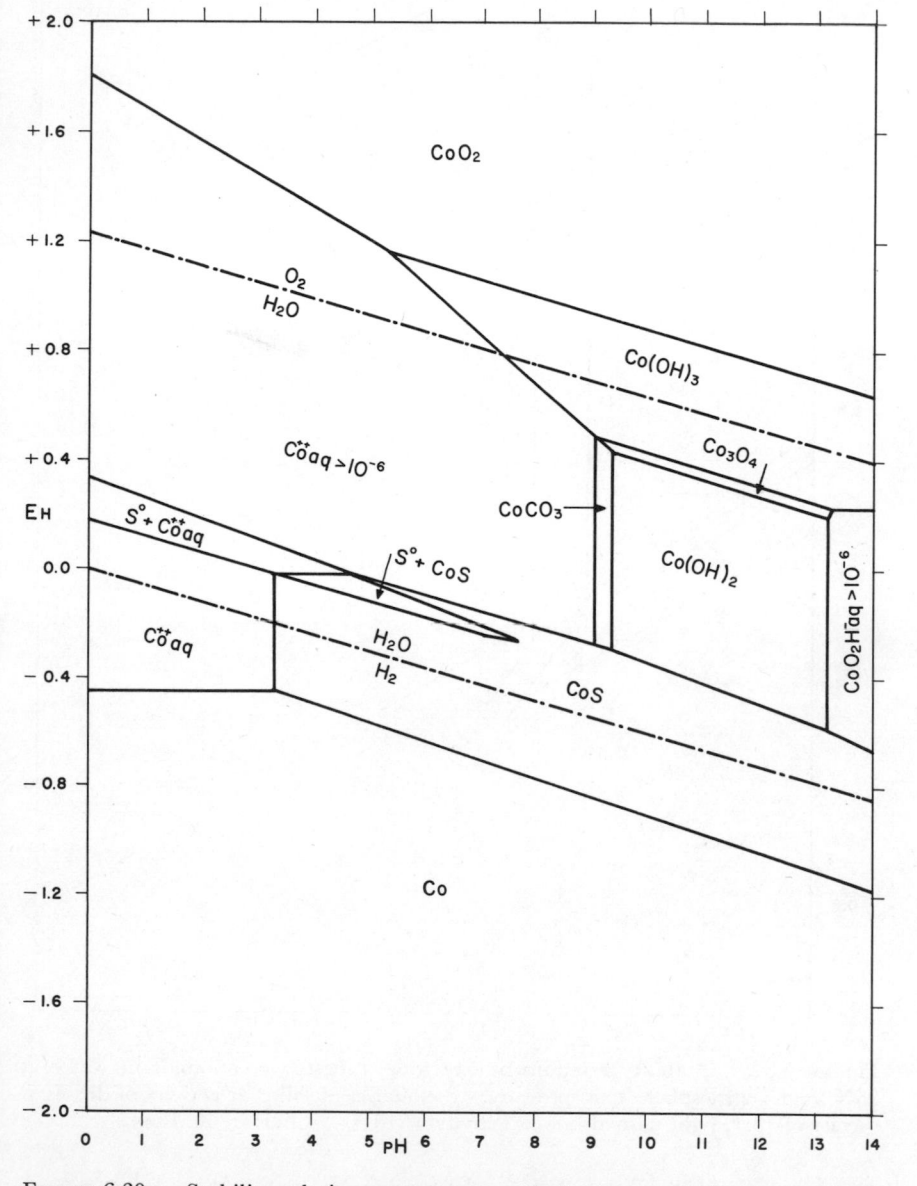

FIGURE 6.30c.   Stability relations among some cobalt compounds in water at 25°C and 1 atmosphere total pressure.   Total dissolved carbonate species $= 10^{-4.9}$, total dissolved sulfur species $= 10^{-1}$.   (Courtesy I. Barnes.)

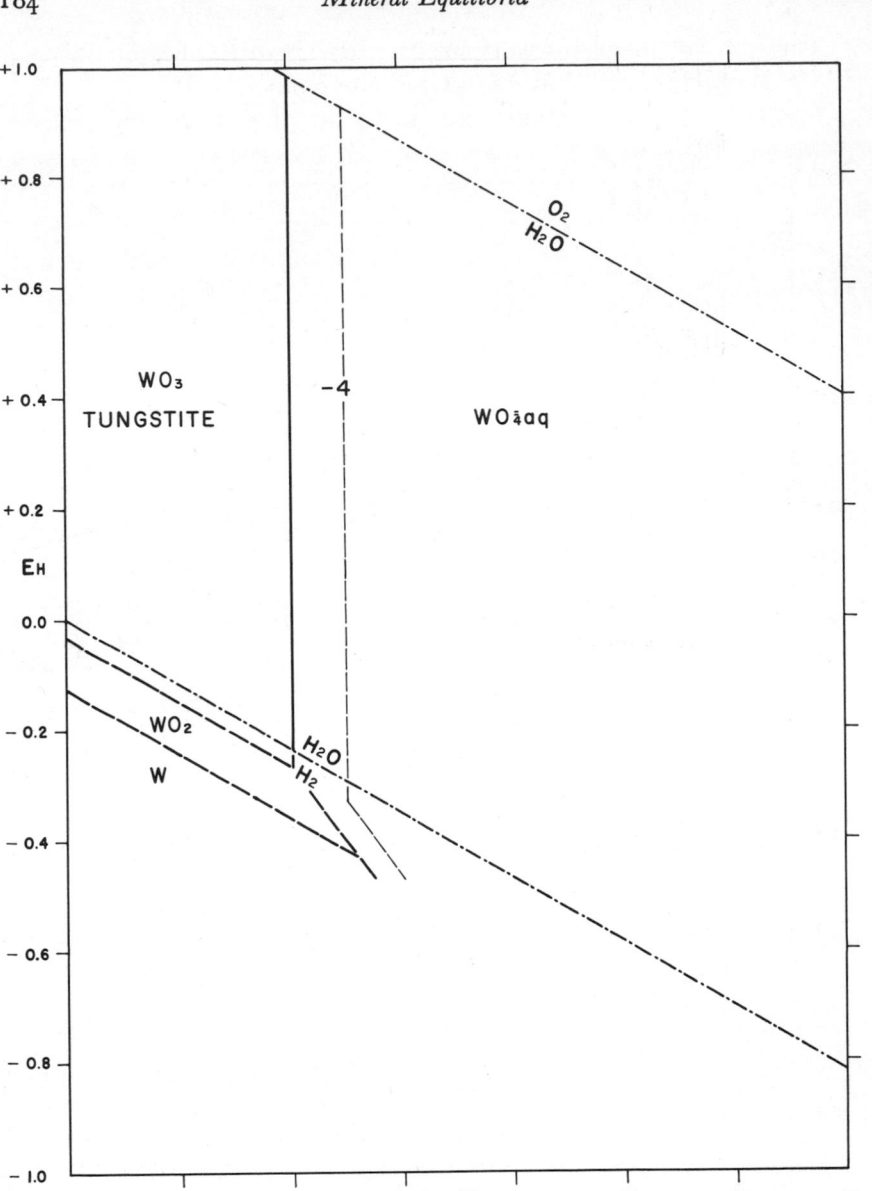

FIGURE 6.31a. Stability relations among some tungsten compounds in water at 25°C and 1 atmosphere total pressure. Boundaries of solids at activity of dissolved species of 10^{-6}, light dashed line at activity = 10^{-4}. (Courtesy K. Linn.)

The strongly amphoteric behavior of tungsten is well shown by the large field of importance of the WO_4^{--} ion, and the stability of WO_3 in acid solutions. In nature the WO_4^{--} ion tends to be fixed by

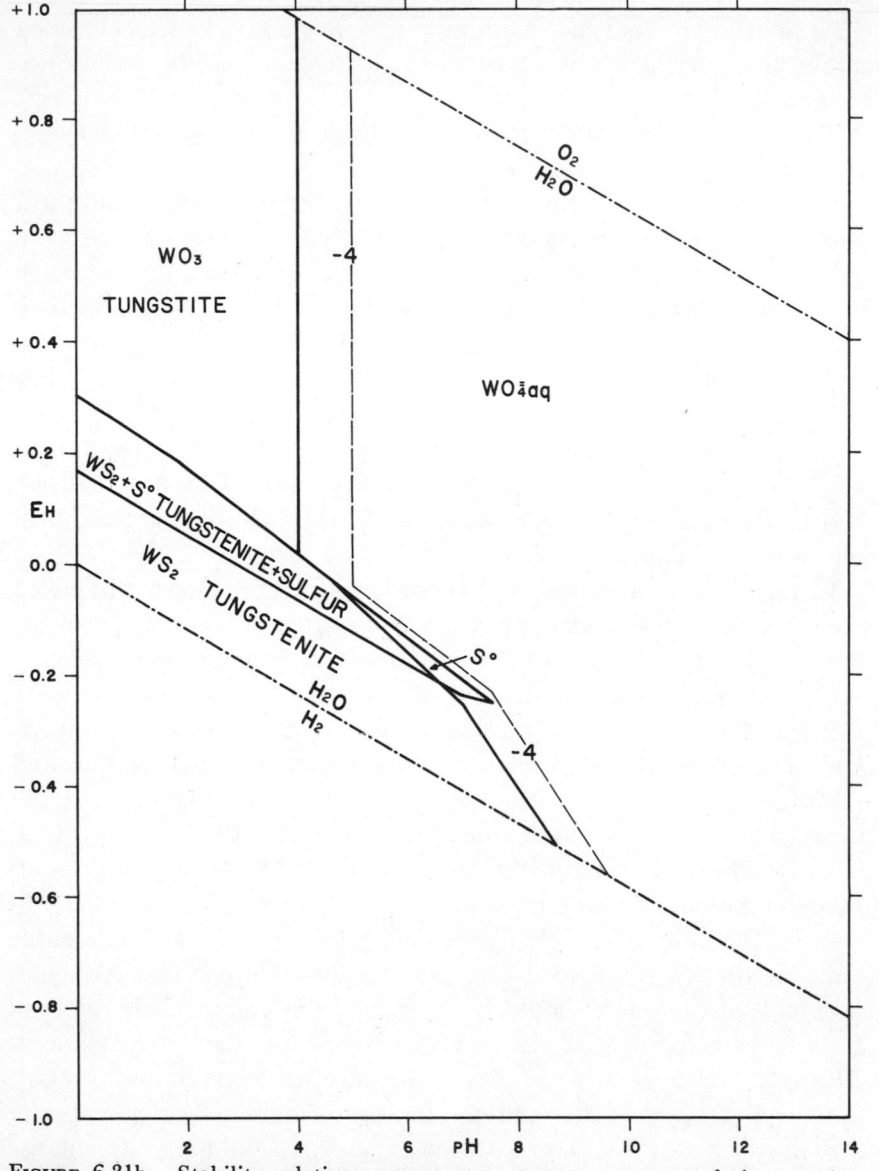

FIGURE 6.31b. Stability relations among some tungsten compounds in water at 25°C and 1 atmosphere total pressure. Total dissolved sulfur species = 10^{-1}. Boundaries of solids at activity of dissolved species of 10^{-6}, dashed line at activity = 10^{-4}. (Courtesy K. Linn.)

cations not shown here, to form such insoluble compounds as $CaWO_4$ and $FeWO_4$. The sulfide is moderately stable, but also tends to be displaced by insoluble tungstates in the presence of various cations.

Note that WO_2 is metastable with respect to water under the conditions shown here, and that metallic tungsten is not to be expected as a stable phase, whatever its resistance to corrosion may be when once formed.

The diagrams were prepared by Kurt Linn, Department of Geology, Harvard Graduate School, 1958.

Figure 6.32a, b, c. Some relations among uranium compounds and ions at 25°C and 1 atmosphere total pressure.

Figure 6.32a and b compare the effect of CO_2 on uranium solubility in the open system (P_{CO_2}) and the closed system ($\sum CO_2$). In both instances sexivalent uranium is complexed strikingly as the diuranyl and triuranyl ionic species, so that with appreciable P_{CO_2} or $\sum CO_2$ the field of stability of the uranyl oxide hydrate (schoepite?) is wiped out. These complexes are so effective that they "eat" down into the field of stability of UO_2 (uraninite) when P_{CO_2} and $\sum CO_2$ are relatively high. It should be clear that carbonate-bearing solutions are excellent solvents for uranium.

In Figure 6.32c a technique that has been little developed but which should have widespread application is illustrated. A major geologic problem in the oxidation of uranium ores is a deciphering of the conditions of migration and fixation of uranium. As shown in Figure 6.32a and b, carbonated water prevents precipitation of uranyl oxide hydrates, but it is well known that carnotite, the potassium uranyl vanadate, is a persistent mineral in the zone of oxidation. In the figure a section of the multicomponent system U-O_2-H_2O-K-V-CO_2 has been drawn at fixed activities of K, V, and CO_2, and the "solubility" relations of uranium examined for this particular set of conditions. The values for $\sum K$, $\sum V$, and $\sum CO_2$ chosen are reasonable ones for the waters of oxidizing uranium-vanadium ores. Although the fields of the solids should be examined through a whole range of these values, a single section serves to illustrate the gross relations. The uranium-carbonate complex ions contribute a "solubility trough" under reducing alkaline conditions, but the formidable field of carnotite is plainly shown. Increase of dissolved V or K would serve to enlarge the carnotite field, whereas increase of CO_2 would diminish its size.

The diagrams were prepared by P. B. Hostetler and R. M. Garrels, in collaboration with C. L. Christ and A. D. Weeks (R. M. Garrels, P. B. Hostetler, C. L. Christ, and A. D. Weeks. Stability of uranium, vanadium, copper, and molybdenum minerals in natural waters at

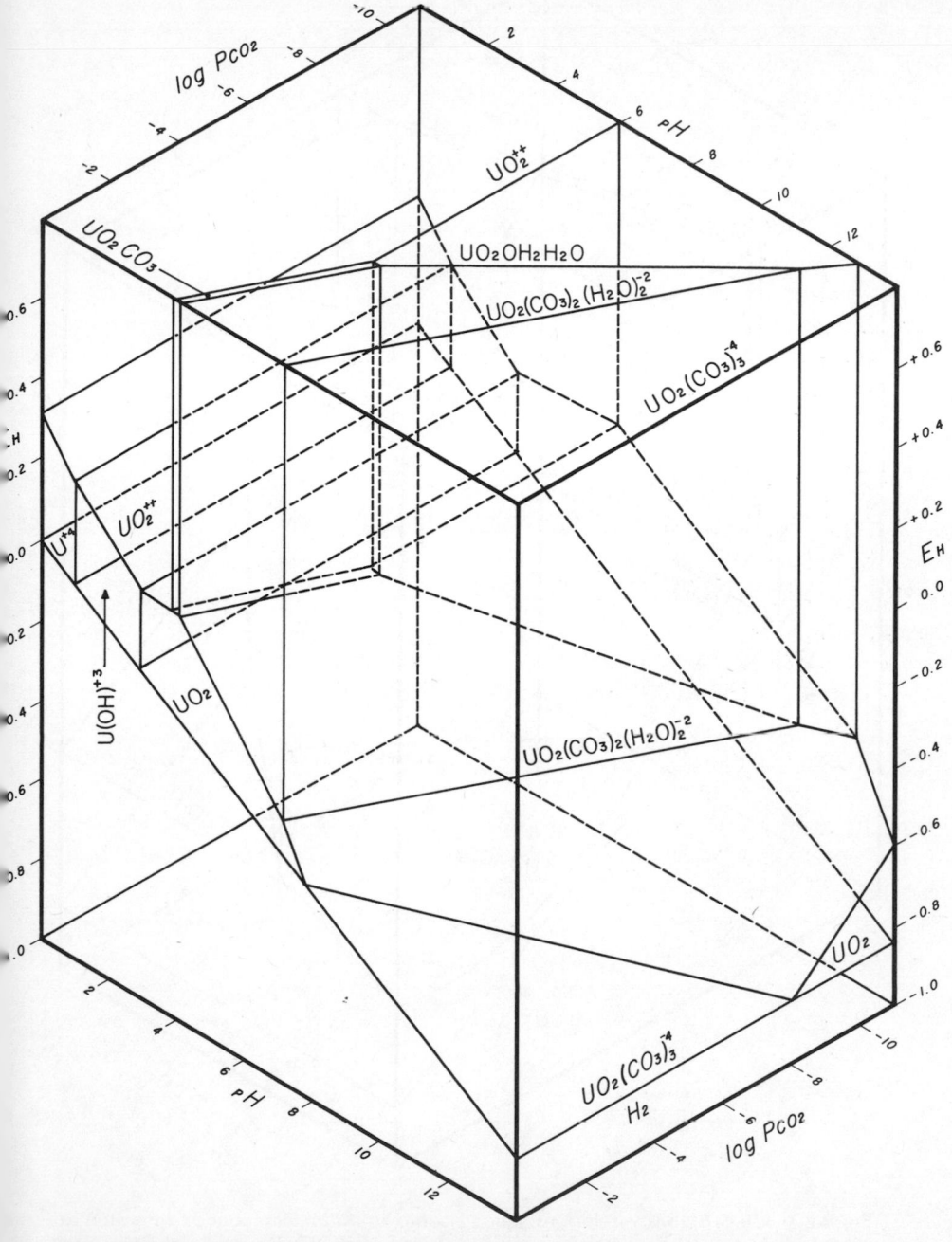

FIGURE 6.32a. Stability relations among some uranium compounds in water at 25°C and 1 atmosphere total pressure as a function of pH, Eh, and P_{CO_2}. Boundaries of solids at activity of total dissolved uranium-bearing species of 10^{-6}. (Courtesy R. Garrels, P. Hostetler, A. Weeks, C. Christ.)

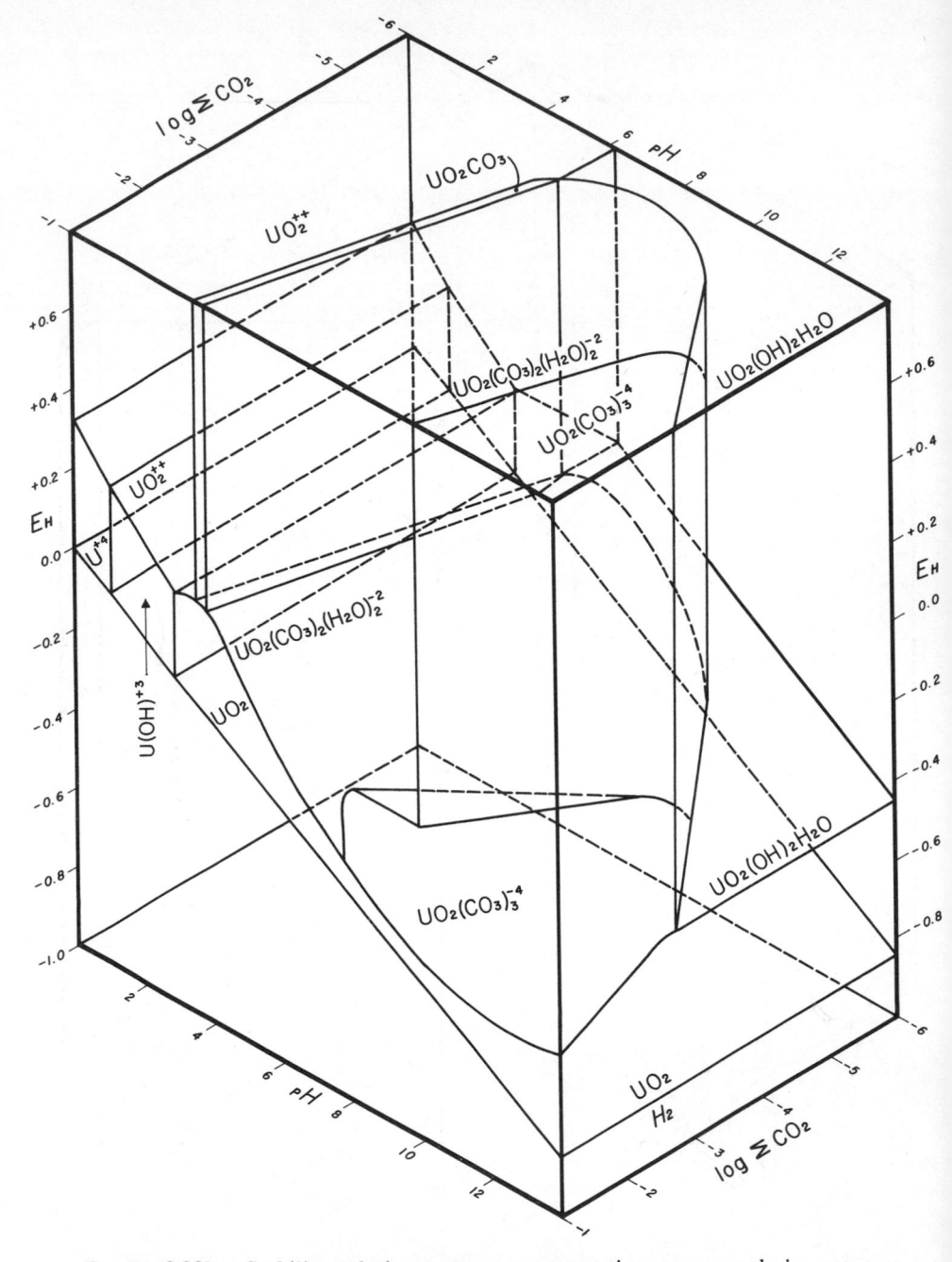

FIGURE 6.32b. Stability relations among some uranium compounds in water at 25°C and 1 atmosphere total pressure as a function of pH, Eh, and total dissolved carbonate species. Boundaries of solids at activity of total dissolved uranium-bearing species of 10^{-6}. (Courtesy R. Garrels, P. Hostetler, A. Weeks, and C. Christ.)

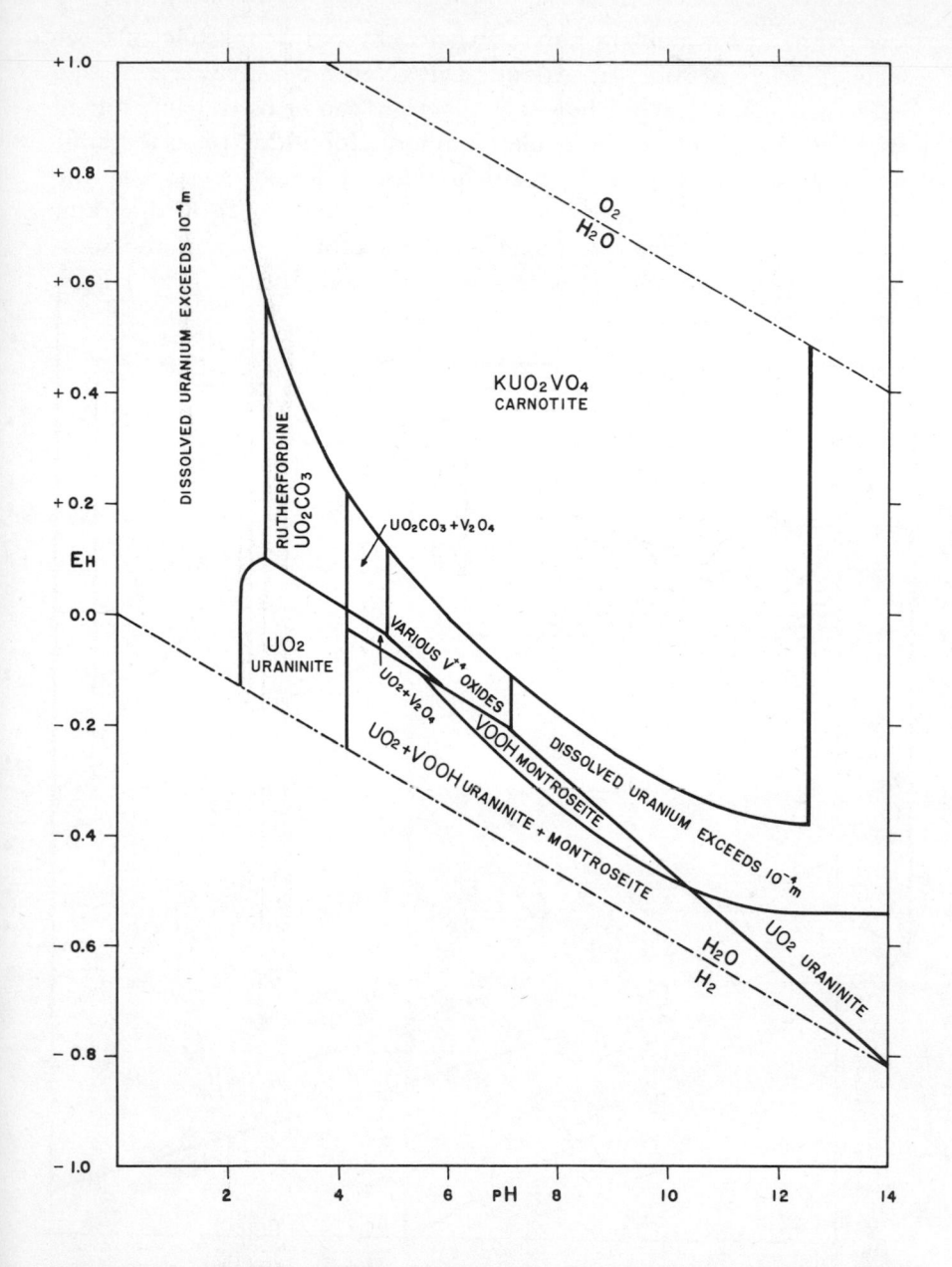

FIGURE 6.32c. Stability relations among some uranium and vanadium compounds in water at 25°C and 1 atmosphere total pressure. Total dissolved vanadium species $= 10^{-3}$, total dissolved carbonate species $= 10^{-1}$, total dissolved potassium species $= 10^{-3}$. (Courtesy R. Garrels, P. Hostetler, A. Weeks, and C. Christ.)

low temperatures and pressures: Paper delivered at meeting of Geological Society of America, Atlantic City, November, 1957).

Figure 6.33a, b. Shows how such diagrams can be used to investigate the effects of complexes on metal solubility. John Phillips, as a graduate student in geology at Harvard in 1957, undertook to portray the effects of sulfide and chloride complexing of gold on an Eh-pH diagram. Many of the relations are based on Krauskopf's study of the solubility of gold [Konrad B. Krauskopf, The solubility of gold. *Econ.*

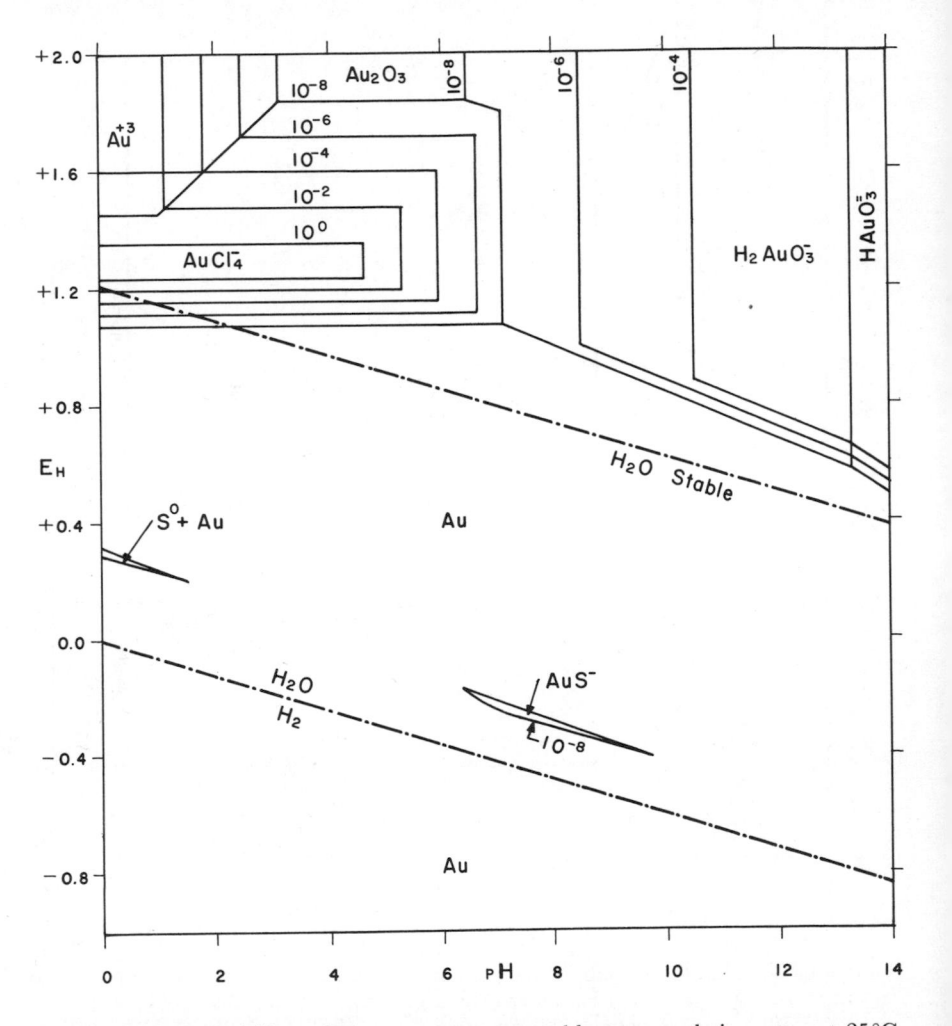

FIGURE 6.33a. Stability relations among some gold compounds in water at 25°C and 1 atmosphere total pressure. Total dissolved chloride species = 10^{-3}, total dissolved sulfur species = 10^{-6}. (Courtesy J. Phillips.)

Geol., *46*, 858–870 (1951)]. The figure shows ionic activities at low and high chloride and sulfur contents of the system. Eh values far above those in equilibrium with water are included, so that the overall relations can be seen, even though the reactions above the water boundary are not truly valid. An Eh-pH diagram for gold in oxygenated water is simple indeed—only native gold appears, with no ions exceeding 10^{-6}. In the presence of high chloride, gold is somewhat soluble in acid oxidizing solutions as $AuCl_4^-$; with high sulfur, a

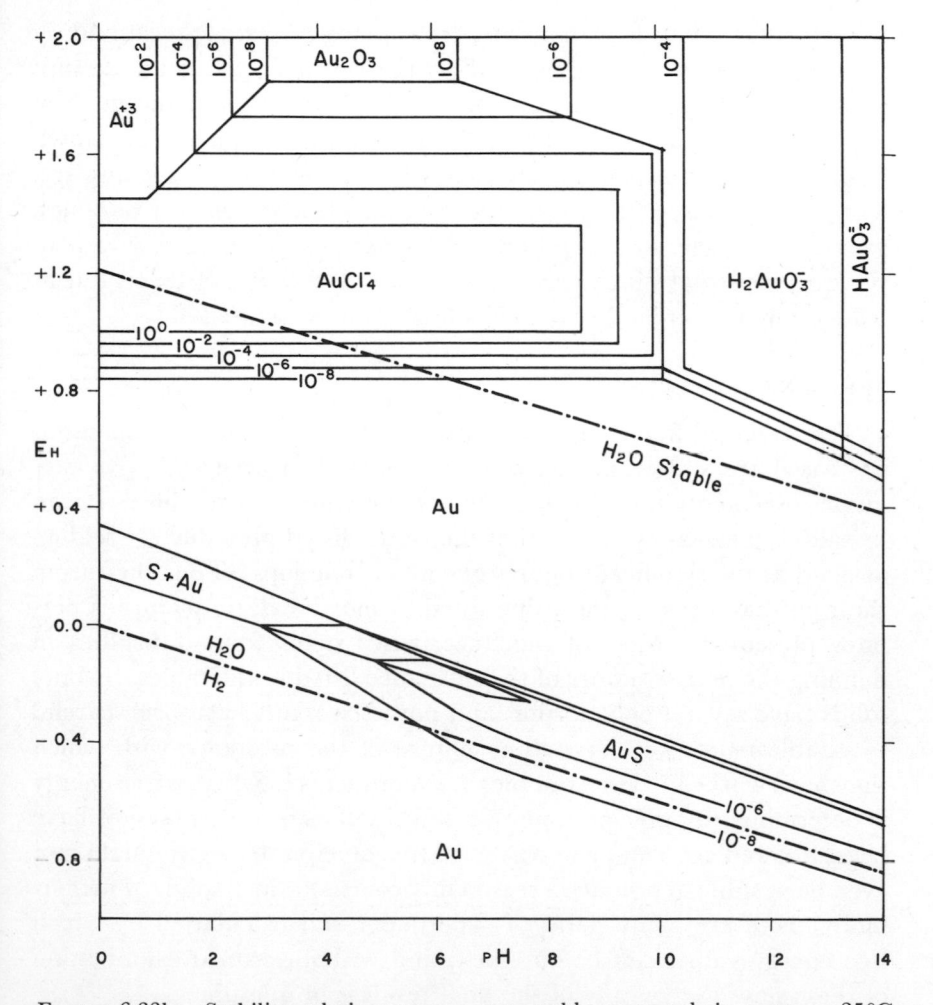

FIGURE 6.33b. Stability relations among some gold compounds in water at 25°C and 1 atmosphere total pressure. Total dissolved chloride species = 10^0. Total dissolved sulfur species = 10^{-1}. (Courtesy J. Phillips.)

little gold dissolves as the AuS^- complex over a wide range of strongly reducing conditions. Both relations are of geologic interest, the first because of the possibility of transport of gold during oxidation of sulfide ores, and the second because of the problem of transporting gold in vein-forming fluids.

SUMMARY OF THE USE AND LIMITATIONS OF Eh-pH DIAGRAMS

In the preceding text there are, from place to place, precautionary statements concerning the use of Eh-pH diagrams. Here an attempt is made to discuss various aspects of this problem, with the hope of showing the kinds of conclusions that can be unequivocally drawn from these diagrams, and the areas in which dangers await the unwary. There is no question that the best safeguard to the user is a thorough grounding in solution chemistry. It is not possible here to cover all the questions that may arise, or even a small fraction of them, but at least the major strengths and weaknesses can be pointed out.

FREE ENERGY DATA

The standard free energy of formation data on which the diagrams are based are, unfortunately, very uneven in their accuracy. No easy guide to estimation of the accuracy of the value is available. It can be said, somewhat cynically, that the values listed probably are seldom as good as the significant figures given. If one lops off one digit from the right-hand side of the value listed, a more realistic picture is perhaps presented. Most of the uncertainty stems from difficulties in defining the precise nature of the substance listed in the tables. Many solids have several polymorphs, and not all workers have been careful to establish the exact crystalline nature of the substance with which they have worked. For example, in experiments in which a free energy is determined by precipitation of a solid, sufficient time may not have been allowed for complete aging of the precipitate, or it might not even be possible to produce a reasonably coarse-grained solid. Furthermore, there are many paths of experiment and calculation by which free energy values can be obtained, and without critical examination of these steps the validity of the final result is in question.

However, these difficulties are not restricted to the use of free energy values in the synthesis of Eh-pH diagrams—they are inherent in any

thermochemical calculations. The best guide, perhaps, is common sense; if a calculation shows that phase A is stable relative to phase B by a small free energy margin, phase B should be eliminated with reservations. This is especially true if the calculation path is a devious one, and involves the difference of several large free energy of formation values.

The ΔF_f° values available for solids are characteristically for materials that correspond analytically as closely as possible to the formula given. Minerals are characteristically "impure" as compared to these standards. Thus a diagram illustrating relations among "pure" chemical compounds must not be mistaken for one representing actual minerals. Generally speaking the difference in free energy of formation caused by minor substitution of other elements in the structure of a given chemical species is not large (the effect is ordinarily approximately proportional to the mole fraction of the substituent). The most serious error likely to be made by the calculator is in forgetting how far minerals do deviate from pure end-member composition, or to what extent certain minerals differ structurally from the analog chemical compound. For example, some natural compounds of dolomite composition are disordered; what this does to stability we would like to know. Also some sphalerites, which we might tend to regard as ZnS for purposes of calculation, in fact contain 10 to 14 percent iron.

Continuing in the same vein, we find ourselves in a geologic difficulty when we attempt to construct a diagram simulating conditions of deposition of the chemically precipitated iron minerals. Should stability relations be calculated for crystalline hematite or goethite, or is the natural system controlled by the freshly precipitated and much less stable hydrous oxide of indefinite water content? The problem again is the choice of the right chemical compound to simulate the natural situation.

THE EFFECT OF TEMPERATURE AND PRESSURE

All calculations given have been for 25°C and 1 atmosphere total pressure. Yet the implication has been clear throughout that the results from using data derived under these conditions would differ but slightly from those that might be obtained within the extremes of the surface and near-surface environments of the earth. Just what is the order of magnitude of the error expected if several atmospheres are impressed upon the system, or if the temperature is 15°C or 35°C?

The effect of a few atmospheres total pressure can be safely ignored, but that of $\pm 10°$ in temperature needs more careful consideration. The change in free energy with temperature of a given reaction at 25°C is given by the relation:

$$\frac{\partial \Delta F_R^\circ}{(\partial T)_P} = -\Delta S_R^\circ$$

where ΔS_R° is the standard entropy change of the reaction. Without going into details of the derivation or significance of standard entropy change, it can be generalized that for most reactions we have considered, ΔS° is but a few hundredths of a kilocalorie per degree centigrade. Therefore the effect of a 10°C temperature change on a given reaction usually results in a change of ΔF_R° of not more than a few tenths of a kilocalorie.

Specifically, if we consider the Eh-pH boundary between magnetite and hematite:

$$2Fe_3O_{4\,c} + H_2O_l = 3Fe_2O_{3\,c} + 2H_{aq}^+ + 2e$$

The equation for the boundary at 25°C is:

$$Eh = 0.221 - 0.059pH$$

At 35°C the equation is:

$$Eh = 0.227 - 0.061pH$$

Thus the difference can barely be plotted. This order of magnitude is about average for the reactions considered; a few boundaries would be affected appreciably more; a few, less. In fact, several diagrams have been constructed at 100°C, and whereas the positions of the fields of various solids shift relative to Eh-pH values of the axes, the shapes and sizes of the fields tend to be maintained.

As a corollary of the effects of temperature and pressure on equilibrium relations, it should be noted that the results of calculations sometimes indicate conditions not justified by the original data. For example, for the reaction

$$3Fe_c + 4H_2O_l = Fe_3O_{4\,c} + 4H_{2\,g}$$

$$\Delta F_R^\circ = \Delta F_{f\,Fe_3O_4}^\circ + 4\Delta F_{f\,H_2}^\circ - 3\Delta F_{f\,Fe}^\circ - 4\Delta F_{f\,H_2O}^\circ$$

$$\Delta F_R^\circ = -15.6 = (-242.4) + (0) - 3(0) - 4(-56.69)$$

Then

$$-15.6 = -1.364 \log k = -1.364 \log P_{H_2}^4$$

$$\log k = \log P_{H_2}^4 = 11.4$$

$$P_{H_2} = 10^{2.85} \text{ atm}$$

The conclusion thus might be drawn that the partial pressure of hydrogen in equilibrium with water, native iron, and magnetite, is 700 atmospheres. But the equilibrium condition predicted is so far away from the conditions of collection of the original free energy data (one atmosphere) that the result cannot be used. The actual effect of the 700 ± atmospheres total pressure on the activities of the constituents of the system would have to be evaluated before any numbers could be obtained that might apply to the real experiment. The conclusion that *can* be drawn from the calculation is that P_{H_2} exceeds 1 atmosphere, and therefore iron plus water would tend to yield magnetite, with hydrogen being lost from a system under a confining pressure of one (or a few) atmospheres.

In other words, the conditions suggested by the calculation violate the original conditions under which the calculation was made, and therefore cannot be accepted as valid. On the other hand, calculations yielding partial pressure of gases less than 1 atmosphere are satisfactory, because they do not violate the original premise of 1 atmosphere *total* pressure.

DIAGRAMS VALID ONLY FOR SPECIES CONSIDERED

In using Eh-pH diagrams, one must remember that the only answers that come out of thermochemical calculations are in response to the questions asked. For instance, one can calculate that FeO and Fe_3O_4 are in equilibrium at a given pair of Eh and pH values, but if one were to assume from such a calculation that FeO and Fe_3O_4 are a stable pair in the iron-water-oxygen system, he would be making a gross error. A given calculation does not tell the results of others that have not been performed. If one considers various possible reactions, he will find that FeO_c will disproportionate at equilibrium into Fe_c and Fe_3O_{4c}:

$$4FeO_c = Fe_3O_{4c} + Fe_c; \quad \Delta F_R^\circ \text{ is negative}$$

For the geologist this type of restriction is not always a serious difficulty. He knows the mineral phases that occur in a certain deposit, and he can ask his questions regarding these minerals. Many of the useful results are negative; one may receive an unequivocal answer that phases A and B *cannot* coexist at equilibrium. Thus calculations give permissive or negative results. A and B *may* coexist at equilibrium in a given system, if neither is unstable with respect to

some other unconsidered species, or if A and B do not interact: alternately, A and B *cannot* coexist at equilibrium.

ACTIVITIES VERSUS SOLUBILITIES

The calculation of the activities of dissolved species in equilibrium with solids is fraught with no more and no fewer dangers than the calculation of the fields of stability of solids. But there is apparently some insidious influence that forces an investigator to attempt to determine solubilities from activities. As pointed out in Chapter 2, the activity of an ion differs from its molality by a factor γ, which can sometimes be estimated fairly accurately from knowledge of the ionic strength. To calculate the solubility of a solid at a given pair of Eh-pH conditions the activities of *all* contributing dissolved species must be known, as well as their activity coefficients. Ignorance of the presence of a given ion, or an error in estimation of an activity coefficient, leads to error in solubility. This point was made firmly in Chapter 2.

A more serious difficulty, from the geologic point of view, stems from the reverse situation: given the composition of a natural water, its Eh and pH, and knowledge of the mineral species in contact with the water, can one deduce whether the minerals present are in equilibrium with their environment? If the stability can be expressed as a function of Eh and pH alone (i.e., Fe_2O_3), then no difficulty arises, because both these values are measurements of activity. But, as for calcite, if it is necessary to know the activity of calcium ion we are back to the problem of calculating the activity of a given ion from an analysis for total dissolved element. This situation is clearly the reverse of an attempt to calculate solubility.

Despite these difficulties, a useful generalization can be made as follows: if a given solid is in equilibrium with a solution, the sum of the activities of all known dissolved species containing a given element is almost always less than the concentration of that element as determined by chemical analysis.

Therefore, it is possible to make calculations of the sum of the activities of ions in equilibrium with a solid, and to assign a *minimum solubility* value to this sum. Again we are faced with a positive or a permissive situation: if the sum of the activities of known ions is a large value, it can be said that the solid in question is soluble; if the sum of the activities of known ions is small, the solid in question *may not* be soluble.

In passing it must be emphasized that few data are currently available on the mineral associations in rocks, together with chemical analyses of the associated aqueous solutions.   With such information we could make rapid strides in assessing our chemical ignorance. By assuming equilibrium between minerals and solution, one can calculate the solubility of a given element to the best of his knowledge. The discrepancy between this value and the analytical concentration of the element in the solution represents ignorance, and one can make tests to see if the discrepancy is due to failure to obtain equilibrium, to unsuspected complexes, to incorrect thermochemical values, or to still other factors.

SELECTED REFERENCES

Pourbaix, M. J. N., *Thermodynamics of Dilute Solutions.*   Edward Arnold & Co., London, 1949, 136 pp.

Technical Reports of the Belgian Center for Study of Corrosion, 24 Rue des Chevaliers, Brussels

1. Pourbaix, M., Sur l'interprétation thermodynamique de courbes de polarisation (1952).
2. Pourbaix, M., Applications de diagrammes tension-pH relatifs au fer et a l'eau oxygénée.   Expériences de démonstration (1954).
3. Deltombe, E., and M. Pourbaix, Comportement électrochimique du cadmium (1953).
4. Schmets, J., and M. Pourbaix, Comportement électrochimique du titane (1953).
5. Deltombe, E., and M. Pourbaix, Comportement électrochimique des cyanures (1953).
6. Deltombe, E., and M. Pourbaix, Comportement électrochimique du cobalt (1954).
7. Deltombe, E., and M. Pourbaix, Comportement électrochimique du fer (1954).
8. Deltombe, E., and M. Pourbaix, Comportement électrochimique du fer en solution carbonique (1954).
9. Pourbaix, M., Sur la phosphation oxydante des aciers ordinaires (1953).
10. Van Muylder, J., La corrosion et la protection des gaines en plomb des câbles enterrés (1953).
11. Van Muylder, J., and M. Pourbaix, Corrosion et protection cathodique du fer.   Expérience de démonstration (1953).
12. Van Muylder, J., Au sujet des hydrures de plomb et de la pulvérisation cathodique du plomb (1954).
13. Van Muylder, J., and M. Pourbaix, Sur le comportement électrochimique du plomb.   Corrosion, protection cathodique, passication (1953).

14. Van Muylder, J., and M. Pourbaix, Corrosion et protection catho-diques du plomb (1954).

15. Magee, G. M., Corrosion electrolytique de l'acier dans le béton (trad. d'un article de G. M. Magee paru dans *Corrosion*, 5, 11 novembre 1949, 378–382) (1954).

16. Wattecamps, P., Progrès récents de la technique américaine d'application des revêtements protecteurs (1953).

17. Bureau of Ships, U.S. Navy (Trad. par P. Wattecamps), Etudes sur des systèmes de revêteùents anticorrosif et antisalissant pour carènes de navires.

18. Moussard, A. M., J. Brenet, F. Jolas, M. Pourbaix, and J. Van Muylder, Comportement électrochimique du manganèse (1954).

19. Abd El Wahed, A. M., and M. Pourbaix, Utilisation des corbes de polarisation pour l'étude des circonstances de corrosion et de protection du fer en présence de chlorures. Phosphatation et phosphatation oxydante (1954).

20. Pourbaix, M., Applications de l'électrochimique à des études de corrosion (1954).

21. Pourbaix, M., Vue d'ensemble sur le comportement électrochimique des métaux (1ère partie) (1953).

22. Comptes-rendus des Journées d'Études du Cebelcor, 13 et 14 avril 1955.

23. Deltombe, E., N. de Zoubov, and M. Pourbaix, Comportement électrochimique du nickel (1955).

24. Laureys, J., J. Van Muylder, and M. Pourbaix, Note sur l'efficacité d'un appareil de traitement magnétique des eaux (1955).

25. Deltombe, E., N. de Zoubov and M. Pourbaix, Comportement électrochimique de l'étain (1955).

26. de Zoubov, N., and E. Deltombe, Enthalpies libres de formation standard de l'hydrure d'étain gazeux.

27. de Zoubov, N., E. Deltombe, and M. Pourbaix, Comportement électrochimique du germanium (1955).

28. Enthalpies libres de formation standards, à 25°C, 1955.

29. Deltombe, E., N. de Zoubov, and M. Pourbaix, Comportement électrochimique du vanadium (1956).

30. Pourbaix, M., Leçons sur la corrosion électrochimique, 2me fascicule (1956).

31. Deltombe, E., N. de Zoubov, and M. Pourbaix, Comportement électrochimique de l'uranium (1956).

32. Deltombe, E., N. de Zoubov, and M. Pourbaix, Comportement électrochimique du tungstène (1956).

33. Deltombe, E., N. de Zoubov, and M. Pourbaix, Comportement électrochimique du tellure (1956).

34. Van Muylder, J., and M. Pourbaix, Comportement des anodes réactives en magnésium et en zinc (1956).

35. Deltombe, E., N. de Zoubov, and M. Pourbaix, Comportement électrochimique du molybdène (1956).

36. Van Eijnsbergen, J. F. H., La protection contre la corrosion de l'acier par der couches métalliques, spécialement par la galvanisation à chaud (1956).
37. Vandervelden, F., and M. Pourbaix, Protection contre la corrosion dans l'emballage et au cours du stockage (1956).
38. Pourbaix, M., Services que peuvent rendre à l'industrie pétrollière les centres de recherche contre la corrosion (1956).
39. Van Muylder, J., and M. Pourbaix, Comportement électrochimique du magnésium (1956).
40. Pourbaix, M., Sur la corrosion du fer et des aciers par les eaux. Influence du pH, des oxydants, des réducteurs, des chlorures, des phosphates et de la température (1956).
41. Deltombe, E., N. de Zoubov, and M. Pourbaix, Comportement électrochimique du chrome (1956).
42. Deltombe, E., and M. Pourbaix, Comportement électrochimique de l'aluminium (1956).
43. Pourbaix, M., and N. de Zoubov, Sur les conditions des passivation du fer par les chromates, molybdates, tungstates et vanadates (1957).
44. Valensi, G., E. Deltombe, N. de Zoubov, and M. Pourbaix, Comportement électrochimique du chlore (1957).
45. Maraghini, M., P. Van Rysselberghe, E. Deltombe, N. de Zoubov, and M. Pourbaix, Comportement électrochimique du zirconium (1957).
46. Van Muylder, J., and M. Pourbaix, Comportement électrochimique de l'arsenic (1957).
47. Deltombe, E., N. de Zoubov, and M. Pourbaix, Comportement électrochimique du bore (1957).
48. Van Muylder, J., and M. Pourbaix, Comportement électrochimique du bismuth (1957).
49. Pourbaix, M., Leçons sur la corrosion électrochimique, 3me fascicule (1957).
50. de Zoubov, N., and M. Pourbaix, Comportement électrochimique du technétium (1957).
51. de Zoubov, N., and M. Pourbaix, Comportement électrochimique du rhénium (1957).
52. Van Muylder, J., and M. Pourbaix, Comportement électrochimique du tantale (1957).
53. Van Muylder, J., N. de Zoubov, and M. Pourbaix, Comportement électrochimique du niobium (1957).
54. Pitman, A. L., M. Pourbaix, N. de Zoubov, Comportement électrochimique de l'antimoine (1957).

Delahay, Paul, Marcel Pourbaix, and Pierre Van Rysselberghe, Potential-pH diagrams. *J. Chem. Education*, 27, 683–688 (1950).
Charlot, G., *Theorie et méthode nouvelle d'Analyse qualitative*, 3rd edition. Masson, Paris, 1949.
Sillen, Lars G., Redox diagrams. *J. Chem. Education*, 29, 600–608 (1952).

7

Some Geologic Applications of Eh-pH Diagrams

This chapter is a review of some of the ways that Eh-pH diagrams have been applied to geologic problems. It should serve as a partial guide to the literature, and should also suggest ways in which the preceding diagrams may be used. The examples are selected because they illustrate use of Eh-pH diagrams showing stability relations of solids.

NATURAL LIMITS OF Eh AND pH

The range of Eh and pH values that must be considered in constructing diagrams is determined by the limits of values observed in nature. Figure 7.1 is a plot showing the approximate values for various natural environments. No attempt is made to give the total range of a given environment, but rather to indicate that values observed or inferred cover a considerable span of both Eh and pH. Numerous values of Eh have been obtained from water-logged soils and from euxenic marine environments that are well below the water boundary, showing that overvoltages can occur in nature. Some of the observed values are more than 0.1 volt below the water stability line. Also of interest is the fact that measurements on most aerated surface waters (note mine waters, rain, streams, normal ocean water on Figure 7.1) fall along a line well below but parallel to the upper water boundary. This line is the "irreversible oxygen potential," and has been explained

by Sato (Motoaki Sato, 1958, A study of the electrochemistry of self-potentials associated with sulfide ore bodies. Paper presented at American Institute of Mining and Metallurgical Engineers, Annual

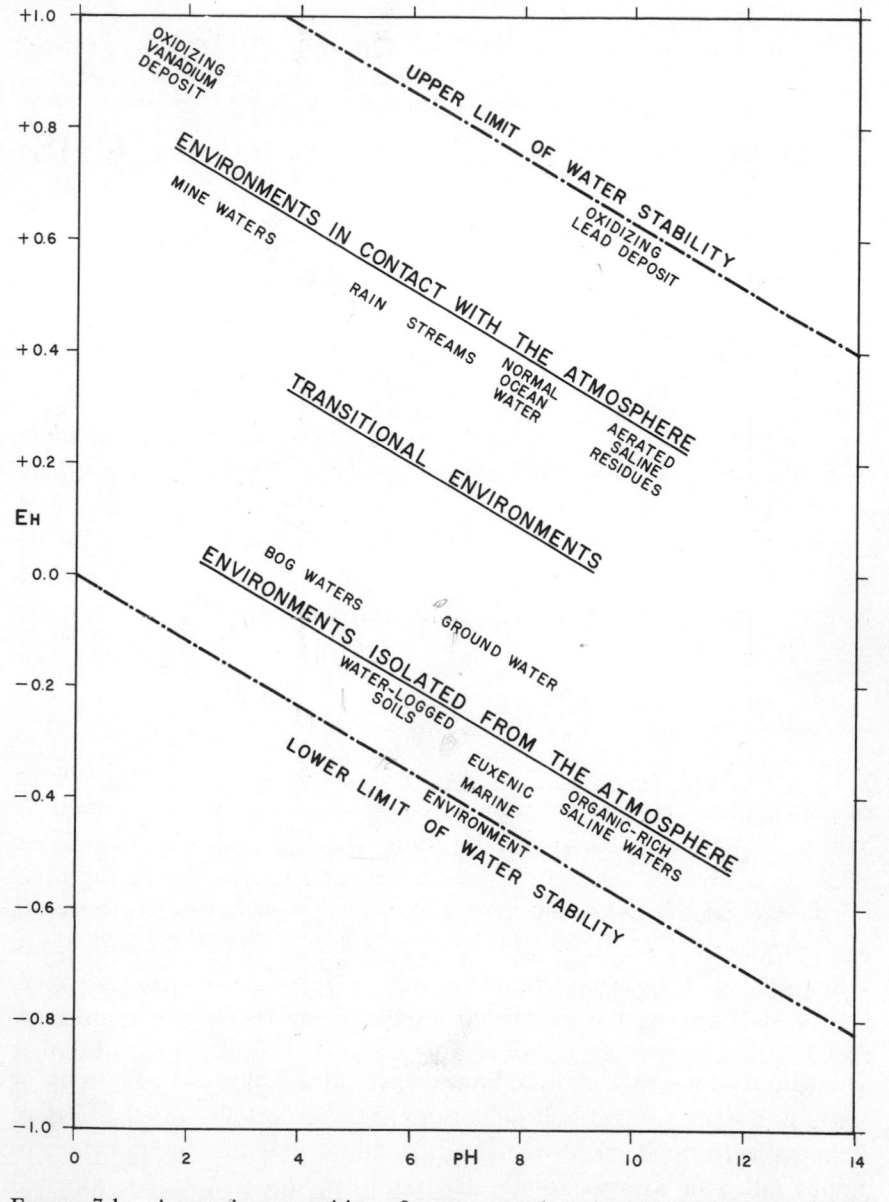

FIGURE 7.1.   Approximate position of some natural environments as characterized by Eh and pH.

Meeting, New York, February 1958) as being the H_2O_2-O_2 stability boundary on the basis that oxidation by dissolved oxygen has to go through a rate-controlling hydrogen peroxide step. If the measured potentials are a true guide to the effect of the oxygen of the atmosphere, then we see that natural waters behave as if they contained a very small amount of dissolved oxygen. On the other hand, oxidized

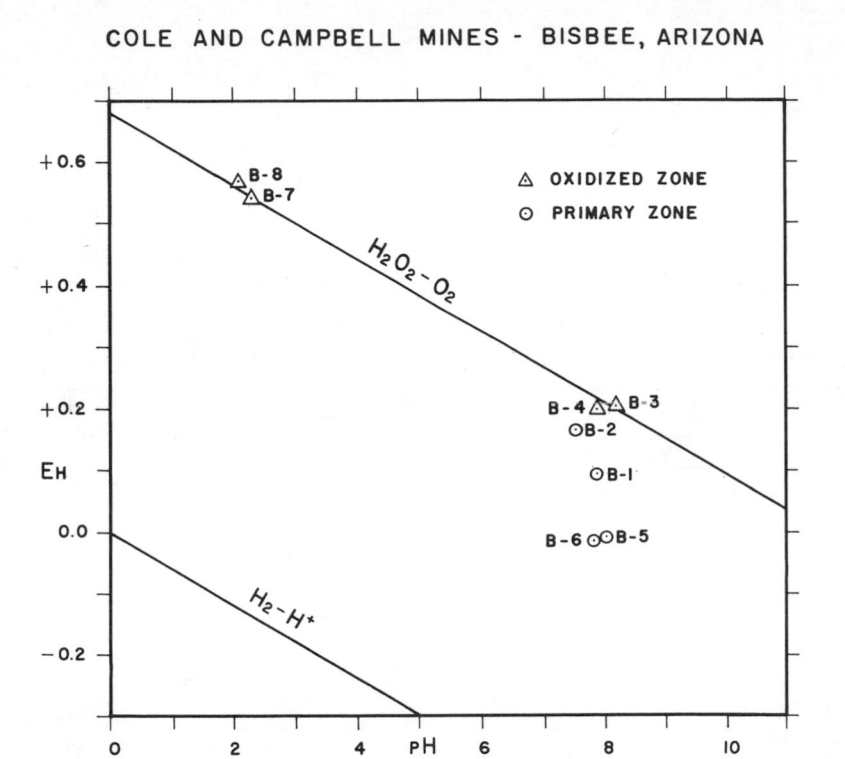

COLE AND CAMPBELL MINES - BISBEE, ARIZONA

OXIDATION POTENTIAL- pH DIAGRAM OF MINE WATERS

FIGURE 7.2. Eh-pH diagram showing relations in mine waters. (From "A study of the electrochemistry of self-potentials associated with sulfide ore bodies," by Motoaki Sato. Paper delivered at American Institute of Mining and Metallurgical Engineers, New York, 1958. Work Sponsored by Atomic Energy Commission at University of Minnesota.)

vanadium ores contain the mineral navajoite, which is stable only at potentials near 1.0 volt and pH values of the order of 1.5 to 2. Figure 7.2, taken from Sato's work (*op. cit.*), shows that measured values in mines fall over a large range of conditions; those samples protected from the atmosphere ("primary zone") falling into the transition zone

of Figure 7.1. Sato's values are among the few available for underground waters. Inasmuch as many rocks—sedimentary, igneous, and metamorphic—contain both magnetite and hematite, it may well be that the potentials of most underground waters approach the magnetite-hematite boundary (Figure 6.3).

Two general sources of Eh-pH values in soils and sediments are ZoBell [E. Claude ZoBell, Studies on redox potentials of marine sediments. *Bull. Am. Assoc. Petrol. Geol.*, *30*, 477–513 (1946)], and Starkey and Wight (R. L. Starkey and K. M. Wight, *Anaerobic Corrosion of Iron in Soil*. American Gas Association, New York, 1945, 108 pp.). An excellent bibliography of papers on oxidation relations in soils is provided by Merkle (F. G. Merkle, Oxidation-reduction processes in soils, in *Chemistry of the Soil*, Firman Bear, editor. Reinhold Publishing Corporation, New York, 1955, 200–218). Krumbein and Garrels have attempted to summarize the Eh-pH characteristics of various environments of chemical sedimentation [W. C. Krumbein and R. M. Garrels, Origin and classification of chemical sediments in terms of pH and oxidation potentials. *J. Geol.*, *60*, 1–33 (1952)].

The general picture that emerges is that only surface waters with good circulation are oxidizing, whereas confined waters rapidly lose their oxygen content, whether confinement results from fixation in rock or soil pores, or by prevention of overturn of open waters. Organic-free waters lose their oxidizing character by reaction with silicates containing ferrous iron, such as biotite, chlorite, amphiboles, pyroxenes, or by contact with sulfides or ferrous iron-containing carbonates. There are many other possible inorganic reducing agents, but the iron compounds are probably the most important quantitatively. The pH tends to rise because of hydrolysis of the silicates, so that the environment becomes alkaline as well as reducing. In environments containing organic matter, biochemical reactions quickly remove oxygen, commonly with marked increase in CO_2, and with production of H_2S. The influence of bacteria is paramount, and deoxygenation tends to be accompanied by pH lowering as CO_2 and H_2S are generated. Some bacteria even release hydrogen, and potentials may sink below the water stability limit. Under inorganic conditions many ions, notably sulfate, may persist metastably during long periods of time, but the presence of organic material and the accompanying bacteria almost guarantees approach to equilibrium as denoted by the measured potentials. Below the water table the environment can be assumed to be alkaline and reducing, except in

local instances of high rates of water flow. The best evidence is the persistence of sulfides in ores for millions of years, without destruction of the finest details of surface characteristics.

SEDIMENTARY IRON ORES

The classic paper on sedimentary iron ores, which ties the environmental characteristics to the observed facies, is the study by James of the Huronian iron ores of Michigan [H. L. James, Sedimentary facies of iron formation. *Econ. Geol.*, *49*, 235–293 (1954)]. His abstract (p. 236) summarizes the relations as succinctly as possible:

The sedimentary iron formations of Precambrian age in the Lake Superior region can be divided on the basis of the dominant original iron mineral in four principal facies: sulfide, carbonate, oxide, and silicate. As chemical sediments, the rocks reflect certain aspects of the depositional environments. The major control, at least for the sulfide, carbonate, and oxide types, probably was the oxidation potential. The evidence indicates that deposition took place in restricted basins, which were separated from the open sea by thresholds that inhibited free circulation and permitted development of abnormalities in oxidation potential and water composition.

. . . The *sulfide facies* is represented by black slates in which pyrite makes up as much as 40 percent of the rock. The free carbon content of these rocks typically ranges from 5 to 15 percent, indicating that ultra-stagnant conditions prevailed during deposition. Locally, the pyrite rocks contain layers of iron-rich carbonate. The *carbonate facies* consists, in its purer form, of interbedded iron-rich carbonate and chert. It is a product of an environment in which oxygen concentration was sufficiently high to destroy most of the organic material but not high enough to permit formation of ferric compounds. The *oxide facies* is found as two principal types, one characterized by magnetite and the other by hematite. Both minerals appear to be of primary origin. The magnetite-banded rock is one of the dominant lithologies in the region; it consists typically of magnetite interlayered with chert, carbonate, or iron silicate, or combinations of the three. Its mineralogy and association suggest origin under weakly oxidizing to moderately reducing conditions, but the mode of precipitation of magnetite is not clearly understood. The hematite-banded rocks consist of finely crystalline hematite interlayered with chert or jasper. Oolitic structure is common. This facies doubtless accumulated in a strongly oxidizing probably near-shore environment similar to that in which younger hematitic ironstones such as the Clinton were deposited. The *silicate facies* contain one or more of the hydrous ferrous silicates (greenalite, minnesotaite, stilpnomelane, chlorite) as a major constituent. . . . The most common association of the silicate rocks is with either carbonate or magnetite-bearing rocks, which suggests that the optimum conditions for deposition ranged from slightly oxidizing to slightly reducing . . .

The relation of James's conclusion to equilibrium stability relations is clear from a consideration of Figure 6.23. With slight under-saturation with amorphous silica, magnetite can replace ferrous silicates; with diminution of $\sum CO_2$, magnetite or ferrous silicate replaces siderite; with increase in sulfide sulfur, pyrite takes over; with oxygenation hematite holds sway. Furthermore, all these facies lie within a very narrow range of pH and Eh values. Castano and Garrels [J. R. Castano and R. M. Garrels, Experiments on the deposition of iron with special reference to the Clinton iron ore deposits. *Econ. Geol.*, *45*, 755–770 (1950)] and Huber and Garrels [N. K. Huber and R. M. Garrels, Relation of pH and oxidation potential to sedimentary iron formation. *Econ. Geol.*, *48*, 337–358 (1953)] demonstrated experimentally that the iron minerals precipitate in the laboratory according to the metastable relations (Figure 6.4), and that the response of freshly precipitated iron "hydroxides" and carbonates to a given Eh-pH environment is rapid. White (David A. White, The stratigraphy and structure of the Mesabi Range, Minnesota. *Bull. 38*, Minnesota Geol. Survey, 1954, 92 pp.) has done an excellent job of deciphering the relation of the iron mineral facies to the environment of deposition (pp. 44–53) and correlates the facies with aeration and distance from shore.

In summary, the study of natural occurrences of iron minerals shows that there is sufficient approach to equilibrium with the environment of deposition to permit use of relations based on thermochemical considerations. The diagrams tell nothing about the rate at which equilibrium might have been attained, nor the path by which it was approached, but if we know what should happen, we are in a position to use the stable associations as a guide to interpreting processes as indicated by replacement sequences among the minerals. We can thus put reasonable limits on the amount of dissolved CO_2 required to have a siderite facies, and can demonstrate that oxygen must be to all intents and purposes absent during formation of siderite, pyrite, magnetite, or silicate facies of iron formation. It is also important to know that any sulfide sulfur in an iron-rich environment will be reflected in pyrite, and that the presence of both pyrite and pyrrhotite in a sedimentary environment puts rather definite limits on the total dissolved sulfur that was in equilibrium with these compounds. Our major gap in knowledge is in thermal data pertaining to the primary iron silicates in sedimentary iron ores—it was necessary to use $FeSiO_3$ in the calculations, and no mineral of this composition is known to

exist. There is a nasty problem in the coexistence of chert and magnetite as primary minerals on the one hand, and iron silicates on the other. The fact that the real silicates are aluminous must enter into the actual equations.

SEDIMENTARY MANGANESE DEPOSITS

Eh-pH relations have been applied to sedimentary deposits of manganese by Krauskopf [K. B. Krauskopf, Separation of manganese from iron in sedimentary processes: *Geochem. et Cosmochim. Acta, 12,* 61–84 (1957)], and by Marchandise [H. Marchandise, Contribution à l'étude des gisements de manganese sedimentaires: Symposium Subre Yasimientos de Manganese, *XX Intern. Geol. Congr. Mexico, 1,* 107–118 (1956)]. Figure 7.3, taken from Krauskopf's paper, shows his plot of the stability boundaries among anhydrous manganese compounds. Note that Krauskopf prefers to plot equations relating mineral pairs, rather than delimiting and labeling mineral fields, as generally used in this text. Figure 7.4 shows his diagram for the manganese hydroxides. Again the best summary of the relation of the diagrams to the observed associations comes from the author's abstract (Krauskopf, *op. cit.,* p. 61):

Thermochemical data on compounds of manganese and iron are in general agreement with reported mineral associations, provided that the more complex mineral compounds, for which data do not exist, be assumed to have somewhat larger stability fields than their nearest simple chemical equivalents. The data show that the iron compounds to be expected in nature are uniformly less soluble than the corresponding manganese compounds, and that ferrous ion is more easily oxidized than manganous ion under any naturally occurring pH-Eh conditions. Thus, inorganic processes should always lead to precipitation of iron before manganese from a solution containing both metals, unless the Mn/Fe ratio is very high.

The oxidation of manganous and ferrous ions by atmospheric oxygen takes place by slow reactions which can be utilized as an energy source by bacteria. Selective oxidation and precipitation by different species of bacteria can lead to partial separation of the metals, but this is probably not a major factor in the formation of large, nearly pure deposits of manganese or iron compounds.

Selective dissolution of the metals from igneous rocks, a mechanism of separation often postulated in the literature, was tested by treating basaltic andesite with a number of solvents at temperatures ranging from 25° to 300°C. The ratios of Mn to Fe in the resulting solutions were all approxi-

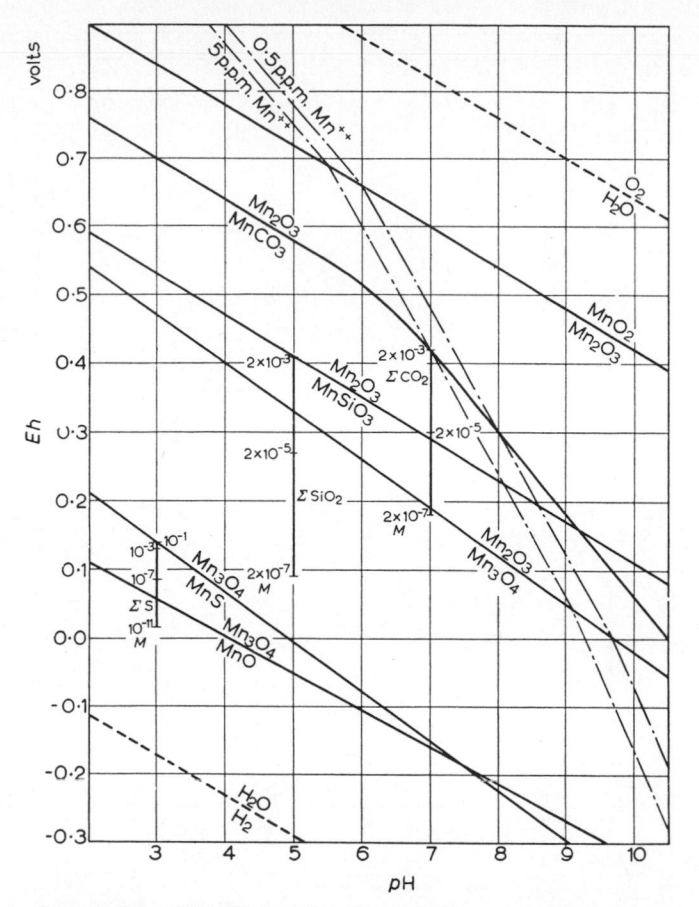

FIGURE 7.3.   Eh-pH diagram for anhydrous manganese compounds.   Solid lines are boundaries of stability fields; each line separates the field of an oxidized form (above) from that of a reduced form (below).   Cross-bars on vertical lines show positions of field boundaries at lower concentrations of carbonate, sulfide, and silica.   Dashed lines are limits of possible redox potentials in water solution.   Dash-dot lines are "isoconcentration" lines, drawn through points where the concentration of Mn^{++} in equilibrium with the oxides is 5 ppm and 0.5 ppm respectively.   (From Konrad B. Krauskopf, 1957, *Separation of iron from manganese in sedimentary processes. Geochim. et Cosmochim. Acta, 12,* 63.)

mately the same as in the original rock, showing that this assumed process of separation is ineffective.

Isolation of manganese in solution can be accomplished by precipitating the iron first.   This is most effectively done by adding alkali gradually to a

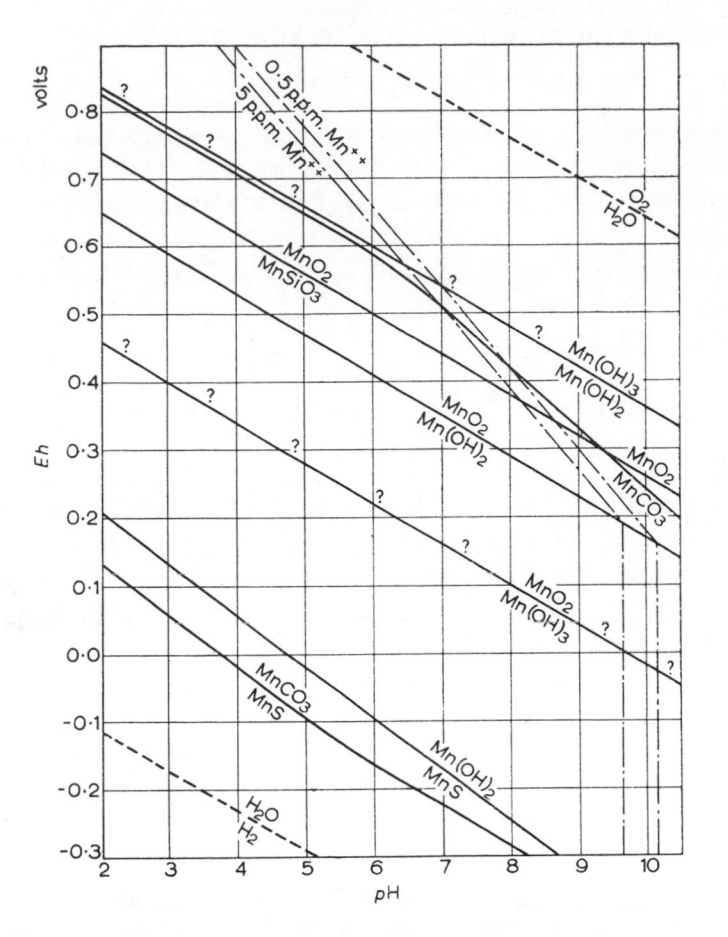

FIGURE 7.4. Eh-pH diagram for manganese hydroxides.
Symbols same as in Figure 7.3.   Question marks along stability
boundaries for Mn(OH)$_3$ indicate that under these conditions
Mn(OH)$_3$ is metastable.   [From Konrad B. Krauskopf, 1957,
Separation of iron from manganese in sedimentary processes.
Geochim. et Cosmochim. Acta, *12*, 66.)

solution containing both metals, keeping the solution in contact with
atmospheric oxygen.   The reaction can be demonstrated in the laboratory
under conditions similar to those in nature by letting dilute acid percolate
through crushed lava and then through limestone: iron dissolved from the
lava is precipitated in the limestone, and the solution is left with a high
Mn/Fe ratio.   This suggests a possible explanation for the origin of many
manganese deposits, especially those associated with lavas and tuffs, but it
requires that iron oxide in amounts many times that of the manganese be
deposited in the rocks through which the solutions have passed.

OXIDATION AND SECONDARY ENRICHMENT OF ORES

Eh-pH diagrams are especially useful in studies of oxidation and secondary enrichment of ore deposits. The temperatures and pressure of the processes are close to 25°C and 1 atmosphere total pressure, and the range of values of Eh and pH encountered is extreme. Also, the concentration of readily oxidizable or reducible material is high compared to most other near-surface environments, and the variety of minerals is great.

WEATHERING OF SANDSTONE-TYPE URANIUM DEPOSITS

Uranium deposits of the so-called sandstone type, which occur in continental sediments as pods, lenses, and blankets, provide the student of mineral associations with an endless variety of relations for investigation. Prior to about 1950, when the best known deposits in the United States were in southwestern Colorado, the chief ore mineral was carnotite, a potassium uranyl vanadate (KUO_2VO_4), and it was believed by many to be a primary sedimentary mineral, precipitated during or shortly after the deposition of the enclosing sediments (cf. R. P. Fischer, Vanadium deposits of Colorado and Utah. *U.S. Geol. Survey Bull.*, *936* P, 1942, 363–394). The mineral is certainly fully oxidized, inasmuch as the uranium is in the sexivalent state, and the vanadium quinquevalent. But discovery of increasing amounts of uraninite in deeper deposits began to raise a valence problem, because at least part of the uranium of uraninite is quadrivalent. The possibility began to develop that uraninite is an early uranium mineral, and that carnotite is an oxidation product. This suggestion was further strengthened by the identification of the mineral montroseite, which contains trivalent vanadium ($VOOH$). To complicate matters still further, other vanadium minerals containing V^{3+} and V^{4+}, V^{4+}, and V^{4+} and V^{5+} were identified.

Today it is generally concluded that carnotite is a weathering product. This view is a result of a great deal of work by a great many people—here we will consider only those aspects relating occurrence of minerals and theoretical stability relations. The specific problem that had to be attacked can be stated somewhat as follows: if an unoxidized uranium ore consists of uraninite, montroseite, and pyrite,

with some sphalerite and galena, will oxidation yield the complex mineral assemblages observed? What oxidation products can coexist stably? Which minerals will oxidize first under near-equilibrium conditions? The use of an Eh-pH framework for representation of

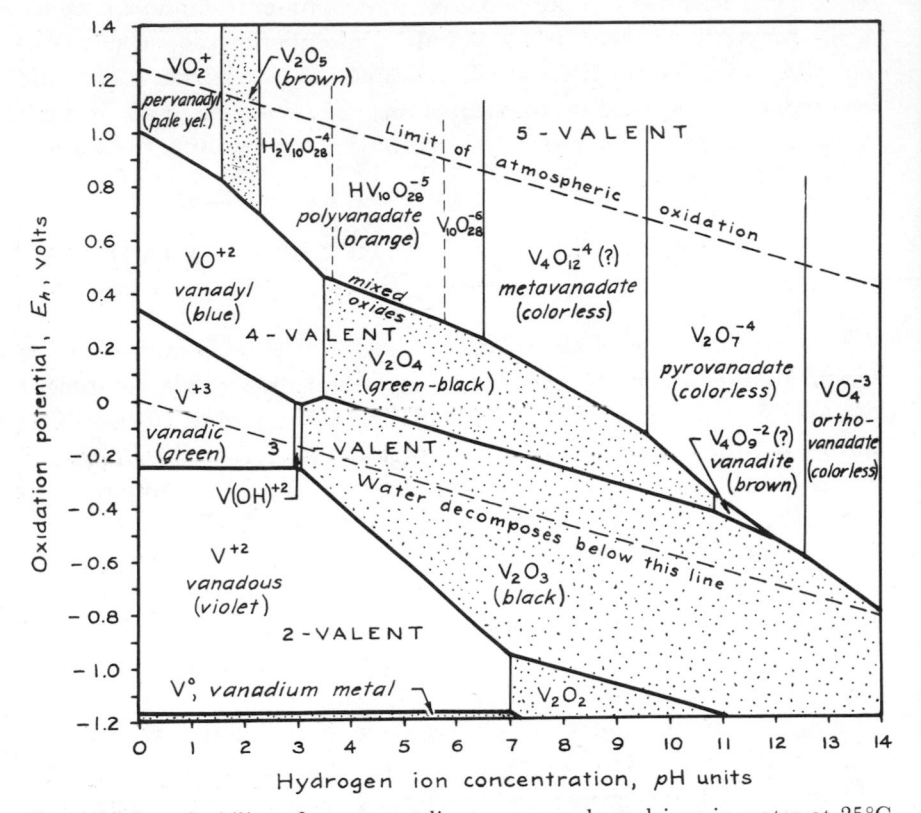

FIGURE 7.5a. Stability of some vanadium compounds and ions in water at 25°C and 1 atmosphere total pressure. (From H. T. Evans, Jr., and R. M. Garrels, Thermodynamic equilibria of vanadium in aqueous systems as applied to the interpretation of the Colorado Plateau ore deposits. *Geochim. et Cosmochim. Acta*, in press.)

stability relations is indicated, so that the various elements can be compared by superposition of individual diagrams.

The first diagrams prepared were rather crude preliminary ones for vanadium and uranium [R. M. Garrels, Some thermodynamic relations among the vanadium oxides, and their relation to the oxidation state of the uranium ores of the Colorado Plateaus: *Am. Mineralogist*, *38*, 1251–1266 (1953); Some thermodynamic relations among the uranium oxides and their relations to the oxidation states of the uranium ores of the Colorado Plateaus. *Ibid.*, *40*, 1004–1021 (1955)].

They did, however, suffice to show that uraninite and montroseite can coexist under strongly reducing conditions, but that montroseite oxidizes at a lower potential than uraninite in water, so that uraninite can coexist with vanadium oxides containing trivalent or quadrivalent

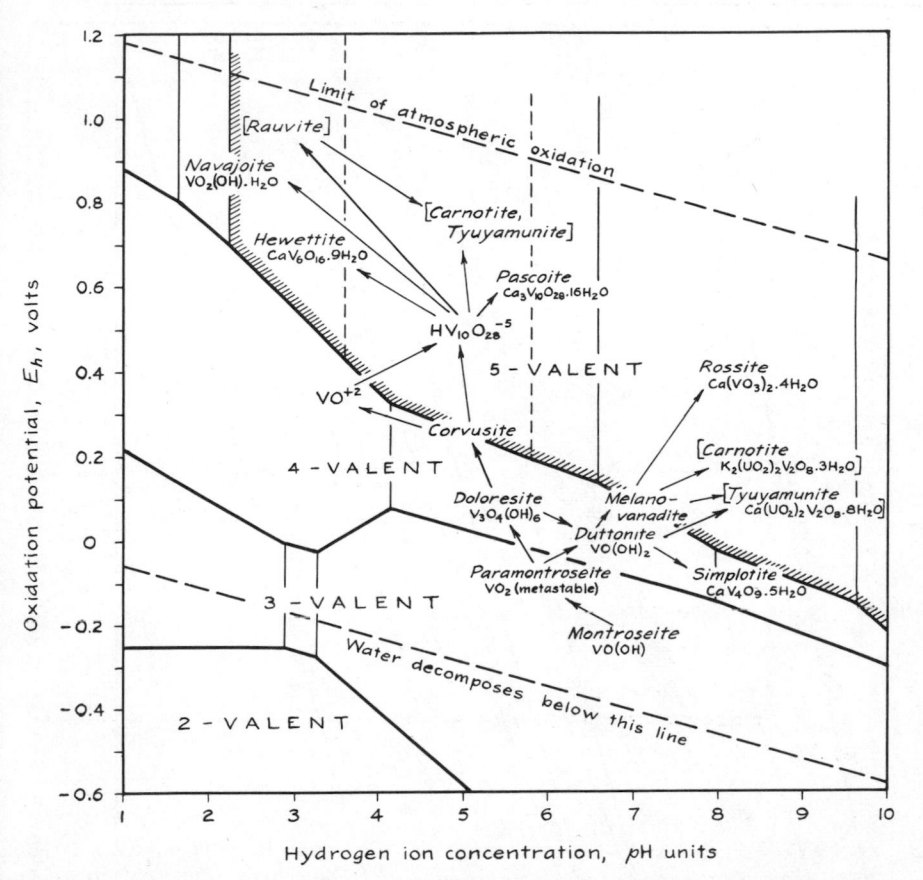

FIGURE 7.5b. Eh-pH diagram showing the oxidation relations of some naturally occurring vanadium compounds. (From H. T. Evans, Jr., and R. M. Garrels, Thermodynamic equilibria of vanadium in aqueous systems as applied to the inter-pretation of the Colorado Plateau ore deposits. *Geochim. et Cosmochim. Acta*, in press.)

vanadium. These crude diagrams were superseded by a pair of diagrams developed chiefly by Evans (H. T. Evans, Jr., and R. M. Garrels, Thermodynamic equilibria of vanadium in aqueous systems as applied to the interpretation of the Colorado Plateau ore deposits. *Geochim. et Cosmochim. Acta*, in press) that compared theoretical relations among a large variety of vanadium-oxygen compounds and ions with the observed sequences of vanadium minerals in Colorado Plateau

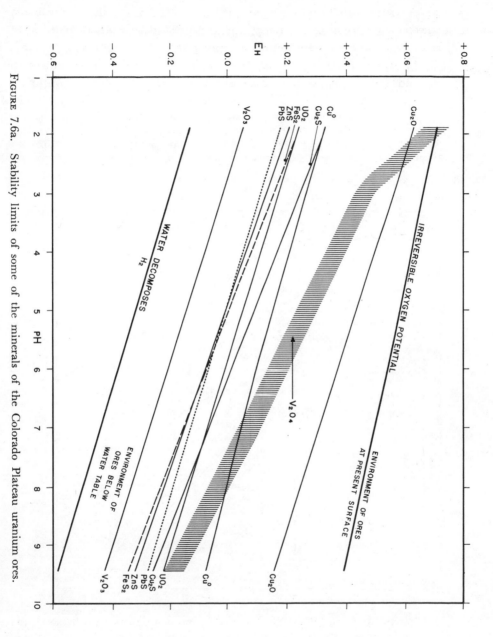

FIGURE 7.6a. Stability limits of some of the minerals of the Colorado Plateau uranium ores.

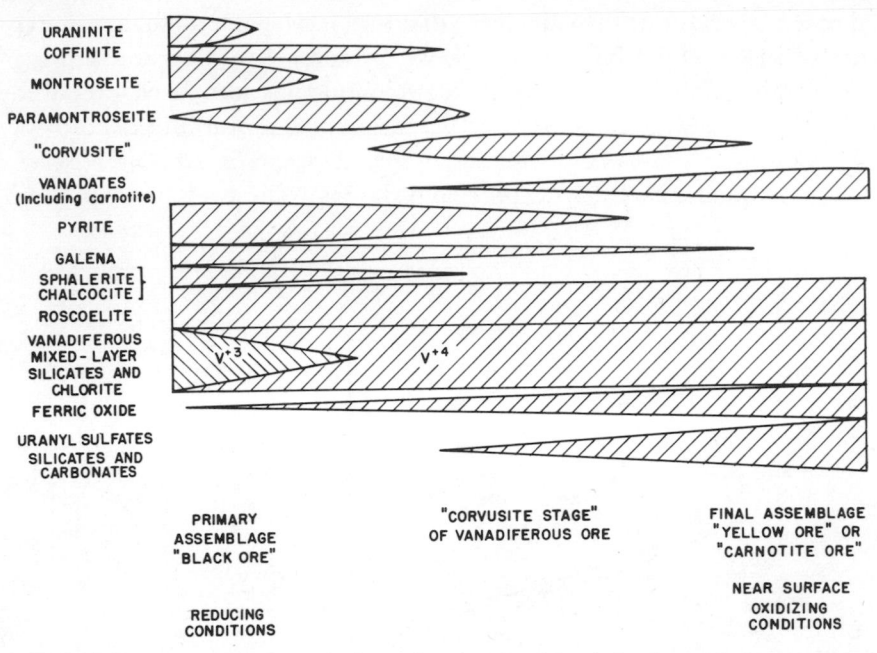

FIGURE 7.6b.   Approximate relations of some ore minerals in the oxidation sequence of the uranium ores of the Colorado Plateau.   (Figure 7.6a, b, c from R. M. Garrels, 1955, Geochemistry of oxidation of the uranium deposits of the Colorado Plateau. *Am. Inst. Chem. Engrs., Nuclear Eng. & Sci. Congr., Preprint 250*, pp. 15.)

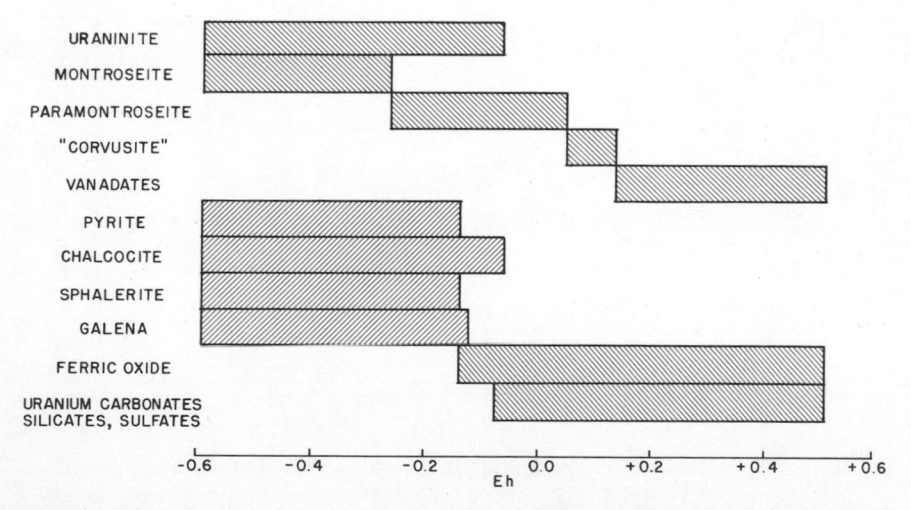

FIGURE 7.6c.   Predicted oxidation sequence of Colorado Plateau uranium ores if equilibrium were maintained during continuous rise of oxidation potential at pH 7.

deposits (Figure 7.5). Not only can the minerals be fitted into the
theoretical relation; the calculated diagram has been a useful predictive
device in searching for new minerals. A composite diagram showing
oxidation boundaries for various compounds has also been prepared
(R. M. Garrels, Geochemistry of oxidation of the uranium deposits of
the Colorado Plateaus. *Am. Inst. Chem. Engrs., Nuclear Eng. & Sci.
Congr., Preprint 250, 1955*, 15 pp.), and the interesting relation has been

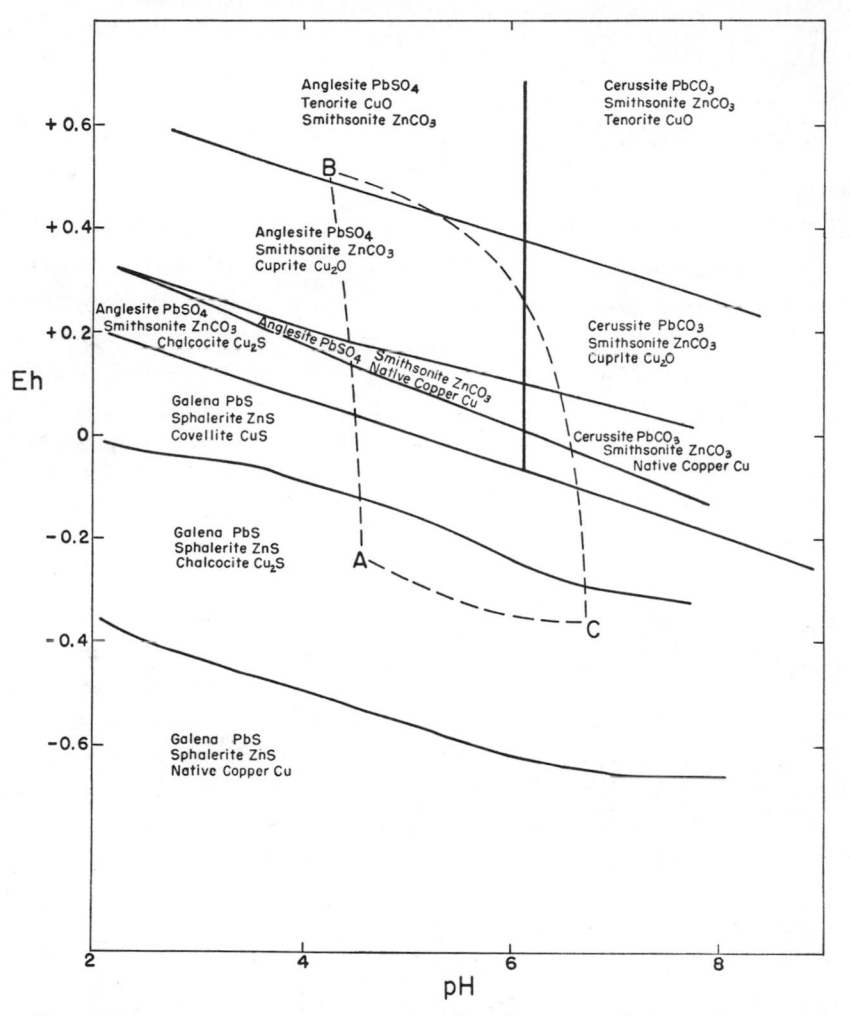

FIGURE 7.7. Composite diagram of stability of metal sulfides and oxidation
products at 25°C and 1 atmosphere total pressure in the presence of total
dissolved carbonate = $10^{-1.5}$, total dissolved sulfur = 10^{-1}. (From R. M.
Garrels, 1953, Mineral species as functions of pH and oxidation potentials.
Geochim. et Cosmochim. Acta, 5, 165.)

found that the observed sequence of minerals during oxidation of a primary uraninite, montroseite, metal sulfide ore corresponds closely to the sequence predicted from the assumption of progressive oxidation of such an ore with near-equilibrium being maintained (Figure 7.6). Coleman and Deleveaux [R. G. Coleman and Maryse Deleveaux, Occurrence of selenium in sulfides from some sedimentary rocks of the United States. *Econ. Geol.*, 52, 499–527 (1957)], used an Eh-pH diagram in explaining the behavior of selenium during weathering.

Thus again the relations calculated from thermochemical data have been useful in studying the behavior of natural deposits.

OXIDATION OF SULFIDE ORES

A composite diagram showing the Eh-pH conditions for the oxidation of the common metal sulfides has been prepared [R. M. Garrels, Mineral species as functions of pH and oxidation-reduction potentials. *Geochim. et Cosmochim. Acta*, 5, 153–168 (1953)]. The nature of the oxidation products and their general behavior in the zone of weathering as calculated correspond fairly well with observed behavior, with the reservation that thermochemical data are not available for many phases known to exist. The diagram is useful in giving a quantitative method of describing the boundary between oxidation and stability of sulfides, and in classifying some individual relationships, such as the stable coexistence of oxidized zinc minerals and copper sulfides such as chalcocite. The diagram shown is rather crude; those developed by Natarajan and Garrels (Figures 6.24 and 6.25) are much more nearly complete and are capable of even greater refinement as better data become available. An interesting comparison of real and theoretical relations has been made by Frondel and Ito [Clifford Frondel and Jun Ito, Geochemistry of germanium in the oxidized zone of the Tsumeb mine, Southwest Africa. *Am. Mineralogist*, 42, 743–754 (1957)], who showed that the germaniferous sulfide ores of the Tsumeb mine oxidize essentially as would be predicted.

THE ENVIRONMENT OF MARINE CHEMICAL SEDIMENTS

There is, of course, a voluminous literature on the environment of marine sediments, but so far little use has been made of Eh-pH diagrams in interpreting the interrelations of the chemical precipitates. On the other hand, there is considerable qualitative use of Eh and pH

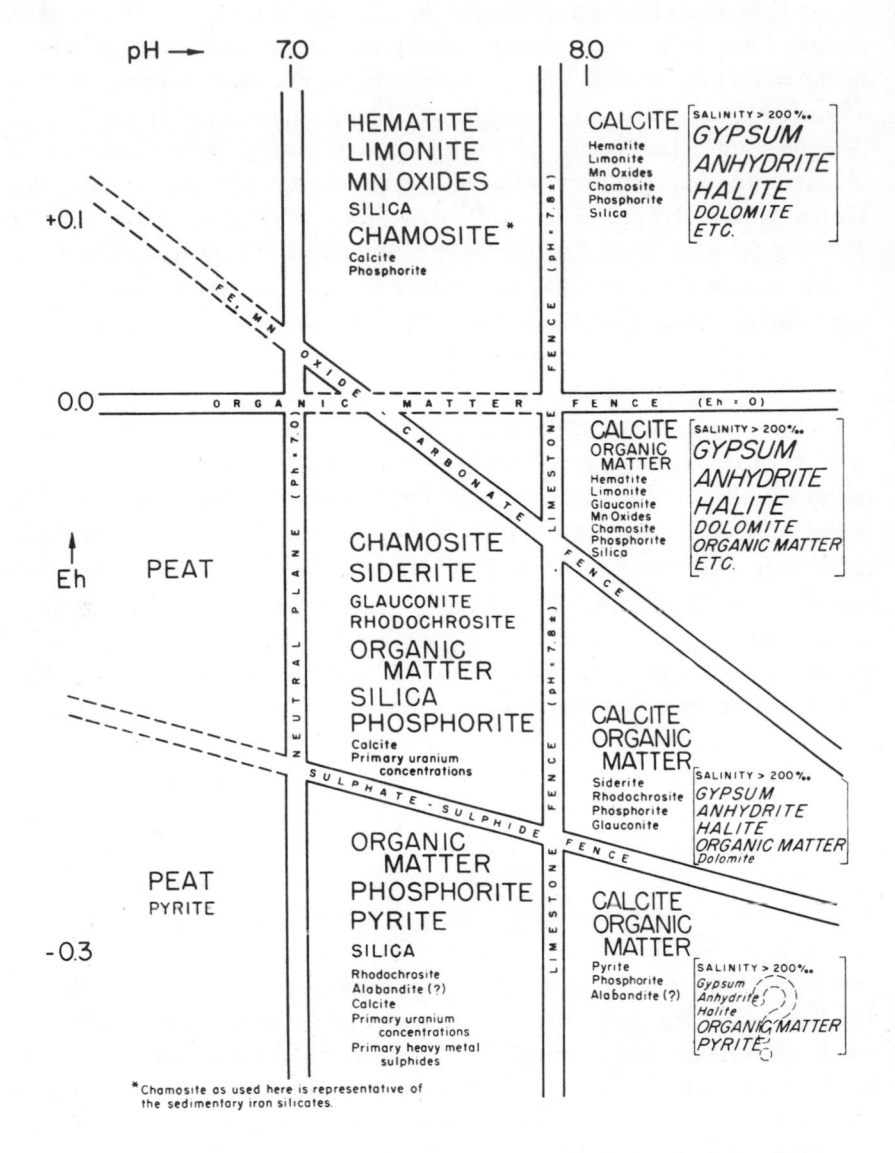

FIGURE 7.8. Sedimentary chemical end-member associations in their relations to environmental limitations imposed by selected Eh and pH values. Associations in brackets refer to hypersaline solutions. (From W. C. Krumbein and R. M. Garrels, 1952, Origin and classification of the chemical sediments in terms of pH and oxidation-reduction potentials. *J. Geol., 60,* 26.)

in describing the environments [cf. K. O. Emery and S. C. Rittenberg, Early diagenesis of California basin sediments. *Am. Assoc. Petrol. Geol. Bull.*, *36*, 735–806 (1952); G. I. Teodorovich, Siderite geochemical facies of seas and saline waters in general as oil producing: *Doklady Akad. Nauk S.S.S.R.*, *69*, 227–230 (1949)]. Krauskopf (K. B. Krauskopf, Sedimentary deposits of rare metals. *Econ. Geol.*, *50th Anniv. Volume*, 1955, pp. 411–463) used stability diagrams to illustrate the activities of ions in equilibrium with various possible stable solids in his study of rare elements in the sea, and Krumbein and Garrels [W. C. Krumbein and R. M. Garrels, Origin and classification of chemical sediments in terms of pH and oxidation potential. *J. Geol.*, *60*, 1–33 (1952)] qualitatively classified a variety of chemical sediments within an Eh-pH framework (Figure 7.8). Unfortunately, so many chemical minerals are so nearly in equilibrium with sea water, metastability is so common, and thermal data so crude, that it will be some time before it is possible to illustrate what should exist at equilibrium on the sea floor. On the other hand, if adequate diagrams showing stability relations could be constructed, we would have a powerful tool in our attempts to decipher the importance of reaction rates; adsorption phenomena as controls of ionic content of ocean waters as opposed to equilibrium with solid phases; the role of various types of soluble complexes in influencing solubility; and the critical questions concerning the ability of organisms to overcome a given set of external environmental conditions as they precipitate mineral substances.

THE ENVIRONMENT OF ORE DEPOSITION

In closing a few words should be said about constructing diagrams of the types discussed here at temperatures other than 25°C and pressures other than 1 atmosphere. It should be obvious that if free energy data are available at any given temperature and pressure that all the techniques used here can be applied. A fair amount of data is available for solids, or can be readily calculated by standard methods. This same statement can be made, although somewhat more guardedly, about gases. A paper by Krauskopf [Konrad B. Krauskopf, The heavy metal content of magmatic vapor at 600°C, *Econ. Geol.*, *52*, 786–807 (1957)] illustrates relations among minerals in terms of the partial pressures of gases at elevated temperatures and pressures. Eugster [H. P. Eugster, Stability of annite. *Ann. Rept. Director Geophys. Lab.*,

Washington, D.C., 1957, 161–164) has done a beautiful piece of work on stability relations of iron oxides and silicates as a function of P_{O_2}. But we are almost totally lacking in data that can be used to obtain standard free energies of formation of ions in aqueous solution. In many instances the temperature coefficient of the standard free energy can be obtained at 25°C, but extrapolation upwards is dangerous business.

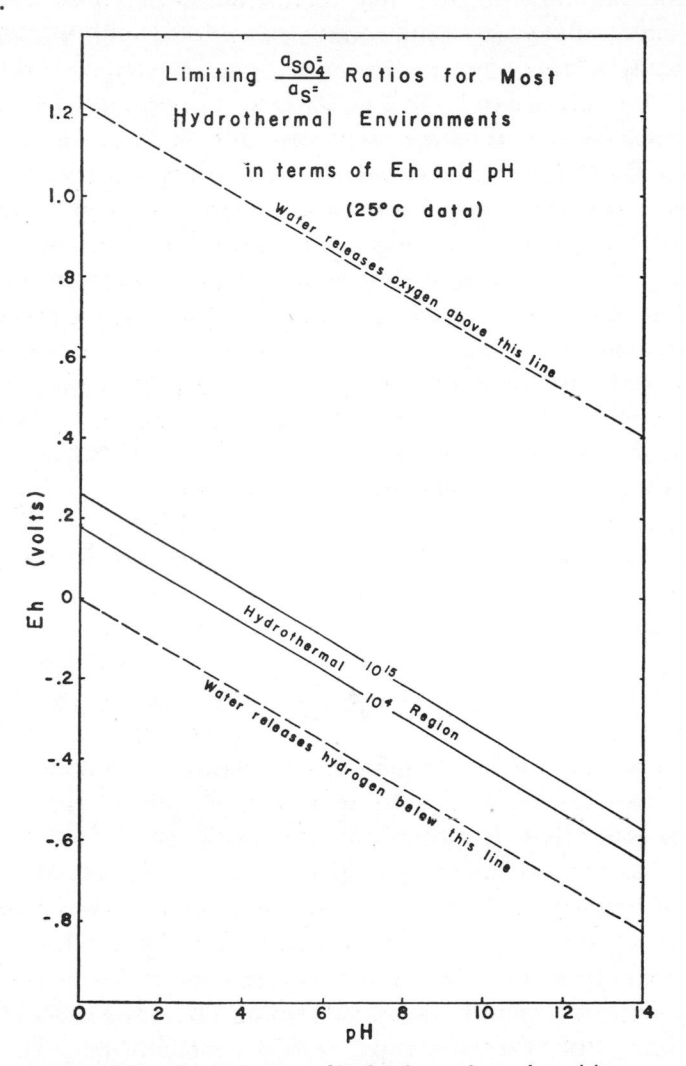

FIGURE 7.9.   Environment of hydrothermal ore deposition as interpreted by Barton. (From Paul B. Barton, Jr., 1957, Some limitations on the possible composition of the ore-forming fluid. *Econ. Geol.*, *52*, 345.)

Some of the possibilities that await have been suggested by Barton [Paul B. Barton, Jr., Some limitations on the possible composition of the ore-forming fluid. *Econ. Geol.*, *52*, 333–353 (1957)] who, using the mineral associations in veins, has done an admirable job of coralling the nature of the ore-forming environment. Figure 7.9 is taken from his paper, and shows his deductions concerning the Eh and pH of formation of some ores. He makes clear his limitation because of lack of free energy data at the high temperatures of actual ore deposition. But if data were available, we could now examine ore deposits in terms of the gas pressures and in terms of the pH and Eh ranges of various mineral associations, and inevitably sharpen our ideas concerning the origin of ore deposits—even unto the point where we might begin to make a few definite statements concerning them.

In addition to the need for thermochemical data on ions, our ignorance is just as great on the influence of the marked amount of solid solution observed in nature on the thermochemical properties of the pure solids. We are in fair shape when it comes to handling pure compounds, the end members of natural series, but lost when interaction must be considered. The diagrams for iron and manganese oxides (Figures 5.12 and 5.13) are good examples. When we superimpose them we are but comparing the behavior of the two separate systems, and are in no position to calculate the stability relations of the actual compounds, in which iron substitutes for manganese, and vice versa.

SUMMARY

It would seem, in retrospect, that this book has presented a number of diagrams, and that the accompanying text has been devoted to their limitations. This is as it should be—it would be unfortunate if attempts are made to read into them a validity and accuracy that are not there. As more information flows in, then we can improve them. But even now, crude as they are, they are useful tools because they suggest relations that might not otherwise have occurred to us. In a way, they represent a memory device. If we calculate reactions one at a time, and do not plot them, we cannot remember from one to the next. Also, they are predictive devices. Right or wrong, they suggest conditions of mutual occurrence, and we can test against the minerals themselves.

Appendix

THE following values of standard free energies of formation of compounds, gases, and ions at 25 °C and 1 atmosphere total pressure have been selected largely from standard sources, with some additions. The values have not been re-examined in detail by the author, so that no attempt has been made to estimate probable error. Some are excellent, some are fair, and some are poor. All are subject to constant revision.

ALUMINUM. Free Energy of Formation in kcal

Formula	Description	State	$\Delta F°$	Source
Al	Metal	c	0.0	2
Al^{+++}		aq	-115.0	1
AlO_2^-		aq	-200.7	7
$H_2AlO_3^-$		aq	-257.4	7
Al_2O_3	Corundum α	c	-376.77	1
$Al_2O_3 \cdot H_2O$	Boehmite	c	-435.0	1
$Al(OH)_3$		Amorph.	-271.9	2
Al_2S_3		c	-117.7	1
$Al_2O_3 \cdot 3H_2O$	Gibbsite	c	-554.6	7
$Al_2O_3 \cdot 3H_2O$	Bayerite	c	-552.5	7
$Al_2Si_2O_5(OH)_4$	Kaolinite	c	-883.0	8

Antimony.   Free Energy of Formation in kcal

Formula	Description	State	$\Delta F°$	Source
Sb		g	51.1	1
Sb	Metal	c	0.0	2
Sb_2		g	40.0	1
SbO^+		aq	-42.0	1
Sb_2O_4		c	-165.9	2
Sb_4O_6	Orth.	c	-298.0	1
Sb_2O_5		c	-200.5	1
SbH_3		g	35.3	2
SbO_2^-		aq	-82.5	2
$HSbO_2$		aq	-97.5	2
SbF_3		c	199.8	2
$SbCl_3$		g	-72.3	1
$SbCl_3$		c	-77.62	1
SbS_3^{--}		aq	(-32.0)	3
Sb_2S_3	Amorph.	c	-32.0	2
SbS_2		aq	-13.0	2

Arsenic.   Free Energy of Formation in kcal

Formula	Description	State	$\Delta F°$	Source
As	$(^4S_{3/2})$	g	50.74	1
As	α gray metal	c	0.0	2
As	β	Amorph.		
As	γ yellow	c		
As_2		g	17.5	1
As_4		g	25.2	1
AsO		g		
AsO^+		aq	-39.1	1
AsO_2^-		aq	-83.7	1
AsO_4^{---}		aq	-152.0	1
As_2O_5		c	-184.6	1
$As_2O_5 \cdot 4H_2O$		c	(-411.1)	3
As_4O_6	Ortho.	c	-275.36	1
AsH_3		g	42.0	2
$HAsO_4^{--}$		aq	-169.0	1
$H_2AsO_3^-$		aq	-140.4	2
$H_2AsO_4^-$		aq	-178.9	1
H_3AsO_3		aq	-152.94	1
H_3AsO_4		aq	-183.8	1
AsF_3		g	-214.7	1
$AsCl_3$		g	-68.5	1
As_2S_2		g		
As_2S_2		c	-32.15	2
As_2S_3		c	-32.46	2

BARIUM. Free Energy of Formation in kcal

Formula	Description	State	$\Delta F°$	Source
Ba	Metal	c	0.0	2
Ba^{++}		aq	−134.0	1
BaO		c	−126.3	1
BaO_2		c	−135.8	1
$BaO_2 \cdot H_2O$		c	−195.0	2
$Ba(OH)_2$		c	−204.7	2
$Ba(OH)_2 \cdot 8H_2O$		c	−666.8	2
BaF_2		c	−272.5	2
BaS		c	−104.5	2
$BaSO_4$		c	−323.4	1
$BaSeO_4$		c	−253.8	2
$Ba_3(PO_4)_2$		c	−944.4	2
$BaCO_3$	Witherite	c	−272.2	1
$BaSiO_3$		c	−338.7	2
Ba_2SiO_3		c	−470.6	2
$BaMnO_4$		c	−257.0	2
$BaMoO_4$		c	−349.3	2
$BaWO_4$		c	−373.6	2

BERYLLIUM. Free Energy of Formation in kcal

Formula	Description	State	$\Delta F°$	Source
Be	Metal	c	0.0	2
Be^{++}		aq	−85.2	2
BeO		c	−139.0	1
BeO_2^{--}		aq	−155.3	2
$Be_2O_3^{--}$		aq	−298.0	2
Be_2O^{++}		aq	−218.0	2
$Be(OH)_2$	α	c	−196.2	2
$Be(OH)_2$	β	c	−195.5	2
$BeO \cdot Be(OH)_2$	Precipitated	c	−338.0	2
BeS		c	−55.9	2

BISMUTH.   Free Energy of Formation in kcal

Formula	Description	State	$\Delta F°$	Source
Bi		g	40.4	1
Bi_2		g	48.0	1
BiO		c	−43.5	2
BiO^+		aq	−34.54	1
Bi_2O_3		c	−118.7	1
Bi_2O_4		c	−109.0	2
BiOOH		g	−88.4	2
$Bi(OH)_3$		c	−137.0	2
BiCl		g	5.2	1
$BiCl_3$		g	−62.2	1
$BiCl_3$		c	−76.23	1
BiOCl		c	−77.0	1
BiBr		g	3.8	1
BiI		g	11.0	1
$BiCl_4^-$		aq	−114.2	2
Bi_2S_3		c	−39.4	1

BORON.   Free Energy of Formation in kcal

Formula	Description	State	$\Delta F°$	Source
B	Crystalline	c	0.0	2
BO_2^-		aq	−169.6 (?)	2
B_2O_3		c	−286.43	1
B_2O_3		glass	−283.89	1
$B_4O_7^{--}$		aq	−616.0 (?)	2
$H_2BO_3^-$		aq	−217.6	1
H_3BO_3		c	−230.2	1
H_3BO_3		aq	−230.24	1
BF_3		g	−262.9	1
BF_4^-		aq	−343.0	1
B_2S_3		c	−53.3	2

BROMINE.   Free Energy of Formation in kcal

Formula	Description	State	$\Delta F°$	Source
Br^-		aq	−24.574	1
Br_2		g	0.751	2
Br_2		aq	0.977	2
BrO_3^-		aq	(5.0)	3

CADMIUM. Free Energy of Formation in kcal

Formula	Description	State	$\Delta F°$	Source
Cd	Metal α	c	0.0	2
Cd	Metal γ	c	0.14	1
Cd^{++}		aq	-18.58	1
$Cd(OH)_2$		c	-112.46	1
CdF_2		c	-154.8	1
$CdCl_2$		c	-81.88	1
$CdCl^+$		aq	-51.8	2
$CdCl_2$	Un-ionized	aq	-84.3	2
$CdCl_3^-$		aq	-115.9	2
CdS		?	-33.60	1
$CdSO_4$		c	-195.99	1
$CdSO_4 \cdot H_2O$		c	-254.84	1
$CdSO_4 \cdot \frac{8}{3}H_2O$		c	-349.63	1
CdTe		c	-23.82	1
$CdCO_3$		c	-160.2	1

CALCIUM. Free Energy of Formation in kcal

Formula	Description	State	$\Delta F°$	Source
Ca	Metal	c	0.0	2
Ca^{++}		aq	-132.18	1
CaO		c	-144.4	1
CaO_2		c	143.0	2
$Ca(OH)_2$		c	-214.33	1
CaF_2		c	-277.7	1
CaS		c	-114.1	1
$CaCO_3$	Calcite	c	-269.78	1
$CaCO_3$	Aragonite	c	-269.53	1
$CaSiO_3$	Pseudowollastonite	c	-357.4	1
$CaSiO_3$	Wollastonite	c	-358.2	1
Ca_2SiO_4	β	c	-512.7	2
Ca_2SiO_4	γ	c	-513.7	2
$CaSO_4$	Anhydrite	c	-315.56	1
$CaSO_4$	Soluble α	c	-313.52	1
$CaSO_4$	Soluble β	c	-312.46	1
$CaSO_4 \cdot \frac{1}{2}H_2O$	α	c	-343.02	1
$CaSO_4 \cdot \frac{1}{2}H_2O$	β	c	-342.78	1
$CaSO_4 \cdot 2H_2O$		c	-429.19	1
$Ca_3(PO_4)_2$	α	c	-929.7	1
$Ca_3(PO_4)_2$	β	c	-932.0	1
$CaHPO_4$		c	-401.5	1
$CaHPO_4 \cdot 2H_2O$		c	-514.6	1
$Ca(H_2PO_4)_2$	Precipitated	c	-672.0	2
$CaWO_4$		c	-368.7	2

Carbon. Free Energy of Formation in kcal

Formula	Description	State	$\Delta F°$	Source
C	Diamond	c	0.6850	1
C	Graphite	c	0.0	1
CO		g	-32.8079	1
CO_2		g	-94.2598	1
CO_2		aq	-92.31	1
CH_4		g	-12.140	1
C_2H_2		g	50.0	1
H_2CO_3		aq	-149.00	1
HCO_3^-		aq	-140.31	1
CO_3^{--}		aq	-126.22	1
COS		g	-40.45	1
CS_2		g	15.55	1
CF_4		g	-151.8	1

Cerium. Free Energy of Formation in kcal

Formula	Description	State	$\Delta F°$	Source
Ce	Metal	c, III	0.000	2
Ce^{+++}		aq	-171.75	2
CeO_2		c	-219.0	2
$Ce(OH)^{+++}$		aq	-188.9	1
$Ce(OH)_2^{++}$		aq	-245.2	1
$Ce(OH)_3$		c	-311.63	2
CeS_2		c	-151.5	2
Ce_2S_3		c	-293.1	2

Cesium. Free Energy of Formation in kcal

Formula	Description	State	$\Delta F°$	Source
Cs	Metal	c	0.000	1
Cs^+		aq	-67.41	1

CHLORINE. Free Energy of Formation in kcal

Formula	Description	State	$\Delta F°$	Source
Cl$^-$		aq	-31.350	1
Cl$_2$		g	0.0	2
Cl$_2$		aq	1.65	2
HCl		g	-22.769	1
HCl		aq	-31.350	1

CHROMIUM. Free Energy of Formation in kcal

Formula	Description	State	$\Delta F°$	Source
Cr	Metal	c	0.0	2
Cr^{++}		aq	-42.1	2
Cr^{+++}	[Cr(6H$_2$O)]$^{+++}$	aq	-51.5	2
Cr$_2$O$_3$		c	-250.2	1
Cr$_2$O$_7^{--}$		aq	-315.4	2
Cr(OH)$^{++}$	[Cr(5H$_2$O)OH]$^{++}$	aq	-103.0	2
HCrO$_4^-$		aq	-184.9	2
CrO$_4^{--}$		aq	-176.1	2
CrO$_2^-$		aq	-125.0	2
Cr(OH)$_2$		c	-140.5	2
Cr(OH)$_3$		c	-215.3	2
Cr(OH)$_3$	Hydrous, prob. [Cr(5H$_2$O)(OH)(OH)$_2$]	c	-205.5	2

COBALT. Free Energy of Formation in kcal

Formula	Description	State	$\Delta F°$	Source
Co	Metal	c	0.0	2
Co^{++}		aq	-12.8	2
Co^{+++}		aq	28.9	2
CoO		c	-49.0	2
Co$_3$O$_4$		c	-179.4	2
Co(OH)$_2$		c	-109.0	2
Co(OH)$_3$		c	-142.6	2
CoS	α precipitated	c	-19.8	2
Co$_2$S$_3$		c		
CoSO$_4$		c	-180.1	2
CoCO$_3$		c	-155.57	2

COPPER. Free Energy of Formation in kcal

Formula	Description	State	$\Delta F°$	Source
Cu	Metal	c	0.0	2
Cu$^+$		aq	12.0	1
Cu^{++}		aq	15.53	1
CuO		c	-30.4	1
HCuO$_2^-$		aq	-61.42	2
CuO$_2^{--}$		aq	-43.5	1
Cu$_2$O		c	-34.98	1
Cu(OH)$_2$		c	-85.3	2
CuS		c	-11.7	1
Cu$_2$S		c	-20.6	1
CuSO$_4$		c	-158.2	1
CuSO$_4$·H$_2$O		c	-219.2	1
CuSO$_4$·3H$_2$O		c	-334.6	1
CuSO$_4$·5H$_2$O	Chalcanthite	c	-449.3	1
CuSe		c	-7.9	2
Cu$_2$(OH)$_2$CO$_3$	Malachite	c	-216.44	9
Cu$_3$(OH)$_2$(CO$_3$)$_2$	Azurite	c	-343.73	9
Cu$_4$(OH)$_6$SO$_4$	Brochantite	c	-434.62	9
Cu$_4$(OH)$_6$SO$_4$·1.3H$_2$O	Langite	c	-505.5	9
Cu$_3$(OH)$_4$SO$_4$	Antlerite	c	-345.5	9
CuCO$_3$		aq	-119.9	9
Cu(CO$_3$)$_2^{--}$		aq	-250.5	9

FLUORINE. Free Energy of Formation in kcal

Formula	Description	State	$\Delta F°$	Source
F$^-$		aq	-66.08	1
HF		g	-64.7	1
HF		aq	-70.41	2
HF$_2^-$		aq	-137.5	2

GERMANIUM. Free Energy of Formation in kcal

Formula	Description	State	$\Delta F°$	Source
Ge		c	0.0	7
GeO	Yellow hydrated	c	-57.7	7
GeO	Brown hydrated	c	-64.9	7
GeO_2	Hexagonal	c	-127.0	7
GeO_2	Tetragonal	c	-131.1	7
Ge^{++}		aq	0.0	7
H_2GeO_3		aq	-181.8	7
$HGeO_3^-$		aq	-170.1	7
GeO_3^{--}		aq	-152.8	7

GOLD. Free Energy of Formation in kcal

Formula	Description	State	$\Delta F°$	Source
Au	Metal	c	0.0	1
Au^+		aq	39.0	2
Au^{+++}		aq	103.6	2
Au_2O_3		c	39.0	1
$H_2AuO_3^-$		aq	-45.8	1
$HAuO_3^{--}$		aq	-27.6	1
AuO_3^{---}		aq	-5.8	1
$Au(OH)_3$		c	-69.3	1
$Au(OH)_3$		aq	-61.8	1

HYDROGEN. Free Energy of Formation in kcal

Formula	Description	State	$\Delta F°$	Source
H^+		aq	0.0	2
H_2		g	0.0	2

Iodine. Free Energy of Formation in kcal

Formula	Description	State	$\Delta F°$	Source
I^-		aq	-12.35	1
I_2		g	4.63	1
I_2		c	0.0	2
I_2		aq	3.926	2
IO_3^-		aq	-32.250	2

Iron. Free Energy of Formation in kcal

Formula	Description	State	$\Delta F°$	Source
Fe		c	0.0	2
Fe^{++}		aq	-20.30	1
Fe^{+++}		aq	-2.53	1
FeO	Wüstite	c	-58.4	1
Fe_2O_3	Hematite	c	-177.1	1
Fe_3O_4	Magnetite	c	-242.4	1
$Fe(OH)^{++}$		aq	-55.91	1
$Fe(OH)_2$		c	-115.57	1
$Fe(OH)_2^+$		aq	-106.2	1
$Fe(OH)_3$		c	-166.0	2
$FeCl^{++}$		aq	-35.9	1
FeO_2H^-		aq	-90.6	7
FeS	α	c	-23.32	1
FeS_2	Pyrite	c	-36.00	10
$FePO_4$		c	-272.0	2
$FeCO_3$	Siderite	c	-161.06	1
FeSe	Precipitated	c	-13.9	2
$FeSiO_3$		c	257.0	2
Fe_2SiO_4		c	-319.8	1
$FeMoO_4$		c	-234.8	2
$FeWO_4$		c	-250.4	2

Lanthanum. Free Energy of Formation in kcal

Formula	Description	State	$\Delta F°$	Source
La	Metal	c, III	0.000	2
La^{+++}		aq	-174.5	2
La_2O_3		c	-426.9	2
$La(OH)_3$		c	-313.2	2
LaS_2		c	-154.7	2
La_2S_3		c	-301.2	2

LEAD. Free Energy of Formation in kcal

Formula	Description	State	$\Delta F°$	Source
Pb	Metal	c	0.0	2
Pb^{++}		aq	-5.81	1
Pb^{+4}		aq	72.3	2
PbO	Red	c	-45.25	1
PbO	Yellow	c	-45.05	1
HPbO$_2^-$		aq	-81.0	2
Pb(OH)$_2$		c	-100.6	1
PbO$_2$		c	-52.34	1
Pb$_3$O$_4$		c	-147.6	1
PbF$_2$		c	-148.1	1
PbCl$_2$		c	-75.04	1
PbS		c	-22.15	1
PbS$_2$O$_3$		c	-134.0	2
PbSO$_4$		c	-193.89	1
PbSO$_4$·PbO		c	-258.9	2
PbSe		c	-15.4	2
PbSeO$_4$		c	-122.0	2
PbTe		c	-18.1	2
Pb$_3$(PO$_4$)$_2$		c	-581.4	1
PbHPO$_3$		c	-208.3	1
PbCO$_3$		c	-149.7	2
PbO·PbCO$_3$		c	-195.6	1
2PbOPbCO$_3$		c	-242.0	1
Pb$_3$(OH)$_2$(CO$_3$)$_2$		c	-406.0	8
PbCrO$_4$		c	-203.6	2
PbMoO$_4$		c	-231.7	2
PbSiO$_3$		c	-239.0	1
Pb$_2$SiO$_4$		c	-285.7	1

LITHIUM. Free Energy of Formation in kcal

Formula	Description	State	$\Delta F°$	Source
Li	Metal	c	0.000	1
Li$^+$		aq	-70.22	1

MAGNESIUM. Free Energy of Formation in kcal

Formula	Description	State	$\Delta F°$	Source
Mg	Metal	c	0.0	2
Mg^{++}		aq	-108.99	1
MgO		c	-136.13	1
MgO	Finely divided	c	-135.31	1
$Mg(OH)_2$		c	-199.27	1
MgS		c	-83.6	2
$Mg_3(PO_4)_2$		c	-904.0	2
$Mg_3(AsO_4)_2$		c	-679.3	2
$MgCO_3$		c	-246.0	1
$MgNH_4PO_4$			-390.0	2

MANGANESE. Free Energy of Formation in kcal

Formula	Description	State	$\Delta F°$	Source
Mn	α	c	0.0	2
Mn	γ	c	0.33	1
Mn^{++}		aq	-54.4	2
Mn^{+++}		aq	(-19.6)	2
MnO		c	-86.8	1
$HMnO_2^-$		aq	-120.9	2
MnO_2	Pyrolusite	c	-111.1	2
MnO_4^-		aq	-107.4	2
MnO_4^{--}		aq	-120.4	2
Mn_2O_3		c	-212.3	2
Mn_3O_4	I	c	-306.0	1
$Mn(OH)_2$	Precipitated	c	-146.9	2
$Mn(OH)_3$		c	-181.0	2
MnS	Green	c	-49.9	1
MnS	Precipitated	c	-53.3	2
$Mn_3(PO_4)_2$	Precipitated	c	-683.0	2
$MnCO_3$		c	-195.4	1
$MnCO_3$	Precipitated	c	-194.3	2
$MnSiO_3$		c	-283.3	1

MERCURY. Free Energy of Formation in kcal

Formula	Description	State	$\Delta F°$	Source
Hg	Metal	l	0.0	2
Hg^{++}		aq	39.38	1
Hg_2^{++}		aq	36.35	2
HgO	Red	c	-13.990	1
HgO	Yellow	c	-13.959	1
$Hg(OH)_2$		aq	-65.70	2
HgCl		g	14.0	1
$HgCl_2$		c	-44.4	2
Hg_2Cl_2		c	-50.35	1
$HgCl_4^{--}$		aq	-107.7	2
$HgBr_4^{--}$		aq	-88.0	2
Hg_2Br_2		c	-42.714	1
$HgBr_2$		c	-35.22	2
HgI		g	23.0	1
Hg_2I_2		c	-26.60	1
HgS	Red, cinnabar	c	-11.67	1
HgS	Black, metacinnabar	c	-11.05	1
HgS_2^{--}		aq	11.6	2
$HgSO_4$		c	-141.0	2
Hg_2SO_4		c	-149.12	1
Hg_2CO_3		c	-105.8	2
Hg_2CrO_4		c	-155.75	2

MOLYBDENUM. Free energy of Formation in kcal

Formula	Description	State	$\Delta F°$	Source
Mo	Metal	c	0.0	2
Mo^{+++}		aq	(-13.8)	3
MoO_2		c	-117.3	2
MoO_3		c	-161.95	1
MoO_4		aq	-154.0	2
MoO_4^{--}		aq	-218.8	2
H_2MoO_4	(Probably complex)	aq	(-227.0)	3
MoS_2		c	-53.8	1
MoS_3		c	-57.6	2

NICKEL. Free Energy of Formation in kcal

Formula	Description	State	$\Delta F°$	Source
Ni		c	0.0	2
Ni^{++}		aq	-11.53	2
NiO$_2$		c	-47.5	2
Ni(OH)$_2$		c	-108.3	1
Ni(OH)$_3$		c	-129.5	2
NiS	α	c	-17.7	2
NiS	γ	c	-27.3	2
NiO		c	-51.7	1
NiSO$_4$		c	-184.9	1
NiSO$_4$·6H$_2$O	Green	c		
NiSO$_4$·6H$_2$O	Blue	c	-531.0	1
NiCO$_3$		c	-147.0	2

NIOBIUM. Free Energy of Formation in kcal

Formula	Description	State	$\Delta F°$	Source
Nb	Metal	c	0.0	2
Nb$_2$O$_4$		c	-362.4	2
Nb$_2$O$_5$		c	-432.0	2
Nb^{+++}		aq	(-76.0)	2

NITROGEN. Free Energy of Formation in kcal

Formula	Description	State	$\Delta F°$	Source
N$_2$		g	0.0	2
NO		g	20.719	1
NO$_2$		g	12.390	1
NO$_2^-$		aq	-8.25	2
NO$_3^-$		aq	-26.43	2
N$_2$O$_2^{--}$		aq	33.2	1
N$_2$O$_4$		g	23.491	1
NH$_3$		g	-3.976	1
NH$_3$		aq	-6.36	2
NH$_4^+$		aq	-19.00	1
HNO$_3$		l	-19.100	1
HNO$_3$		aq	-26.43	1
NH$_4$OH		aq	-63.05	2

OXYGEN.   Free Energy of Formation in kcal

Formula	Description	State	$\Delta F°$	Source
O_2		g	0.0	2
OH^-		aq	-37.595	1
H_2O		g	-54.635	1
H_2O		l	-56.690	1
H_2O_2		aq	-31.470	2
O_2^-		aq	$+13.0$	2

PALLADIUM.   Free Energy of Formation in kcal

Formula	Description	State	$\Delta F°$	Source
Pd		c	0.0	2
Pd^{++}		aq	45.5	2
PdO		c	-14.4	2
$Pd(OH)_2$		c	-72.0	2
$Pd(OH)_4$		c	-126.2 (?)	2

PHOSPHORUS.   Free Energy of Formation in kcal

Formula	Description	State	$\Delta F°$	Source
P	White	c, III	0.0	2
P	Red	c, II	-3.3	1
P	Black	c, I		
PO_4^{---}		aq	-245.1	1
$H_2PO_2^-$		aq	-122.4	2
HPO_3^{--}		aq	-194.0	2
HPO_4^{--}		aq	-261.5	1
$H_2PO_3^-$		aq	-202.35	2
$H_2PO_4^-$		aq	-271.3	1
H_3PO_4		aq	-274.2	2

PLATINUM.   Free Energy of Formation in kcal

Formula	Description	State	$\Delta F°$	Source
Pt		c	0.0	2
Pt++		aq	(54.8)	3
Pt(OH)$_2$		c	-68.2	1
PtS		c	-21.6 (?)	2
PtS$_2$		c	-25.6	2

POTASSIUM.   Free Energy of Formation in kcal

Formula	Description	State	$\Delta F°$	Source
K	Metal	c	0.000	1
K+		aq	-67.46	1
K$_2$O		c	-76.2	2
KOH		c	-89.5	1
K$_2$S		c	-96.6	1
K$_2$CO$_3$		c	-255.5	1
KAlSi$_3$O$_8$	Feldspar	c	-856.0	8
KAl$_3$Si$_3$O$_{10}$(OH)$_2$	Mica	c	-1298.0	8

RUBIDIUM.   Free Energy of Formation in kcal

Formula	Description	State	$\Delta F°$	Source
Rb	Metal	c, I	0.000	1
Rb+		aq	-67.45	1
Rb$_2$S		c	-80.6	1
Rb$_2$CO$_3$		c	-249.3	2

Scandium. Free Energy of Formation in kcal

Formula	Description	State	$\Delta F°$	Source
Sc	Metal	c	0.0	2
Sc^{+++}		aq	-143.7	2
$Sc(OH)_3$		c	(-293.5)	2

Selenium. Free Energy of Formation in kcal

Formula	Description	State	$\Delta F°$	Source
Se		g	38.77	1
Se	I, gray, hexagonal	c	0.0	2
Se^{--}		aq	42.6	1
Se_2		g	21.15	1
SeO_2		c	-41.5	2
SeO_3^{--}		aq	-89.33	1
SeO_4^{--}		aq	-105.42	1
HSe^-		aq	23.5	1
H_2Se		g	17.0	1
H_2Se		aq	18.4	1
$HSeO_3^-$		aq	-98.3	1
$HSeO_4^-$		aq	-108.2	1
H_2SeO_3		aq	-101.8	1
H_2SeO_4		aq	-105.42	1
SeF_6		g	-222.0	1

SILICON.   Free Energy of Formation in kcal

Formula	Description	State	$\Delta F°$	Source
Si		g	77.41	1
SiO_2	Quartz	c	− 192.4	1
SiO_2	Cristobalite II	c	− 192.1	1
SiO_2	Tridymite IV	c	− 191.9	1
SiO_2	Vitreous	glass	− 190.9	1
SiH_4		g	− 9.4	1
SiF_6^{--}		aq	− 511.0	2
H_4SiO_4		aq	− 300.2	5
$H_3SiO_4^-$		aq	− 286.8	6

SILVER.   Free Energy of Formation in kcal

Formula	Description	State	$\Delta F°$	Source
Ag	Metal	c	0.0	2
Ag^+		aq	18.430	1
Ag^{++}		aq	64.1	2
AgO^+		aq	53.9	2
AgO^-		aq	− 5.49	2
Ag_2O		c	− 2.586	1
AgO		c	2.6	1
Ag_2O_3		c	20.8	2
AgCl		c	− 26.224	1
AgBr		c	− 22.930	1
AgI		c	− 15.85	1
Ag_2S	Rhombic α	c	− 9.62	1
Ag_2S	β	c	− 9.36	1
Ag_2SO_4		c	− 147.17	1
Ag_2SeO_4		c	− 68.5	1
Ag_2CO_3		c	− 104.48	1
Ag_2MoO_4		c	− 196.4	2
Ag_2WO_4		c	− 206.0	2
Ag_2CrO_4		c	− 154.7	2

Sodium. Free Energy of Formation in kcal

Formula	Description	State	$\Delta F°$	Source
Na	Metal	c	0.000	1
Na$^+$		aq	-62.589	1
NaCl		aq	-93.939	1
Na$_2$S		c	-86.6	2
Na$_2$CO$_3$		c	-250.4	1
Na$_2$CO$_3$		aq	-251.4	2
NaHCO$_3$		c	-203.6	1
NaHCO$_3$		aq	-202.89	2
Na$_2$SiO$_3$		c	-341.0	1

Strontium. Free Energy of Formation in kcal

Formula	Description	State	$\Delta F°$	Source
Sr	Metal	c	0.0	2
Sr^{++}		aq	-133.2	1
SrO		c	-133.8	1
SrO$_2$		c	-139.0	2
Sr(OH)$_2$		c	-207.8	2
SrF$_2$		c	-277.8	2
SrS		c	-97.4	2
SrSO$_4$		c	-318.9	1
Sr$_3$(PO$_4$)$_2$		c	-932.1	2
SrHPO$_4$		c	-399.7	2
SrCO$_3$	Strontianite	c	-271.9	1
SrSiO$_3$		c	-350.8	2
Sr$_2$SiO$_4$		c	-495.7	2
Sr(WO$_4$)		c	-366.5	2

Formula	Description	State	$\Delta F°$	Source
S	Rhombic	c	0.0	2
S	Monoclinic	c	0.023	1
S		g	44.06	1
S^{--}		aq	22.1	2
S$_2$		g	19.13	4
S$_2^{--}$		aq	21.8	2
S$_3^{--}$		aq	21.1	2
S$_4^{--}$		aq	19.4	2
SO$_2$		g	-71.75	1
SO$_3$		g	-88.50	1
SO$_3^{--}$		aq	-116.1	2
SO$_4^{--}$		aq	-177.34	1
S$_2$O$_3^{--}$		aq	-124.0	2
S$_2$O$_4^{--}$		aq	-143.4	2
S$_2$O$_5^{--}$		aq	-189.0	2
S$_2$O$_6^{--}$		aq	-231.0	2
S$_2$O$_8^{--}$		aq	-262.0	1
S$_3$O$_6^{--}$		aq	-229.0	2
S$_4$O$_6^{--}$		aq	-244.3	2
S$_5$O$_6^{--}$		aq	-228.5	2
HS$^-$		aq	3.01	1
H$_2$S		g	-7.898	1
H$_2$S		aq	-6.54	1
HSO$_3^-$		aq	-126.0	2
HSO$_4^-$		aq	-179.94	1
H$_2$SO$_3$		aq	-128.59	2
H$_2$SO$_4$		aq	-177.34	1
HS$_2$O$_4^-$		aq	-140.0	2
H$_2$S$_2$O$_4$		aq	-140.0	2
H$_2$S$_2$O$_8$		aq	-262.0	1
SF$_6$		g	-237.0	1
S$_2$Cl$_2$		l	-5.9	2
SO$_2$Cl$_2$		g	-73.6	2

TANTALUM. Free Energy of Formation in kcal

Formula	Description	State	ΔF°	Source
Ta	Metal	c	0.0	2
Ta_2O_5		c	-470.6	1

TELLURIUM. Free Energy of Formation in kcal

Formula	Description	State	ΔF°	Source
Te		c, II	0.0	1
Te^{--}		aq	52.7	2
Te_2^{--}		aq	38.75	2
Te_2		g	29.0	1
HTe^-		aq	37.7	2
H_2Te		g	33.1	1
H_2Te		aq	34.1	2
TeO_2		c	-64.60	1
TeO_3^{--}		aq	-108.0	2
H_6TeO_6		c	-167.9	2
H_2TeO_3		c	-115.7	1
$TeOOH^+$		aq	-61.78	2
TeF_6		g	-292.0	1
$TeCl_4$		c	-56.7	2
$TeCl_6^{--}$		aq	-137.4	2

THORIUM. Free Energy of Formation in kcal

Formula	Description	State	ΔF°	Source
Th	Metal	c	0.0	2
Th^{4+}		aq	-175.2	2
ThO_2		c	-278.4	2
$Th(OH)_4$	"Soluble"	c	-379.0	2
Th_2S_3		c	-257.7	2

TIN. Free Energy of Formation in kcal

Formula	Description	State	$\Delta F°$	Source
Sn	Gray	c	1.1	1
Sn	White	c	0.0	2
Sn^{++}		aq	-6.275	2
Sn^{4+}		aq	0.65	2
SnO		c	-61.5	1
SnO_2		c	-124.2	1
$HSnO_2^-$		aq	-98.0	2
$Sn(OH)_2$		c	-117.6	1
SnF_6^{--}		aq	-420.0	2
$Sn(OH)_4$		c	-227.5	2
$Sn(OH)_6^{--}$		aq	-310.5	2
SnS		c	-19.7	1
$Sn(SO_4)_2$		c	-346.8	2

TITANIUM. Free Energy of Formation in kcal

Formula	Description	State	$\Delta F°$	Source
Ti	Metal	c	0.0	2
Ti^{++}		aq	(-75.1)	2
Ti^{+++}		aq	(-83.6)	2
TiO_2	Rutile	c	-212.3	7
TiO_2	Hydrated	c	-196.3	2
$TiO(OH)_2$		c	-253.0	2
TiO^{++}		aq	-138.0	2
Ti_2O_3		c	-342.3	7
Ti_3O_5		c	-535.1	7
$FeTiO_3$		c	-268.9	1
$HTiO_3^-$		aq	-228.5	7
TiO_2^{++}		aq	-111.7	7

TUNGSTEN. Free Energy of Formation in kcal

Formula	Description	State	$\Delta F°$	Source
W		c	0.0	2
WO_2		c	-124.4	2
WO_3	Yellow	c	-182.47	1
W_2O_5		c	-306.9	2
WO_4^{--}		aq	-220.0	2
WS_2		c	-46.2	1

URANIUM. Free Energy of Formation in kcal

Formula	Description	State	$\Delta F°$	Source
U	Metal	c, III	0.000	2
U^{+++}		aq	-124.4	1
U^{4+}		aq	-138.4	1
UO_2		c	-246.6	7
UO_2^+		aq	-237.6	1
UO_2^{++}		aq	-236.4	1
UO_3		c	-273.0	7
$UO_3 \cdot H_2O$		c	-343.0	2
$U(OH)^{+++}$		aq	-193.5	1
$U(OH)_3$		c	(-263.2)	3
$U(OH)_4$		c	(-351.6)	2
Na_2UO_4		c	-475.0	2
UO_2SO_4		aq	-413.7	1
$UO_2(CO_3)_3^{4-}$		aq	-640.0	11
$UO_2(CO_3)_2(H_2O)_2^{--}$		aq	-622.0	11
UO_2CO_3		c	-377.0	11
$UO_2(OH)_2H_2O$		c	-437.0	11

VANADIUM. Free Energy Formation in kcal

Formula	Description	State	$\Delta F°$	Source
V		c	0.0	12
V^{++}		aq	54.2	,,
V^{+++}		aq	-60.1	,,
VO^{++}		aq	-109.0	,,
VO_2^+		aq	-142.6	,,
V_2O_2		c	-189.0	,,
V_2O_3		c	-271.0	,,
V_2O_4		c	-318.0	,,
V_2O_5	Aged precipitate		-344.0	,,
V_2O_5	Fresh precipitate		-342.0	,,
$V(OH)_3$	Precipitate		-218.0	,,
$V(OH)^{++}$		aq	-112.8	,,
$VO(OH)_2$	Precipitate		-213.6	,,
NH_4VO_3		c	-221.8	,,
$V_4O_9^{2-}$		aq	-665.3	,,
$H_2V_{10}O_{28}^{4-}$		aq	-1875.2	,,
$HV_{10}O_{28}^{5-}$		aq	-1875.3	,,
$V_{10}O_{28}^{6-}$		aq	-1862.4	,,

YTTRIUM.   Free Energy of Formation in kcal

Formula	Description	State	$\Delta F°$	Source
Y	Metal	c	0.0	2
Y+++		aq	-164.1	2
Y(OH)$_3$		c	-307.1	2

ZINC.   Free Energy of Formation in kcal

Formula	Description	State	$\Delta F°$	Source
Zn		c	0.0	2
Zn++		aq	-35.184	1
ZnO		c	-76.05	1
ZnO$_2^{--}$		aq	-93.03	2
Zn(NH$_3$)$_4^{++}$		aq	-73.5	2
Zn(OH)$^+$		aq	-78.8	2
Zn(OH)$_2$		c	-132.6	2
ZnS	Sphlalerite	c	-47.4	1
ZnS	Wurtzite	c	-44.2	2
ZnS	Precipitated	c	-43.2 (?)	2
ZnSO$_4$		c	-208.31	1
ZnSO$_4$·H$_2$O		c	-269.9	1
ZnSO$_4$·6H$_2$O		c	-555.0	1
ZnSO$_4$·7H$_2$O		c	-611.9	1
ZnSe		c	-34.7	2
ZnSiO$_3$		c	-274.8	2
ZnCO$_3$		c	-174.8	1

ZIRCONIUM.   Free Energy of Formation in kcal

Formula	Description	State	$\Delta F°$	Source
Zr	Metal	c	0.0	2
Zr^{4+}		aq	-141.0	2
ZrO++		aq	-201.5	7
ZrO$_2$		c	-244.4	1
ZrO(OH)$_2$		c	-311.5	1
Zr(OH)$_4$		c	-370.0	1
HZrO$_3^-$		aq	-287.7	2
Zr^{4+}		aq	-142.0	7

REFERENCES

1. Rossini, F. D., D. D. Wagman, W. H. Evans, Samuel Levine, and Irving Jaffe, Selected values of chemical thermodynamic properties. *Natl. Bur. Standards Circ. 500*, 1952, U.S. Dept. Commerce, 1268 pp. (plus later supplements).

2. Latimer, W. M., *Oxidation Potentials*. Prentice-Hall, Englewood Cliffs, N.J., 1952, 392 pp.

3. *Ibid.*, but values are estimated.

4. Stephenson, C. C., personal communication.

5. Siever, Raymond, The silica budget in the sedimentary cycle. *Am. Mineralogist*, *42*, 826 (1957).

6. Estimated by R. M. G. from reference 5 and dissociation constant H_4SiO_4.

7. *Technical Report 28*, Enthalpies libre de formation standards, à 25°C. Centre Belge d'Etude de la Corrosion, Brussels, 1955, 9 pp.

8. Garrels, R. M., Some free energy values from geologic relations. *Am. Mineralogist*, *42*, 789 (1957).

9. Silman, J. R., Ph.D. Thesis, Department of Geology, Harvard University, 1958.

10. Kelley, K. K., The thermodynamic properties of sulfur and its inorganic compounds: *U.B. Bur. Mines Bull. 406*, 1937, 44 pp.

11. Bullwinkel, E. P., The chemistry of uranium in carbonate solutions: U.S. Atomic Energy Comm., Raw Materials Division, RMO-2614, 1954, 59 pp.

12. Evans, H. T., Jr., and R. M. Garrels, Thermodynamic equilibria of vanadium in aqueous systems as applied to the interpretation of the Colorado Plateau ore deposits. *Geochim. et Cosmochim. Acta*, in press.

Index